A Beka Book

HOME SCHOOL

Arithmetic 4

Curriculum / Lesson Plans

Part 1   General Information
Part 2   Arithmetic Curriculum

A Beka Book® Pensacola, FL 32523-9100
a ministry of PENSACOLA CHRISTIAN COLLEGE

Arithmetic 4 Home School Curriculum

Editors: P. Oslin, J. Howe

Copyright © 2000 Pensacola Christian College
All rights reserved. Printed in U.S.A. 2003 C03

A Beka Book, a Christian textbook ministry affiliated with Pensacola Christian College, is designed to meet the need for Christian textbooks and teaching aids. The purpose of this publishing ministry is to help Christian schools reach children and young people for the Lord and train them in the Christian way of life.

General Information

Contents

General Information

PHILOSOPHY OF
CHRISTIAN CURRICULUM

This curriculum, which has been devised by professional Christian teachers and administrators, contains day-by-day lesson plans for an entire year. The purpose of this curriculum is to help you, the parent. Thousands of Christian schools and home schools around the world successfully use the *A Beka Book* curriculums because they are based on sound scholarship, common sense, and the Word of God.

Why Christian Home Schoolers Should Use a Standard Curriculum

1. This curriculum makes available the accumulated wisdom of experienced educators.
2. An organized curriculum saves you hours of time planning *when* and *what* to do so that you can concentrate on *how* to do it.
3. Using a prepared curriculum helps even a parent teaching for the first time to be successful.
4. The *A Beka Book* curriculum ensures that a child will be taught new material on each grade level and that there will be sufficient review of old material each year. A child can progress steadily from year to year.
5. This curriculum provides for review in a variety of ways to ensure thorough learning.

Why Christian Home Schoolers Should Use a Christian Curriculum

The Christian home school is not merely for the sake of academics, but also for the sake of fulfilling the God-ordained role in carrying out the Christian education mandate (Deut. 6:7, Prov. 22:6, 2 Tim. 3:15–17). Just as we believe it would be wrong to place a child under the influence of godless teachers, so we believe it would be wrong to place him under the influence of godless, humanistic textbooks and teaching materials. It is imperative to follow a curriculum that is based on the Scriptures, one that has the Christian approach to education and life woven throughout it. This curriculum was written on the premise that all truth comes from God and that any teaching of man that is contrary to the clear teaching of the Word of God must be rejected and refuted.

The *A Beka Book* curriculums and their correlated materials teach, for example, that **mathematics, grammar,** and **spelling** are all rule-governed activities. If they are not taught that way (if, on the contrary, they are taught as arbitrary matters in which the individual may "do his own thing"), then the purpose of mathematics, grammar, and spelling in society is destroyed. This common-sense approach fully accords with Scriptural principles about orderliness and authority. The teaching materials for these subjects also abound with specific examples aimed at Christian character building.

Well-selected **literature** helps a child grow intellectually, emotionally, and spiritually by demonstrating discernment, aesthetic values, and character. Good literature points a child to Christ, to the wonderful world of creation, to Christian principles (such as the law of sowing and reaping), and to a study of human nature. The child meets characters in his reading who successfully conquer by doing what is right. He also realizes the inevitable results of wrongdoing. The classics in the *A Beka Book* literature texts introduce the child to good writing by men and women who strive to teach important truths about the world around him, about man, and about God.

History gives a child the record of God's plan for mankind as related to man's creation and fall, the redemptive plan of God, and the fulfillment of God's perfect will and purpose for His creatures. The history texts again and again show the consequences of sin for men and empires and extol those who are good examples of godly living.

The **science** curriculum presents the universe as the direct creation of the God of the Scriptures and refutes the man-made idea of evolution. Further, it presents God as the great Designer, Sustainer, and Lawgiver, without Whom the evident design and laws of nature would be inexplicable. Science is presented as one way that man can fulfill the Genesis command to subdue the earth and exercise dominion over it (Gen. 1:28a).

The *A Beka Book* curriculums are designed to provide time each day for the teaching of **Bible,** the most important subject taught. All parents, whether they teach Bible or not, should be concerned with leading the child to a saving knowledge of Christ and then helping him to grow spiritually in the Lord. The teaching materials suggested in the curriculum have been designed to give specific examples of how Christians should and should not live, but you as the parent must also be a living example of the Christian life.

Hints on Using an *A Beka Book* Curriculum

1. First-year Christian home school parents should follow the lesson plans very closely. Experienced home school parents may have additional ideas that they know work well and should feel free to use them.

2. If your child is not keeping up with the lesson plans, ask yourself these questions:
    a. Am I making good use of every minute?
    b. Am I spending some time each day reviewing basic concepts in order to give my child the opportunity to master the material?
    c. Am I sufficiently prepared to make clear explanations of the new material?
    d. Am I allowing my child to practice the material after I explain it?
    e. Am I providing extra time to work with my child if he is having trouble?
    If you can answer all of these questions affirmatively, think about slowing the curriculum (reteaching previous lessons) until the child is ready to continue in the curriculum.
3. Please remember that it is illegal to reproduce pages of the curriculum other than those indicated.

FOURTH GRADE
HOME SCHOOL KIT

Child Kit

Read and Think 4 Skill Sheets
Salute to Courage
Liberty Tree
Flags Unfurled
Trails to Explore
Adventures in Other Lands
Language A
    Student Test Book
Spelling, Vocabulary, Poetry 4
    Student Test Book
Penmanship Mastery I
Arithmetic 4
    Student Speed Drills and Tests
Understanding God's World
    Student Test and Quiz Book
    Student Activity Book
Developing Good Health
    Student Test and Study Book
The History of Our United States
    Student Geography/Map/Review Book
    Student Test and Quiz Book
My State Notebook

Optional

Art Projects A
Saved at Sea (highly recommended)
Song of the Brook (highly recommended)

(See *A Beka Book* order form for
additional book report titles.)

Parent Kit

Home School Language Arts 4 Curriculum/
    Lesson Plans
        (language, reading, penmanship, spelling)
    Language A Teacher Edition
        Teacher Test Key
    Oral Language Exercises
    Home School Language 4–6 Charts
    Spelling 4 Teacher Test Key
Home School *Arithmetic 4* Curriculum/
    Lesson Plans
    Teacher Key
    Speed Drills/Test Key
Home School Science/Health 4 Curriculum/
    Lesson Plans
    Science 4 Answer Key
    Science 4 Test/Quiz Key
    Science 4 Activity Key
    Home School Science Teaching Charts 4–6
    Health 4 Answer Key
    Health 4 Test/Study Key
    Home School Health Teaching Charts 4–6
Home School *History of Our United States*
    Curriculum/Lesson Plans
    History 4 Answer Key
    History 4 Test/Quiz Key
    Geography/Map/Review Key
    Home School Geography Teaching Maps

Recommended (purchase from *A Beka Book* or make them)
    Addition Flashcards
    Subtraction Flashcards
    Multiplication Flashcards
    Division Flashcards
    Arithmetic 3–4 Concept Cards (highly
        recommended)
    Home School Arithmetic 3–8 Charts (highly
        recommended)

Optional

Songs We Enjoy 4
Red, Red Robin Cassette
Birds of North America Flashcards
Spelling, Vocabulary, Poetry 4 Teacher Edition
Reading 4 Answer Key

How to Use *A Beka Book* Home School Curriculum/Lesson Plans

A Beka Book home school curriculum/lesson plans are designed to guide parents in teaching average children. 170 lessons allow for one lesson each day of the school year. On the first day, lesson one in each subject will be done, on the second day, lesson two, etc. The suggestions for each lesson are guidelines for the parent. Parents using the curriculum/lesson plans need to cover each point under Preparation and Procedure with their child. Each aspect of the lesson is important to the complete education of the child. *A Beka Book* curriculum/lesson plans will save hours of planning and assure that each page of the textbooks, quiz books, and test books is assigned at an average pace for the grade.

Because children need reinforcement of material that has been taught, the curriculum/lesson plans include oral and written review. The review sections may go quickly but are a vital part of the child's learning.

Yearly Schedule

You may want to make a tentative schedule for the year by using a calendar and writing in the lesson numbers for each day. Plan for holidays and vacations also. This will help you finish fourth grade in a timely manner.

Daily Schedule

A suggested daily time schedule is given on the following page. The times may vary slightly. You may make adjustments to fit your own needs. An extra column is included to record any necessary adjustments you need to make to the suggested times.

A parent often has several children to teach at one time. A sample of how to set up a master time schedule at home is included. Notice that the child needs parental instruction from the curriculum/lesson plans as well as independent work or practice time. Keep in mind a kindergarten child does not have a long attention span and generally cannot do independent work until second semester. Grades 1–2 have similar schedules and grades 3–6 are very much alike in format. This should help you in planning your own master time schedule for your home school.

Habits and Procedures

Appropriate habits and procedures produce an orderly room that is conducive to effective learning. During the early lessons, the daily plans allow time for the practice and reinforcement of these habits.

Grading

Grades in fourth grade will be given in Bible, reading, language, spelling, penmanship, arithmetic, science, health, and history. Further details about grading each subject are given in that curriculum. Reading, penmanship, language, and spelling are found in the Language Arts 4 Home School Curriculum. Arithmetic grading details are given in the Arithmetic 4 Home School Curriculum. Science and health grading details are found in the Science/Health 4 Home School Curriculum, and history in the History 4 Home School Curriculum. The Bible memory course and grading details are found in all curriculums.

Progress Reports

The fourth grade program is divided into four grading periods. The progress reports, found in this section, will give forms needed to keep track of your child's progress. These will allow you to have accurate records for each grading period for your child. Two copies are included for your convenience.

Suggested Grading Scale

A	95–100
B	85–94
C	77–84
D	70–76
F	0–69

SUGGESTED DAILY SCHEDULE

You may make adjustments to fit your own needs. The chart contains an extra column which may be used to record any necessary adjustment of the suggested time.

Suggested Time	Time	Minutes	Activity
8:15 – 8:25		10	Bible
8:25 – 9:00		35	Arithmetic
9:00 – 9:25		25	Language
9:25 – 9:35		10	Penmanship
9:35 – 9:55		20	Reading
9:55 – 10:10		15	Break
10:10 – 10:25		15	Spelling / Poetry
10:25 – 10:45		20	History
10:45 – 11:05		20	Science
11:05 – 12:00		55	Independent Work / Art / Homework (some children may need more time to complete their independent work or homework)

A Beka Book
Home School
Combination Grade Schedule

SAMPLE

Time	Kindergarten	Grade 2	Grade 4
8:15	. . . .*Bible / Devotions		
8:45			Language
9:00		Phonics	Independent—Language
9:15	Phonics / Writing or Reading	Seatwork— Letters and Sounds	Independent— Language / Spelling
9:30	Social Studies / Science / Art	Seatwork—Language	Independent—Read
9:45	Play / Art (5 min.)	Seatwork—Spelling	Read (10 min.)
10:00	Art / Read (5 min.)	Read (10 min.)	Independent—Arithmetic
10:15	Phonics Review (5 min.)/ Numbers (10 min.)	Silent Reading	Independent—Arithmetic
10:30	Numbers (5 min.)	Seatwork— Arithmetic	Arithmetic (10 min.)
10:45		Arithmetic	Independent—History
11:00		Arithmetic / Writing	Independent—Science
11:15		Seatwork—Writing	Arithmetic
11:30		Read (5 min.)	Spelling / Penmanship (10 min.)
11:45	. . . . LUNCH		
12:00	. . . . LUNCH		
12:15		Read	Independent—Penmanship
12:30			History
12:45			Science
1:00	. . . . Additional Activities		

*Underline indicates directed teaching by parent. Allow some time (10–30 min.) each day for children to do homework in grade one and above. Most homework in grades four and above is independently done.

Actual Bible instruction should be given by the parent; however, you will find below the memory verses that are learned by fourth grade children throughout the year.

Ten minutes each day should be spent memorizing verses. The parent should have the child say the memorized verses at a regular time each day. Generally spend three to four weeks on one passage. Have your child say the verses from memory for a grade and then begin to teach the next passage. Listed below is the approximate time for completion of the passages in four grading periods.

As the child is tested, be sure to record the grade on the progress report. A suggested grading scale for oral verses is given below.

Grading Scale for Verses

Guide for subjective verse grades: *(Can use "plus" and "minus" on letter grades.)*

Child knows the verse/passage.	A	Says verse correctly or with just 1 mistake (a missed word, wrong word, or hesitation)
	B	a few mistakes
Child needs help.	C	several mistakes
Child is struggling.	D	many mistakes—requires excessive help
Child doesn't know verse/passage.	F	Child obviously does not know the verse.

FOURTH GRADE BIBLE VERSES

1st Nine Weeks

Isaiah 53:1–6

Books of the Bible

2nd Nine Weeks

Isaiah 53:7–12

Isaiah 9:6–7

1 Corinthians 13

3rd Nine Weeks

Matthew 7:24–27

Matthew 6:19–24

Matthew 20:25–28

Isaiah 40:28–31

John 20:30–31

4th Nine Weeks

1 Thessalonians 4:13–18

Matthew 22:36–40

John 16:7–14

A Beka Book
Fourth Grade Progress Report

Student Name _____
               Last   First   Middle

Home Teacher _____

Mailing Address _____

City, State ZIP CODE _____

Country _____

ARITHMETIC TESTS

Lesson	**Test**	Grade
12	**1**	_____
22	**2**	_____
32	**3**	_____
42	**4**	_____
	Average	_____

ARITHMETIC QUIZZES

Lesson	Quiz	Grade
7	1	_____
17	2	_____
27	3	_____
37	4	_____
	Average	_____

ARITHMETIC SPEED DRILLS

Lesson	Grade
9	_____
14	_____
16	_____
25	_____
28	_____
34	_____
39	_____
44	_____
Average	_____
Final Average	_____

Home Teacher:

Record numerical grades on lines.

Subtract the number of wrong points from 100.

BIBLE

Verses	Grade
Isaiah 53:1–6	_____
Books of the Bible	_____
Average	_____

Note: Record Bible grades here only if not using Home School Language Arts 4 Curriculum.

Date _____

◢◣ *A Beka Book*®
Fourth Grade Progress Report

Student Name _____
Last   First   Middle

Home Teacher _____

Mailing Address _____

City, State ZIP CODE _____

Country _____

ARITHMETIC TESTS

Lesson	Test	Grade
12	1	_____
22	2	_____
32	3	_____
42	4	_____
	Average	_____

ARITHMETIC QUIZZES

Lesson	Quiz	Grade
7	1	_____
17	2	_____
27	3	_____
37	4	_____
	Average	_____

ARITHMETIC SPEED DRILLS

Lesson	Grade
9	_____
14	_____
16	_____
25	_____
28	_____
34	_____
39	_____
44	_____
Average	_____
Final Average	_____

Home Teacher:

Record numerical grades on lines.

Subtract the number of wrong points from 100.

BIBLE

Verses	Grade
Isaiah 53:1–6	_____
Books of the Bible	_____
Average	_____

Note: Record Bible grades here only if not using Home School Language Arts 4 Curriculum.

A Beka Book®
Fourth Grade Progress Report

Student Name _____
Last   First   Middle

Home Teacher _____

Mailing Address _____

City, State ZIP CODE _____

Country _____

ARITHMETIC TESTS

Lesson	Test	Grade
52	5	_____
62	6	_____
72	7	_____
82	8	_____
	Average	_____

ARITHMETIC QUIZZES

Lesson	Quiz	Grade
47	5	_____
57	6	_____
67	7	_____
77	8	_____
87	9	_____
	Average	_____

ARITHMETIC SPEED DRILLS

Lesson	Grade
48	_____
51	_____
58	_____
65	_____
69	_____
74	_____
76	_____
85	_____
86	_____
Average	_____
Final Average	_____

Home Teacher:

Record numerical grades on lines.

BIBLE

Verses	Grade
Isaiah 53:7–12	_____
Isaiah 9:6–7	_____
1 Corinthians 13	_____
Average	_____

Note: Record Bible grades here only if not using Home School Language Arts 4 Curriculum.

A Beka Book®
Fourth Grade Progress Report

Student Name _____
        Last   First   Middle

Home Teacher _____

Mailing Address _____

City, State ZIP CODE _____

Country _____

ARITHMETIC TESTS

Lesson	Test	Grade
52	5	_____
62	6	_____
72	7	_____
82	8	_____
	Average	_____

ARITHMETIC QUIZZES

Lesson	Quiz	Grade
47	5	_____
57	6	_____
67	7	_____
77	8	_____
87	9	_____
	Average	_____

ARITHMETIC SPEED DRILLS

Lesson	Grade
48	_____
51	_____
58	_____
65	_____
69	_____
74	_____
76	_____
85	_____
86	_____
Average	_____
Final Average	_____

Home Teacher:

Record numerical grades on lines.

BIBLE

Verses	Grade
Isaiah 53:7–12	_____
Isaiah 9:6–7	_____
1 Corinthians 13	_____
Average	_____

Note: Record Bible grades here only if not using Home School Language Arts 4 Curriculum.

Date _____

◢◤ A Beka Book®

Fourth Grade Progress Report

Student Name _____
                  Last   First   Middle

Home Teacher _____

Mailing Address _____

City, State ZIP CODE _____

Country _____

ARITHMETIC TESTS

Lesson	**Test**	Grade
92	**9**	_____
102	**10**	_____
112	**11**	_____
122	**12**	_____
132	**13**	_____
	Average	_____

ARITHMETIC QUIZZES

Lesson	Quiz	Grade
97	10	_____
107	11	_____
117	12	_____
127	13	_____
	Average	_____

ARITHMETIC SPEED DRILLS

Lesson	Grade
95	_____
100	_____
105	_____
109	_____
115	_____
116	_____
125	_____
130	_____
133	_____
Average	_____
Final Average	_____

Home Teacher:

Record numerical grades on lines.

BIBLE

Verses	Grade
Matthew 7:24–27	_____
Matthew 6:19–24	_____
Matthew 20:25–28	_____
Isaiah 40:28–31	_____
John 20:30–31	_____
Average	_____

Note: Record Bible grades here only if not using Home School Language Arts 4 Curriculum.

Date _____

◀◀ A Beka Book®
Fourth Grade Progress Report

Student Name _____
             Last   First   Middle

Home Teacher _____

Mailing Address _____

City, State ZIP CODE _____

Country _____

ARITHMETIC TESTS

Lesson	Test	Grade
92	9	_____
102	10	_____
112	11	_____
122	12	_____
132	13	_____
	Average	_____

ARITHMETIC QUIZZES

Lesson	Quiz	Grade
97	10	_____
107	11	_____
117	12	_____
127	13	_____
	Average	_____

ARITHMETIC SPEED DRILLS

Lesson	Grade
95	_____
100	_____
105	_____
109	_____
115	_____
116	_____
125	_____
130	_____
133	_____
Average	_____
Final Average	_____

Home Teacher:

Record numerical grades
on lines.

BIBLE

Verses	Grade
Matthew 7:24–27	_____
Matthew 6:19–24	_____
Matthew 20:25–28	_____
Isaiah 40:28–31	_____
John 20:30–31	_____
Average	_____

Note: Record Bible grades here only if not
using Home School Language Arts 4
Curriculum.

Date _____

A Beka Book.
Fourth Grade Progress Report

Student Name _____
Last   First   Middle

Home Teacher _____

Mailing Address _____

City, State ZIP CODE _____

Country _____

ARITHMETIC TESTS

Lesson	**Test**	Grade
142	**14**	_____
152	**15**	_____
162	**16**	_____
170	Final Exam	_____
	Average	_____

ARITHMETIC QUIZZES

Lesson	Quiz	Grade
137	14	_____
147	15	_____
157	16	_____
	Average	_____

ARITHMETIC SPEED DRILLS

Lesson	Grade
138	_____
144	_____
148	_____
155	_____
159	_____
Average	_____
Final Average	_____

Home Teacher:

Record numerical grades on lines.

BIBLE

Verses	Grade
1 Thessalonians 4:13–18	_____
Matthew 22:36–40	_____
John 16:7–14	_____
Average	_____

Note: Record Bible grades here only if not using Home School Language Arts 4 Curriculum.

Fourth Grading Period
Lessons 136–178

Date _____

A Beka Book®
Fourth Grade Progress Report

Student Name _____

Last   First   Middle

Home Teacher _____

Mailing Address _____

City, State ZIP CODE _____

Country _____

ARITHMETIC TESTS

Lesson	Test	Grade
142	**14**	_____
152	**15**	_____
162	**16**	_____
170	Final Exam	_____
	Average	_____

ARITHMETIC QUIZZES

Lesson	Quiz	Grade
137	14	_____
147	15	_____
157	16	_____
	Average	_____

ARITHMETIC SPEED DRILLS

Lesson	Grade
138	_____
144	_____
148	_____
155	_____
159	_____
Average	_____
Final Average	_____

Home Teacher:

Record numerical grades
on lines.

BIBLE

Verses	Grade
1 Thessalonians 4:13–18	_____
Matthew 22:36–40	_____
John 16:7–14	_____
Average	_____

Note: Record Bible grades here only if not
using Home School Language Arts 4
Curriculum.

HOME SCHOOL
ARITHMETIC 4
Curriculum/Lesson Plans

CONTENTS

 *A Beka Book*® Pensacola, FL 32523-9100
a ministry of PENSACOLA CHRISTIAN COLLEGE

Why Traditional Arithmetic?
Seven Reasons to Choose *A Beka* Arithmetic

Traditional arithmetic gives glory to God.

Do you believe that God created the heavens and the earth? Do you believe that God had a plan for creation just as He had a plan for the salvation of man? God is never surprised by His actions. Our orderly, rational God used mathematics as He created the world and set it into motion. **Traditional arithmetic promotes structure and order and shows children an aspect of the order of the real world.** It helps children to know more about the character of the God Who created them. Children find exactness, preciseness, and completeness in traditional arithmetic, just as is expected in God's world.

Traditional arithmetic promotes absolute truth.

Do you believe that there is a right answer and a wrong answer? Do you believe that Jesus Christ died for your sins and rose from the dead? A Christian answers *yes* because a Christian believes that in this world of changing social standards, truth remains unchanged and unchangeable. **Traditional arithmetic is the mathematics program that promotes absolute truth.** In traditional arithmetic, children are not taught to manipulate sets and thus change truth. Instead, they are taught truth as created by an orderly, rational God.

Traditional arithmetic encourages good work habits.

Do you believe that a job worth doing is worth doing well? Colossians 3:23 says, *And whatsoever ye do, do it heartily, as to the Lord, and not unto men.* More than any other subject, arithmetic requires the stretching of the brain, constant thinking and remembering, and complete attention. Just as the body is tired after a physical workout, the mind is tired after a math workout using traditional math. But also as the physical workout strengthens the body, **the traditional arithmetic workout strengthens the mind.** C. T. Studd, missionary to Africa, understood this principle of doing a job well and used it in his work with a people who had just risen from the depths of cannibalism. Studd's reasoning is described:

> Every pole had to be exactly the right length, placed at the right angle, etc.; and he had a purpose in it, for the natives must be taught that good Christianity and lazy or bad workmanship are an utter contradiction. He believed that one of the best ways to teach a native that righteousness is the foundation of God's Throne was by making him see that absolute straightness and accuracy is the only law of success in material things.

(*C. T. Studd,* Norman Grubb, Fort Washington, Pennsylvania, Christian Literature Crusade, 1972, 1974)

Traditional arithmetic trains the intellect.

Would you read this article more closely if a graded quiz followed or if you were given an oral examination? If you were expected to know these facts, you might make a list of them and say them over and over until you had them memorized. You would probably review them every day for several days to make sure you remembered them. **Traditional arithmetic expects children to learn and remember necessary facts.** A traditional arithmetic program is not ashamed that children must memorize facts, because memorization of facts promotes an acceptance of absolute truth. Children need to memorize facts for these three additional reasons:

1. **It lays the correct foundation for understanding mathematics.**
   Just as a Christian memorizes Bible verses and principles to build strong Christian character, the math student memorizes facts to build mathematical knowledge.

2. **It increases the child's capacity to understand concepts.**
   Math is a building-block subject in which facts are needed to learn new concepts. A child can easily understand that 2 x 6 = 12 because he knows that 6 + 6 = 12.

3. **It helps the child develop concepts.**
   Have a child memorize that there are twelve things in a dozen. Teach the concept that two halves are two equal parts of a whole. The child can then bring together the two learned facts to tell that there are six things in one-half dozen. He can also tell that six inches are one-half foot because he has memorized that there are twelve inches in a foot.

Traditional arithmetic is usable.

Why do you enjoy a beautiful painting? You may like to look at its beauty of color and light. You may enjoy the memories it brings to your mind. All would agree that the painting brings beauty to our lives. These are appropriate responses to art. The modern mathematician views math in the same way you view your painting. He sees the beauty of structure and form. Modern math inappropriately tries to make all children learn and appreciate this structure. The appreciation of math for its **structure** is a mistaken view of mathematics, for God used mathematics as a **tool** to benefit mankind. The using of mathematics in science, architecture, business, technology, etc., is what makes math beneficial—not the learning of its rigid structure. **Children are taught in traditional arithmetic to count, add, tell time, give change, find interest, etc., because it is useful for them to do so.**

Traditional arithmetic builds Christian character.

Do you believe Philippians 4:8? *Finally, brethren, whatsoever things are true, whatsoever things are honest, whatsoever things are just, whatsoever things are pure, whatsoever things are lovely, whatsoever things are of good report; if there be any virtue, and if there be any praise, think on these things.* Story problems do more than help children apply mathematical knowledge. They influence the thinking of the children by the way they are presented and the subject matter of the word problem. They can show people working, tithing, enjoying God's world, and engaging in Christian activities, or they can show only secular interests and behavior. **The *A Beka* traditional arithmetic program uses word problems that help to develop strong Christian character.**

Traditional arithmetic lays the foundation for higher mathematics.

Elementary arithmetic, quite naturally, begins with the most elementary, basic arithmetic processes. Children learn best when they proceed from the particular to the general, from the concrete to the abstract. Traditional elementary arithmetic properly emphasizes the facts of addition, subtraction, multiplication, and division that accord with the child's stage of mental development and have immediate practical application. **Traditional arithmetic lays a solid foundation for high school math, which appropriately (but still gradually) introduces the children to a higher level of abstraction.** The child learns and understands algebra and all higher math better if he masters arithmetic first.

Instructional Materials

Child Materials

Arithmetic 4 Student Workbook
The pages in the workbook are designed as practice and review over the material the parent teaches.

Tests and Speed Drills
Four speed drills and either a test or a quiz are included for each week.

Parent Materials

Teacher Key
This spiral-bound teacher text/answer key contains all student exercises and their solutions. Answers for story problems are given with the story problems, but solutions are in a special section of this book.

Tests and Speed Drills Key
It is like the student copy except that the answers for the speed drills, quizzes, and tests are included. The quizzes and tests also have a suggested grading scale.

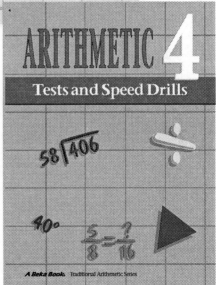

Home School Curriculum / Lesson Plans
This idea-packed daily guide ensures the best use of the text. The lesson plans are easy to read and follow, and a minimum of study time is required for each lesson.

Visual Aids

Flashcards and More

- *Addition Flashcards* (recommended)—189 cards for Addition Families 1–18 (pp. T15–T18 of this curriculum)
- *Subtraction Flashcards* (recommended)—189 cards for Subtraction Families 1–18 (pp. T15–T18)
- *Multiplication Flashcards* (recommended)—156 cards for Multiplication Tables 1–12 (pp. T18–T21)
- *Division Flashcards* (recommended)—156 cards for Division Tables 1–12 (pp. T18–T21)
- *Arithmetic 3–4 Concept Cards* (recommended)—193 cards for many categories, such as place value, measures, fractions, decimals, and geometry
- Coins (recommended)—20 pennies, 10 nickels, 10 dimes, 4 quarters, and 2 half dollars
- Fractional Circles (recommended)—many felt pieces that make teaching fractions fun and easy

  Using 8 different colors of felt or construction paper, cut 8 circles of the same size, one from each color. Leave one circle whole. Cut one in halves, one in thirds, one in fourths, one in fifths, one in sixths, one in eighths, and one in tenths. This set will be used first through sixth grade.
- *Arithmetic 3–8 Tables and Facts Charts* (pp. T18–T22)

Home School Arithmetic 3–8 Charts (essential)

Place Value Charts	*Angles*
Division Steps	*Ratios*
Multiplication and Division Tables	*Triangles*
English Linear Measures	*Percent*
English Measures of Weight	*Circle*
English Measures of Capacity	*Protractor*
Measures of Time	*1–100 Chart, 101–200 Chart*
Averaging Numbers	*Rolling Rulers* (in. and cm)
Fractions	*Calculator*
Metric Units of Length	*"Lion" Graph*
Metric Units of Weight	
Metric Units of Capacity	
Roman Numerals	
Divisibility Rules	
Geometry	
Decimals	
Perimeter	
Area	
Rounding Charts	
Fraction/Decimal Equivalents	
Temperatures	

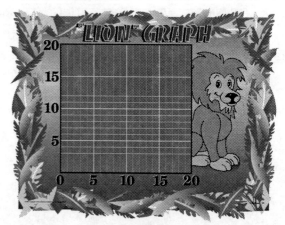

Yearly Goals

- Recognize the place-value of numbers through millions.
- Know addition facts and be able to work and check addition problems with carrying.
- Know subtraction facts and be able to work and check subtraction problems with borrowing.
- Know 0–12 multiplication tables and be able to work multiplication problems with carrying. Multiplication problems may have up to three digits in the second factor.
- Know 1–12 division tables and be able to work and check division problems. Division problems may have up to two digits in the divisor. It may be necessary to use estimation when finding the quotient.
- Know terminology of four processes.
- Solve story problems.
- Average numbers.
- Estimate answers.
- Know English and metric measures.
- Convert measures and solve measurement equations.
- Know Roman numerals 1–1,000.
- Know fraction terminology and how to solve problems containing fractions. Add and subtract fractions and mixed numbers with a common or uncommon denominator. Recognize proper and improper fractions. Change mixed numbers to improper fractions and change improper fractions to mixed numbers. Reduce fractions to lowest terms. Write answers in fraction problems in lowest terms. Subtract fractions involving borrowing. Write a remainder as a fraction. Multiply fractions using cancellation. Write a fraction as a decimal.
- Factor numbers to find the greatest common factor.
- Find the least common multiple shared by two or more numbers.
- Know divisibility rules for 2, 3, 4, 5, 9, and 10.
- Recognize the place-value of decimals. Write a decimal as a fraction. Add and subtract decimals. Use the decimal in money problems.
- Make correct change.
- Read a thermometer.
- Solve equations containing an unknown number.
- Recognize and read pictographs, bar graphs, and line graphs.
- Draw and read scale drawings of maps.
- Recognize and draw some of the geometric shapes and figures.
- Find the perimeter of a polygon. Find the perimeter of a rectangle and a square using the correct formula.
- Find the area of a rectangle and a square using the correct formula.

Scope and Sequence

Week	Lessons	Review Material	New Material
1	1–5	One-step story problems Addition with carrying Addition terminology Checking addition Money values and problems Subtraction with borrowing Subtraction terminology Checking subtraction Multiplication terminology Multiplication process involving carrying	Place value of large numbers Recognition of story problem clue words
2	6–10	Missing factors Counting bills and coins Two-digit multiplication Division with a one-digit divisor Division terminology Continued review of previous lessons	Checking multiplication
3	11–15	Time lapse Two-step story problems Checking division Continued review of previous lessons	Multiplication by 10 and 100
4	16–20	English linear measures Simple measurement problems Simple measurement equations Measurement equations Continued review of previous lessons	
5	21–25	English liquid measures Symbols for greater than and less than English table of weight measures Checking division with a remainder Continued review of previous lessons	8 fluid ounces = 1 cup
6	26–30	Measuring to the nearest inch Division with a money dividend Averaging numbers Continued review of previous lessons	
7	31–35	Fraction terminology Finding fractional part of an object Continued review of previous lessons	Multiplying by a three-digit factor
8	36–40	Fractional parts of a group Measuring to the nearest half inch Division with a two-digit divisor Remainders as fractions Continued review of previous lessons	Estimating quotients

Week	Lessons	Review Material	New Material
9	41–45	Adding fractions with common denominators Subtracting fractions with common denominators Terms: whole number, fraction, mixed number Continued review of previous lessons	
10	46–50	Addition and subtraction of mixed numbers Metric units of length Continued review of previous lessons	Metric prefixes
11	51–55	Measures of time Continued review of previous lessons	Factoring 10 years = 1 decade 20 years = 1 score 100 years = 1 century 1,000 years = 1 millennium
12	56–60	Measuring to the nearest centimeter Measuring to the nearest quarter inch Continued review of previous lessons	Finding common factors Greatest common factor
13	61–65	Reducing fractions Continued review of previous lessons	
14	66–70	Metric units of weight Continued review of previous lessons	Proper and improper fractions Fraction bar as a division symbol Changing improper fractions to whole numbers or mixed numbers
15	71–75	Dry measures Equivalent fractions Continued review of previous lessons	Simplifying sums that contain improper fractions
16	76–80	Continued review of previous lessons	Least common multiple Finding least common denominators Addition and subtraction of fractions with uncommon denominators
17	81–85	Roman numerals 1–1,000 Continued review of previous lessons	Roman numeral rules Estimation
18	86–90	Continued review of previous lessons	Estimating two-digit divisors ending in 5, 6, 7, 8, or 9 Whole numbers as improper fractions Subtraction of fractions with borrowing
19	91–95	Continued review of previous lessons	Borrowing when subtracting fractions when the minuend is not one
20	96–100	Continued review of previous lessons	Borrowing with uncommon denominators Changing mixed numbers to improper fractions

Week	Lessons	Review Material	New Material
21	101–105	Continued review of previous lessons	Multiplying fractions
22	106–110	Continued review of previous lessons	Divisibility rules Using divisibility rules to reduce fractions Cancellation
23	111–115	Story problems with missing information Continued review of previous lessons	Multiplying a fraction and a whole number
24	116–120	Estimating money to the nearest dollar Continued review of previous lessons	Estimating distances Multiplying fractions and mixed numbers
25	121–125	Continued review of previous lessons	Pictographs Bar graphs
26	126–130	Continued review of previous lessons	Line graphs Introduction to decimals Decimal place-value Writing decimals as fractions
27	131–135	Continued review of previous lessons	Addition and subtraction of decimals Scale drawings
28	136–140	Metric units of liquid measure Measuring temperature Temperature reference points Continued review of previous lessons	Counting back change Checking change
29	141–145	Continued review of previous lessons	Using algebraic principles to solve equations
30	146–150	Continued review of previous lessons	1 tbsp. = 3 tsp. Introduction to geometry Geometric shapes
31	151–155	Continued review of previous lessons	Concept of perimeter Finding perimeter of a rectangle Finding perimeter of a square
32	156–160	Continued review of previous lessons	Concept of area Finding area of a rectangle Finding area of a square
33	161–165	Continued review of previous lessons	Square measures
34	166–170	Continued review of previous lessons	

Parent Information

🍎 What books are needed?

Your child needs a copy of *Arithmetic 4*. Most days, two pages are completed during class. *Arithmetic 4* contains a variety of exercises involving new and review material taught in each lesson. Although all new material is discussed at the top of the workbook page, it is vital that your child hears a thorough explanation of each concept and sees procedures demonstrated step by step by the parent. The workbook contains 169 lessons excluding 16 tests. The final exam is lesson 170. **Many pages of supplementary exercises are included after the 169 lessons.** These can be used throughout the year as remedial help, as a reward for children who work quickly, or as review lessons to complete the 180 days of school. For the child's benefit, a handbook is included at the end of the book. This handbook contains facts, rules, and measures which are given throughout the workbook.

The parent needs a copy of the *Arithmetic 4 Teacher Edition*. The spiral-bound text has all child exercises and solutions.

🍎 How long is arithmetic class?

Allow approximately **thirty five to forty minutes** for arithmetic class. The arithmetic class includes oral and written review, the introduction of new concepts, and the practice of new concepts. Your child does a written speed drill and the pages of the workbook during the arithmetic time. Most pages include *Class Practice* and *Review/Boardwork*. Class time will depend on whether *Review/Boardwork* is done with a parent or independently.

Class Practice follows the teaching of the new concept or skill. It often includes concepts that were taught recently but explained by the parent again. Many story problems are worked together as part of *Class Practice*. Your child is helped to develop strong story problem attack skills.

Review/Boardwork follows the teaching of new concepts and review of previously learned concepts. Daily written *Review* is necessary for any successful arithmetic program. Three days each week a *Homework* section is included.

Homework is always review and is easily completed by most children. Your child should complete this section during independent study time. Of course, if he successfully completes the worksheet during class before the thirty-five minutes are over, he can do the *Homework* section during class.

🍎 How is an oral review drill conducted?

Arithmetic class begins with an oral review drill, which is probably the most important part of the arithmetic class. The time allotted is usually nine minutes, although the time does change occasionally. Children look forward to this time when it is conducted in an interesting, challenging, and exciting manner.

Although the oral review activities are listed in a specific order in the daily plans, parents do not need to follow that order. However, all oral review listed for a particular day should be reviewed. Oral review can be used at times other than the beginning of class. Occasionally, review multiplication tables at other times. Be imaginative and time-conscious.

Mental arithmetic and rapid calculations play an important part of oral review. The parent sets the pace for the long addition problems and the multiple combinations. Children become faster as they push themselves to concentrate and do their best. You may want to have a math champ or other incentives to cause child to do his best. Children find that if they stretch their minds during these mental work times, that they develop speed that helps them finish the worksheet quickly.

The key to good oral review is variety and a review time that moves rapidly from one review to another. Oral review is successful for the child only if he participates. A child who is actively involved in oral review is alert and participating verbally in every drill.

During oral review, challenge the child to become faster each day, and be quick to notice progress made. Make good use of games, for they require your child to know the answer.

Many suggestions for oral review are included in this *Curriculum / Lesson Plans*.

What is the purpose of the written speed drills?

The written speed drill follows the oral review. Speed drills are in the *Student Tests and Speed Drills*. The speed drills, quizzes, and tests are arranged in the order that you use them. The time to allow for each speed drill is on the drill and in the *Curriculum / Lesson Plans*. If a child seems slow at first, encourage him to work up to your time. Eventually the child's hard work results in a better speed.

Always encourage him to do his best work and to work quickly by competing with himself. If a child missed seven yesterday, he should try to miss six or fewer today. Gradual improvement is certainly better than no improvement. Children work hard and strive for excellence if you recognize improvement. Parents who use a variety of motivational ideas have children who enjoy and do well with speed drills.

One speed drill per week is marked as a quiz. Grade this speed drill. Record as a speed drill/quiz grade on the progress report.

How is a new concept introduced?

Approach each new concept with enthusiasm and confidence. Your excitement of learning is caught by the most reluctant child, and your belief that he can learn encourages the timid child. This *Curriculum / Lesson Plans* gives suggestions for introducing each new concept. **Adjust the suggestions to your child to present the most effective explanation.**

Usually something new is introduced or reviewed each day. The time allotted depends on the difficulty and the newness of the con-

cept. When teaching a new concept, be sure you understand the concept and study carefully the steps given in this *Curriculum / Lesson Plans* and the workbook. It helps to anticipate the questions your child will ask. Build up his interest in the new concept and expect him to do well. The explanations are made concrete by using visual aids and experiences the child understands.

Don't expect a child to understand a new concept the first time it is presented. Your child has varying degrees of understanding. The spiral review allows him to understand at his level and to master important concepts and facts. Many suggestions are given for reviewing concepts. You may want to read the suggestions for introducing the concept again the first few times a concept is reviewed.

How do I conduct a review time?

Often there is a review time after the introduction and practice of the new concept. This is a time for the child to master the material and get it firmly planted in his mind. Direct questions to your child as you reteach a topic. You will then be able to discern if he understands the steps to follow and if he has memorized the necessary tables, measurements, rules, etc., in order to solve the problem correctly.

Many of your questions should be directed to those areas where child is weak or average in arithmetic. When a child does not respond with a correct answer or with any answer, visualize the problem or reword the question so he can give a correct answer. If he still does not know a correct response, tell him the answer. Then, have him give the correct response. If he gives an incorrect response to the same question, stop the review and reteach the concept.

Where does the child work the story problems?

Story problems need to be set up in the proper manner as shown in lesson 1 of *Arithmetic 4* and should be written neatly. **They are worked on the child's notebook paper, since space is not available on the**

worksheet. He should write just the answer in the workbook. You may want him to use the same sheet of paper until it is filled. That means he must keep it in a place that is easily accessible.

Story problems are designed to teach the child to think and plan the solving of problems by himself. At first, the parent needs to guide the child's thinking. Gradually the child works more independently.

🍎 When does the child do *review/boardwork?*

The section *Review / Boardwork* is the last activity in arithmetic time. This is a time for your child to review. Stress neatness, accuracy, and speed.

🍎 What is *Extra Practice?*

A few lessons have a section called *Extra Practice*. It is not necessary for these problems to be completed. They are problems that can be done if there is sufficient time. They are great for a child who is faster and is left with nothing to do at the end of the arithmetic time.

🍎 Do I assign homework?

A *Homework* section is included on three lessons per week and falls on Mondays, Thursdays, and Fridays. Of course, adjustments can easily be made to fit your schedule. *Homework* assignments are review material and can be completed by most children in ten to fifteen minutes. A child who is new to *A Beka Book* may take up to thirty minutes if he is weak with his facts. As he participates in oral and written drill, he will improve and become faster with his homework and all arithmetic work.

A child does the *Homework* section during independent study time since this section was designed to be completed after *Class Practice* and *Review / Boardwork*.

The *Homework* section is checked the following day for completeness.

🍎 How are multiplication and division tables taught?

Use the charts from *Multiplication and Division Tables and Facts* (pp T15–T22) to review the tables. Child should say the tables at the beginning of the year by looking at them. Keep several tables displayed so child can study during any free time.

When child says the multiplication facts, he says the entire sentence as *3 times 2 equals 6*. The division sentence he says is *6 divided by 2 equals 3*.

He learns the multiplication tables faster if the twins in multiplication are stressed. A twin of a multiplication fact is the fact with the order of the factors switched. 2 x 3 = 6 is the twin of 3 x 2 = 6. **Because the order of the factors is changed without changing the product, reverse the order in which factors are said by the child.** For instance, when saying Multiplication Table 5, sometimes say 5 as the second factor and sometimes say 5 as the first factor.

If a child understands the concept of multiplication twins, he has fewer combinations to learn as the table number increases. For example, when he gets to Multiplication Table 9, he will have already learned 0 x 9 = 0 to 8 x 9 = 72 in Tables 0–8.

The *Curriculum / Lesson Plans* also devotes time to mastering the subtraction and addition facts. If a child is weak with the facts, have him study the *Supplementary Exercises* at the end of the book.

🍎 How do I use the *Supplementary Exercises?*

These pages were designed to be helpful to children and parents. They can be used in a multitude of ways, and they help to make the arithmetic program a great success.

The first few pages are devoted to the four processes and number facts that the child should memorize. You may want your child to write just the answers to the facts on a piece of paper so the fact pages can be used again and again.

Later pages in *Supplementary Exercises* are many additional problems arranged by categories according to the concept. For example, there is a whole page of problems dealing with averaging. If a child is having trouble with averaging, refer him to this page. You can have the child work in the workbook or on a sheet of paper. If the child works on paper, the problems can be used more than once.

All of the *Supplementary Exercises* can be used for review days. You can also use the problems if you want to give additional help. They are also great for children who quickly finish their worksheet and have nothing to do. These children will love the additional story problems and the brain boosters.

🍎 How do I test?

Arithmetic tests and quizzes are in the *Student Tests and Speed Drills*. A test is given every other week. On the weeks that no test is given, a fifteen minute quiz is given. Tests and quizzes are scheduled for Tuesday beginning the second week of school. Another day can be used if it fits your schedule better. One speed drill per week is graded. Both this *Curriculum/Lesson Plans* and *Teacher Tests and Speed Drills* denote the graded speed drills.

When taking the arithmetic test, the child needs a checking sheet. On the checking sheet, the child recopies a portion of his test and works the problems again. Then he checks these answers against the ones on his test. If an answer is not the same, the problem should be worked until the same answer is reached two times. **Checking should not begin until the child has completed the entire test.** This procedure is helpful in eliminating careless mistakes.

A child will benefit greatly if he is able to see his graded test within a day or two after the test is given. If a child did poorly, it is helpful for him to rework the test problems he missed on a sheet of paper. This would not change his grade but would help him understand where he made his errors.

How do I grade my child?

The *Teacher Tests and Speed Drills* has complete instructions for giving and grading the speed drills, quizzes, and tests. Suggested grading scales for the quizzes, weekly graded speed drills, and tests are also in the book. Record grades on the progress reports.

Only record the one graded speed drill per week. This graded speed drill is recorded as a speed drill/quiz grade. Average all speed drill/quiz grades together for a grading period. **The speed drill/quiz average is equal to one quiz grade.**

Grade and record quizzes. Average all quiz grades together for a grading period. **The quiz average is equal to one test grade.**

Grade and record tests. **The tests and the quiz average are averaged together to get the final grade for the grading period.**

It is not necessary to grade the pages in *Arithmetic 4*. Go over the answers so the child has immediate feedback. Check his paper to make sure he understands and is doing his best. Display the pages so the family can see the child's progress.

🍎 How do I give remedial help?

You may find your child needs extra help about two weeks into the school year. Plan help time two to three times per week for about ten minutes. Spend help time on multiplication and division tables, practicing addition and subtraction facts, learning measures, and working problems that are difficult for the child. Use the process flashcards, *Concept Cards,* and oral combinations. Have a balance of oral drill, chalkboard practice, and fun games. Praise him as he works hard to make progress.

If a child is doing poorly with the facts, occasionally do not give the ungraded speed drill for the day. Practice the facts on the speed drill for the five minutes allotted it. Do not make up the speed drill.

Supplementary Exercises are at the end of *Arithmetic 4*. Facts for all four processes are given for the child to study. Problems are given for him to work. To be able to use the problems over and over, have the child answer on a sheet of paper. You may want to have him give answers orally to the fact problems.

Addition and Subtraction Families

1 Family

0 + 1 = 1	1 − 1 = 0
1 + 0 = 1	1 − 0 = 1

2 Family

0 + 2 = 2	2 − 2 = 0
1 + 1 = 2	2 − 1 = 1
2 + 0 = 2	2 − 0 = 2

3 Family

0 + 3 = 3	3 − 3 = 0
1 + 2 = 3	3 − 2 = 1
2 + 1 = 3	3 − 1 = 2
3 + 0 = 3	3 − 0 = 3

4 Family

0 + 4 = 4	4 − 4 = 0
1 + 3 = 4	4 − 3 = 1
2 + 2 = 4	4 − 2 = 2
3 + 1 = 4	4 − 1 = 3
4 + 0 = 4	4 − 0 = 4

5 Family

0 + 5 = 5	5 − 5 = 0
1 + 4 = 5	5 − 4 = 1
2 + 3 = 5	5 − 3 = 2
3 + 2 = 5	5 − 2 = 3
4 + 1 = 5	5 − 1 = 4
5 + 0 = 5	5 − 0 = 5

6 Family

0 + 6 = 6	6 − 6 = 0
1 + 5 = 6	6 − 5 = 1
2 + 4 = 6	6 − 4 = 2
3 + 3 = 6	6 − 3 = 3
4 + 2 = 6	6 − 2 = 4
5 + 1 = 6	6 − 1 = 5
6 + 0 = 6	6 − 0 = 6

7 Family

0 + 7 = 7	7 − 7 = 0
1 + 6 = 7	7 − 6 = 1
2 + 5 = 7	7 − 5 = 2
3 + 4 = 7	7 − 4 = 3
4 + 3 = 7	7 − 3 = 4
5 + 2 = 7	7 − 2 = 5
6 + 1 = 7	7 − 1 = 6
7 + 0 = 7	7 − 0 = 7

8 Family

0 + 8 = 8	8 − 8 = 0
1 + 7 = 8	8 − 7 = 1
2 + 6 = 8	8 − 6 = 2
3 + 5 = 8	8 − 5 = 3
4 + 4 = 8	8 − 4 = 4
5 + 3 = 8	8 − 3 = 5
6 + 2 = 8	8 − 2 = 6
7 + 1 = 8	8 − 1 = 7
8 + 0 = 8	8 − 0 = 8

Addition and Subtraction Families

9 Family

0 + 9 = 9		9 − 9 = 0		
1 + 8 = 9		9 − 8 = 1		
2 + 7 = 9		9 − 7 = 2		
3 + 6 = 9		9 − 6 = 3		
4 + 5 = 9		9 − 5 = 4		
5 + 4 = 9		9 − 4 = 5		
6 + 3 = 9		9 − 3 = 6		
7 + 2 = 9		9 − 2 = 7		
8 + 1 = 9		9 − 1 = 8		
9 + 0 = 9		9 − 0 = 9		

10 Family

0 + 10 = 10	10 − 10 = 0
1 + 9 = 10	10 − 9 = 1
2 + 8 = 10	10 − 8 = 2
3 + 7 = 10	10 − 7 = 3
4 + 6 = 10	10 − 6 = 4
5 + 5 = 10	10 − 5 = 5
6 + 4 = 10	10 − 4 = 6
7 + 3 = 10	10 − 3 = 7
8 + 2 = 10	10 − 2 = 8
9 + 1 = 10	10 − 1 = 9
10 + 0 = 10	10 − 0 = 10

11 Family

0 + 11 = 11	11 − 11 = 0
1 + 10 = 11	11 − 10 = 1
2 + 9 = 11	11 − 9 = 2
3 + 8 = 11	11 − 8 = 3
4 + 7 = 11	11 − 7 = 4
5 + 6 = 11	11 − 6 = 5
6 + 5 = 11	11 − 5 = 6
7 + 4 = 11	11 − 4 = 7
8 + 3 = 11	11 − 3 = 8
9 + 2 = 11	11 − 2 = 9
10 + 1 = 11	11 − 1 = 10
11 + 0 = 11	11 − 0 = 11

12 Family

0 + 12 = 12	12 − 12 = 0
1 + 11 = 12	12 − 11 = 1
2 + 10 = 12	12 − 10 = 2
3 + 9 = 12	12 − 9 = 3
4 + 8 = 12	12 − 8 = 4
5 + 7 = 12	12 − 7 = 5
6 + 6 = 12	12 − 6 = 6
7 + 5 = 12	12 − 5 = 7
8 + 4 = 12	12 − 4 = 8
9 + 3 = 12	12 − 3 = 9
10 + 2 = 12	12 − 2 = 10
11 + 1 = 12	12 − 1 = 11
12 + 0 = 12	12 − 0 = 12

13 Family

0 + 13 = 13	13 − 13 = 0
1 + 12 = 13	13 − 12 = 1
2 + 11 = 13	13 − 11 = 2
3 + 10 = 13	13 − 10 = 3
4 + 9 = 13	13 − 9 = 4
5 + 8 = 13	13 − 8 = 5
6 + 7 = 13	13 − 7 = 6
7 + 6 = 13	13 − 6 = 7
8 + 5 = 13	13 − 5 = 8
9 + 4 = 13	13 − 4 = 9
10 + 3 = 13	13 − 3 = 10
11 + 2 = 13	13 − 2 = 11
12 + 1 = 13	13 − 1 = 12
13 + 0 = 13	13 − 0 = 13

14 Family

0 + 14 = 14	14 − 14 = 0
1 + 13 = 14	14 − 13 = 1
2 + 12 = 14	14 − 12 = 2
3 + 11 = 14	14 − 11 = 3
4 + 10 = 14	14 − 10 = 4
5 + 9 = 14	14 − 9 = 5
6 + 8 = 14	14 − 8 = 6
7 + 7 = 14	14 − 7 = 7
8 + 6 = 14	14 − 6 = 8
9 + 5 = 14	14 − 5 = 9
10 + 4 = 14	14 − 4 = 10
11 + 3 = 14	14 − 3 = 11
12 + 2 = 14	14 − 2 = 12
13 + 1 = 14	14 − 1 = 13
14 + 0 = 14	14 − 0 = 14

15 Family

0 + 15 = 15	15 − 15 = 0
1 + 14 = 15	15 − 14 = 1
2 + 13 = 15	15 − 13 = 2
3 + 12 = 15	15 − 12 = 3
4 + 11 = 15	15 − 11 = 4
5 + 10 = 15	15 − 10 = 5
6 + 9 = 15	15 − 9 = 6
7 + 8 = 15	15 − 8 = 7
8 + 7 = 15	15 − 7 = 8
9 + 6 = 15	15 − 6 = 9
10 + 5 = 15	15 − 5 = 10
11 + 4 = 15	15 − 4 = 11
12 + 3 = 15	15 − 3 = 12
13 + 2 = 15	15 − 2 = 13
14 + 1 = 15	15 − 1 = 14
15 + 0 = 15	15 − 0 = 15

16 Family

0 + 16 = 16	16 − 16 = 0
1 + 15 = 16	16 − 15 = 1
2 + 14 = 16	16 − 14 = 2
3 + 13 = 16	16 − 13 = 3
4 + 12 = 16	16 − 12 = 4
5 + 11 = 16	16 − 11 = 5
6 + 10 = 16	16 − 10 = 6
7 + 9 = 16	16 − 9 = 7
8 + 8 = 16	16 − 8 = 8
9 + 7 = 16	16 − 7 = 9
10 + 6 = 16	16 − 6 = 10
11 + 5 = 16	16 − 5 = 11
12 + 4 = 16	16 − 4 = 12
13 + 3 = 16	16 − 3 = 13
14 + 2 = 16	16 − 2 = 14
15 + 1 = 16	16 − 1 = 15
16 + 0 = 16	16 − 0 = 16

17 Family

0 + 17 = 17	17 − 17 = 0
1 + 16 = 17	17 − 16 = 1
2 + 15 = 17	17 − 15 = 2
3 + 14 = 17	17 − 14 = 3
4 + 13 = 17	17 − 13 = 4
5 + 12 = 17	17 − 12 = 5
6 + 11 = 17	17 − 11 = 6
7 + 10 = 17	17 − 10 = 7
8 + 9 = 17	17 − 9 = 8
9 + 8 = 17	17 − 8 = 9
10 + 7 = 17	17 − 7 = 10
11 + 6 = 17	17 − 6 = 11
12 + 5 = 17	17 − 5 = 12
13 + 4 = 17	17 − 4 = 13
14 + 3 = 17	17 − 3 = 14
15 + 2 = 17	17 − 2 = 15
16 + 1 = 17	17 − 1 = 16
17 + 0 = 17	17 − 0 = 17

18 Family

0 + 18 = 18	18 − 18 = 0
1 + 17 = 18	18 − 17 = 1
2 + 16 = 18	18 − 16 = 2
3 + 15 = 18	18 − 15 = 3
4 + 14 = 18	18 − 14 = 4
5 + 13 = 18	18 − 13 = 5
6 + 12 = 18	18 − 12 = 6
7 + 11 = 18	18 − 11 = 7
8 + 10 = 18	18 − 10 = 8
9 + 9 = 18	18 − 9 = 9
10 + 8 = 18	18 − 8 = 10
11 + 7 = 18	18 − 7 = 11
12 + 6 = 18	18 − 6 = 12
13 + 5 = 18	18 − 5 = 13
14 + 4 = 18	18 − 4 = 14
15 + 3 = 18	18 − 3 = 15
16 + 2 = 18	18 − 2 = 16
17 + 1 = 18	18 − 1 = 17
18 + 0 = 18	18 − 0 = 18

Multiplication and Division Tables/Facts

Chart 1

Mult. Table

0	x	0	=	0
1	x	0	=	0
2	x	0	=	0
3	x	0	=	0
4	x	0	=	0
5	x	0	=	0
6	x	0	=	0
7	x	0	=	0
8	x	0	=	0
9	x	0	=	0
10	x	0	=	0
11	x	0	=	0
12	x	0	=	0

Chart 2

Mult. Table

0	x	1	=	0
1	x	1	=	1
2	x	1	=	2
3	x	1	=	3
4	x	1	=	4
5	x	1	=	5
6	x	1	=	6
7	x	1	=	7
8	x	1	=	8
9	x	1	=	9
10	x	1	=	10
11	x	1	=	11
12	x	1	=	12

Div. Table

0	÷	1	=	0
1	÷	1	=	1
2	÷	1	=	2
3	÷	1	=	3
4	÷	1	=	4
5	÷	1	=	5
6	÷	1	=	6
7	÷	1	=	7
8	÷	1	=	8
9	÷	1	=	9
10	÷	1	=	10
11	÷	1	=	11
12	÷	1	=	12

Chart 3

Mult. Table

0	x	2	=	0
1	x	2	=	2
2	x	2	=	4
3	x	2	=	6
4	x	2	=	8
5	x	2	=	10
6	x	2	=	12
7	x	2	=	14
8	x	2	=	16
9	x	2	=	18
10	x	2	=	20
11	x	2	=	22
12	x	2	=	24

Div. Table

0	÷	2	=	0
2	÷	2	=	1
4	÷	2	=	2
6	÷	2	=	3
8	÷	2	=	4
10	÷	2	=	5
12	÷	2	=	6
14	÷	2	=	7
16	÷	2	=	8
18	÷	2	=	9
20	÷	2	=	10
22	÷	2	=	11
24	÷	2	=	12

Chart 4

Mult. Table

0	x	3	=	0
1	x	3	=	3
2	x	3	=	6
3	x	3	=	9
4	x	3	=	12
5	x	3	=	15
6	x	3	=	18
7	x	3	=	21
8	x	3	=	24
9	x	3	=	27
10	x	3	=	30
11	x	3	=	33
12	x	3	=	36

Div. Table

0	÷	3	=	0
3	÷	3	=	1
6	÷	3	=	2
9	÷	3	=	3
12	÷	3	=	4
15	÷	3	=	5
18	÷	3	=	6
21	÷	3	=	7
24	÷	3	=	8
27	÷	3	=	9
30	÷	3	=	10
33	÷	3	=	11
36	÷	3	=	12

Chart 5

Mult. Table	Div. Table
0 x 4 = 0	0 ÷ 4 = 0
1 x 4 = 4	4 ÷ 4 = 1
2 x 4 = 8	8 ÷ 4 = 2
3 x 4 = 12	12 ÷ 4 = 3
4 x 4 = 16	16 ÷ 4 = 4
5 x 4 = 20	20 ÷ 4 = 5
6 x 4 = 24	24 ÷ 4 = 6
7 x 4 = 28	28 ÷ 4 = 7
8 x 4 = 32	32 ÷ 4 = 8
9 x 4 = 36	36 ÷ 4 = 9
10 x 4 = 40	40 ÷ 4 = 10
11 x 4 = 44	44 ÷ 4 = 11
12 x 4 = 48	48 ÷ 4 = 12

Chart 6

Mult. Table	Div. Table
0 x 5 = 0	0 ÷ 5 = 0
1 x 5 = 5	5 ÷ 5 = 1
2 x 5 = 10	10 ÷ 5 = 2
3 x 5 = 15	15 ÷ 5 = 3
4 x 5 = 20	20 ÷ 5 = 4
5 x 5 = 25	25 ÷ 5 = 5
6 x 5 = 30	30 ÷ 5 = 6
7 x 5 = 35	35 ÷ 5 = 7
8 x 5 = 40	40 ÷ 5 = 8
9 x 5 = 45	45 ÷ 5 = 9
10 x 5 = 50	50 ÷ 5 = 10
11 x 5 = 55	55 ÷ 5 = 11
12 x 5 = 60	60 ÷ 5 = 12

Chart 7

Mult. Table	Div. Table
0 x 6 = 0	0 ÷ 6 = 0
1 x 6 = 6	6 ÷ 6 = 1
2 x 6 = 12	12 ÷ 6 = 2
3 x 6 = 18	18 ÷ 6 = 3
4 x 6 = 24	24 ÷ 6 = 4
5 x 6 = 30	30 ÷ 6 = 5
6 x 6 = 36	36 ÷ 6 = 6
7 x 6 = 42	42 ÷ 6 = 7
8 x 6 = 48	48 ÷ 6 = 8
9 x 6 = 54	54 ÷ 6 = 9
10 x 6 = 60	60 ÷ 6 = 10
11 x 6 = 66	66 ÷ 6 = 11
12 x 6 = 72	72 ÷ 6 = 12

Chart 8

Mult. Table	Div. Table
0 x 7 = 0	0 ÷ 7 = 0
1 x 7 = 7	7 ÷ 7 = 1
2 x 7 = 14	14 ÷ 7 = 2
3 x 7 = 21	21 ÷ 7 = 3
4 x 7 = 28	28 ÷ 7 = 4
5 x 7 = 35	35 ÷ 7 = 5
6 x 7 = 42	42 ÷ 7 = 6
7 x 7 = 49	49 ÷ 7 = 7
8 x 7 = 56	56 ÷ 7 = 8
9 x 7 = 63	63 ÷ 7 = 9
10 x 7 = 70	70 ÷ 7 = 10
11 x 7 = 77	77 ÷ 7 = 11
12 x 7 = 84	84 ÷ 7 = 12

Multiplication and Division Tables/Facts

Chart 9

Mult. Table	Div. Table
0 x 8 = 0	0 ÷ 8 = 0
1 x 8 = 8	8 ÷ 8 = 1
2 x 8 = 16	16 ÷ 8 = 2
3 x 8 = 24	24 ÷ 8 = 3
4 x 8 = 32	32 ÷ 8 = 4
5 x 8 = 40	40 ÷ 8 = 5
6 x 8 = 48	48 ÷ 8 = 6
7 x 8 = 56	56 ÷ 8 = 7
8 x 8 = 64	64 ÷ 8 = 8
9 x 8 = 72	72 ÷ 8 = 9
10 x 8 = 80	80 ÷ 8 = 10
11 x 8 = 88	88 ÷ 8 = 11
12 x 8 = 96	96 ÷ 8 = 12

Chart 10

Mult. Table	Div. Table
0 x 9 = 0	0 ÷ 9 = 0
1 x 9 = 9	9 ÷ 9 = 1
2 x 9 = 18	18 ÷ 9 = 2
3 x 9 = 27	27 ÷ 9 = 3
4 x 9 = 36	36 ÷ 9 = 4
5 x 9 = 45	45 ÷ 9 = 5
6 x 9 = 54	54 ÷ 9 = 6
7 x 9 = 63	63 ÷ 9 = 7
8 x 9 = 72	72 ÷ 9 = 8
9 x 9 = 81	81 ÷ 9 = 9
10 x 9 = 90	90 ÷ 9 = 10
11 x 9 = 99	99 ÷ 9 = 11
12 x 9 = 108	108 ÷ 9 = 12

Chart 11

Mult. Table	Div. Table
0 x 10 = 0	0 ÷ 10 = 0
1 x 10 = 10	10 ÷ 10 = 1
2 x 10 = 20	20 ÷ 10 = 2
3 x 10 = 30	30 ÷ 10 = 3
4 x 10 = 40	40 ÷ 10 = 4
5 x 10 = 50	50 ÷ 10 = 5
6 x 10 = 60	60 ÷ 10 = 6
7 x 10 = 70	70 ÷ 10 = 7
8 x 10 = 80	80 ÷ 10 = 8
9 x 10 = 90	90 ÷ 10 = 9
10 x 10 = 100	100 ÷ 10 = 10
11 x 10 = 110	110 ÷ 10 = 11
12 x 10 = 120	120 ÷ 10 = 12

Chart 12

Mult. Table	Div. Table
0 x 11 = 0	0 ÷ 11 = 0
1 x 11 = 11	11 ÷ 11 = 1
2 x 11 = 22	22 ÷ 11 = 2
3 x 11 = 33	33 ÷ 11 = 3
4 x 11 = 44	44 ÷ 11 = 4
5 x 11 = 55	55 ÷ 11 = 5
6 x 11 = 66	66 ÷ 11 = 6
7 x 11 = 77	77 ÷ 11 = 7
8 x 11 = 88	88 ÷ 11 = 8
9 x 11 = 99	99 ÷ 11 = 9
10 x 11 = 110	110 ÷ 11 = 10
11 x 11 = 121	121 ÷ 11 = 11
12 x 11 = 132	132 ÷ 11 = 12

Multiplication and Division Tables/Facts

Chart 13

Mult. Table	Div. Table
0 x 12 = 0	0 ÷ 12 = 0
1 x 12 = 12	12 ÷ 12 = 1
2 x 12 = 24	24 ÷ 12 = 2
3 x 12 = 36	36 ÷ 12 = 3
4 x 12 = 48	48 ÷ 12 = 4
5 x 12 = 60	60 ÷ 12 = 5
6 x 12 = 72	72 ÷ 12 = 6
7 x 12 = 84	84 ÷ 12 = 7
8 x 12 = 96	96 ÷ 12 = 8
9 x 12 = 108	108 ÷ 12 = 9
10 x 12 = 120	120 ÷ 12 = 10
11 x 12 = 132	132 ÷ 12 = 11
12 x 12 = 144	144 ÷ 12 = 12

Addition Facts—Chart 14

4 +3	9 +9	5 +6	9 +7	7 +6	4 +7	6 +5
6 +8	9 +3	3 +6	9 +1	8 +6	3 +2	3 +5
2 +5	9 +4	8 +3	4 +2	2 +1	6 +4	6 +9
9 +8	2 +3	8 +7	4 +5	7 +7	2 +8	4 +6
5 +2	9 +6	8 +9	6 +6	8 +2	7 +5	3 +3
9 +5	4 +8	2 +6	3 +7	6 +3	8 +8	6 +1
7 +4	3 +9	7 +8	2 +7	5 +5	5 +9	8 +4
2 +4	5 +8	2 +9	7 +3	8 +5	5 +7	6 +7

Subtraction Facts—Chart 15

13 −8	9 −3	18 −9	16 −7	12 −8	15 −6	8 −3
6 −5	16 −9	13 −7	11 −7	17 −9	9 −6	12 −3
12 −6	15 −8	11 −9	9 −8	10 −9	15 −9	13 −9
10 −4	11 −3	14 −7	12 −9	8 −5	11 −5	15 −7
14 −9	12 −4	6 −3	13 −4	11 −6	12 −5	17 −8
7 −5	10 −6	14 −5	8 −4	13 −6	14 −8	10 −2
12 −7	10 −8	16 −8	8 −6	7 −4	10 −3	8 −7
14 −6	7 −6	10 −7	13 −5	5 −3	10 −5	9 −2

Multiplication Facts—Chart 16

6 ×3	4 ×4	8 ×2	9 ×6	3 ×2	9 ×8	7 ×6
9 ×3	2 ×8	8 ×6	8 ×8	7 ×8	5 ×9	4 ×9
8 ×4	6 ×9	5 ×5	8 ×9	9 ×7	9 ×4	8 ×3
9 ×2	4 ×7	9 ×9	8 ×7	9 ×5	5 ×7	3 ×8
6 ×5	4 ×3	7 ×9	6 ×7	4 ×8	7 ×3	5 ×3
5 ×4	2 ×3	6 ×8	7 ×5	6 ×4	3 ×7	4 ×5
3 ×9	7 ×2	4 ×2	7 ×7	8 ×5	7 ×4	3 ×3
6 ×6	5 ×8	4 ×6	3 ×6	5 ×6	3 ×4	2 ×5

Multiplication and Division Tables/Facts

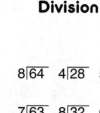

Division Facts—Chart 17

8)64	4)28	5)15	9)18	5)45	5)20
7)63	8)32	6)24	7)42	9)27	8)40
6)48	3)21	4)16	6)18	8)56	7)28
9)81	9)45	8)24	5)25	5)35	3)24
7)14	6)30	4)8	7)49	5)30	7)35
8)48	7)21	5)10	6)42	6)12	8)72
4)12	6)36	7)56	8)16	9)36	4)32
9)63	6)54	4)20	9)72	5)40	9)54

Mixed Facts—Chart 18

18 − 9	18 ÷ 9	9 x 6	17 − 9
8 + 3	64 ÷ 8	16 − 7	9 x 8
28 ÷ 4	13 − 8	6 x 3	8 + 5
4 x 4	8 x 8	7 + 4	32 ÷ 8
5 + 7	12 − 6	42 ÷ 7	7 + 7
12 − 8	7 x 6	40 ÷ 8	15 − 6
3 + 9	7 + 8	12 x 9	8 + 7
45 ÷ 5	8 x 6	48 ÷ 6	9 + 5
9 + 8	24 ÷ 6	15 − 8	63 ÷ 9
5 x 8	16 − 9	7 x 8	11 − 3
8 + 9	7 + 5	15 − 9	54 ÷ 6
13 − 7	63 ÷ 7	9 + 6	9 x 3

Review Drills and Games

●●

A variety of concepts are studied throughout fourth grade. For accuracy in computation, the basic facts must be mastered. To accomplish this, effective daily drill is required. Drills and games that can be used effectively are described.

DRILLS

Flashcards

Arrange flashcards in mixed order. Flip cards quickly from back to front, setting the pace for the child. If answers are missed frequently, set those cards aside for extra drill.

- Instruct child to have pencil and paper ready. Flash the cards and have him write the answers. Check answers. Give 2 points for each correct answer.
- Using flashcards, instruct child to add or subtract a certain number from each answer mentally, then call out the final answer.

Example:

7
x 5
___

(35 + 2 = 37)

Child answers only 37.

Division Drill

Pick a multiplication table to work on. Announce: divide by 7 (or any other division table). Call out various products of seven. Have the child divide mentally and give the quotient. The products can also be put on cards to be flashed. (Do not mix tables.)

Just the Facts

Put the answer to multiplication or division facts on flashcards, or the chalkboard, or call them out from a list. Have the child write the division or multiplication fact that fits the answer. Check by going through each flashcard and having him answer orally.

Skip Counting

Count by threes, fours, sevens, etc. starting from any number. Example: 5, 9, 13, 17 (counting by fours from 5). Reverse and (using subtraction) count backward. Example: 81, 75, 69, 63, 57, etc. (counting backward by six, starting with 81).

Missing Link

The parent gives two numbers and a process sign to the child. The child gives the answer and then gives another process sign and number to the parent. The first one to break the chain becomes the "missing link." Start a new chain with the next person. Example: Parent, "7 times 3." Child, "21 minus 4."

Measurement Drill

Call out two measures. Have the child give the number used to convert from one to the other ("inches to feet"—"12").

Variation: Call out two measures, having him give the process needed to convert from the first to the last (inches—feet, "divide").

Progressive Addition (or multiplication)

The parent writes an addition (or multiplication) fact on a paper. The paper is passed to the child who puts the answer and another number to be added. Continue to pass the paper back and forth several times. When the paper is done, child must check for any errors.

Sign Language

On flashcards, have problems with answers but no process sign. Have a gesture or sign planned for each process. For example raise left hand for addition, stand for subtraction, put hands on head for multiplication, and raise right hand for division. As the parent holds up the flashcards, the child responds with the gesture planned for the correct process.

Example:

| 9 __ 5 = 14 | Child raises left hand to indicate addition. |

Beat the Machine

On paper have number facts or multiple combinations written in a vertical column. Lay it on a table and cover the list with a piece of paper. Move down the page at a steady pace, having the child answer each fact or combination as it becomes visible. See how quickly he can go.

Rithmetic Rhythm

Using the "clap, clap, snap, snap" of the regular Rhythm game, the parent calls out a multiplication fact on the "snap, snap" such as *three fives*. The child responds with the answer on the next "snap, snap" *(fifteen)*. The parent then calls another multiplication fact, etc. Try to go as far as possible without breaking the rhythm. Be sure the rhythm is well started and child is ready before calling any number facts.

Balance the Budget

Put up pictures of objects or foods from a magazine (using masking tape or plastic tape) or draw them on the chalkboard. Put a price under each one. Then tell child: "You have $10.30. What can you buy so that you will spend exactly ½ of your money?" Let him use paper to add up prices until he can find what will add up to exactly $5.15. (Be sure there are a few combinations of prices that will add up to the total.) Other pictures, prices, and totals may be used another time.

CHALKBOARD DRILLS

Number Drill

Place eight to ten numbers (1–12) in a scrambled position on the chalkboard. Tell the child to multiply by a certain number. As you point to each number, the child gives the answer obtained by multiplying by the given number. (All four processes and various numbers may be used.)

Missing Number

Put the answers to one of the multiplication tables (out of order) on the chalkboard. Have the child put his head down. Erase one of the numbers from the chalkboard. Then the child raises his head. When he finds the missing number he may stand. When called on, he must give the fact and the answer: 2 x 7 = 14, 14 is missing. Show the child how to go through the table mentally until he finds the missing answer. As child progresses, 2 or 3 answers may be erased at one time. The child should be able to tell all missing answers. (This can also be used with Roman numerals.)

Climbing Higher (variation of Number Drill)

Draw simple ladders on the chalkboard. Above each rung place a number. On the bottom rung, place a number and process. Have the child climb ladders on his practice paper.

| 54 |
| 66 |
| 12 |
| 3 |
| 18 |
| 42 |
| ÷ 6 |

Up and Down the Ladder

Have on the chalkboard:

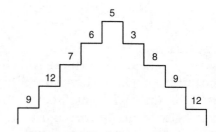

Have child multiply by 9 going up the ladder, add 9 going down the ladder. (Use numbers he is having trouble adding, subtracting, multiplying, or dividing.)

REVIEW GAMES

Around the World

Choose a path around the room with a certain number of places to stop. (The number of stops will vary with the number of flashcards your child has learned.) Show him a flashcard, count silently to three, if he answers within that time he moves to the next stop. If he can not answer in the allotted time, have him repeat the combination with the answer three times. The object of the game is to travel all the way around the "world." You could have the same number of flashcards as stops to make the game a greater challenge.

Variation: Let your child take one step around the room for every correct answer.

Baseball

Call out combinations. When child answers a combination correctly, he gets to hold up one finger. When he has 4 fingers up to indicate that he ran all the bases and made it home, he gets a run. Repeat.

Beat the Clock

Let child answer twenty flashcards as quickly as possible. Encourage him to answer quickly and accurately. Time him to see how long it takes to go through twenty cards. Record the time. Make it a goal to beat the record each time this game is played.

Capture the Card

Show a flashcard to your child. If he answers correctly within 3 seconds, he captures the card. If he cannot capture the card, set it aside for later. After the game is over, practice the cards that were not captured.

Four Corners

Have your child go to one corner of the room. Show a flashcard. If he answers correctly he gets to move to the next corner. When he returns to his original corner he is a winner. Repeat.

Circles in a Box

Draw a box on the chalkboard. Write the numbers 0–9 inside the box. Your child comes to the chalkboard and circles 2 numbers. After he has circled 2 numbers, tell him to either multiply or divide the 2 circled numbers and write the correct answer. Mark through the 2 circled numbers and have him circle 2 numbers in the box. Continue until all numbers have been used.

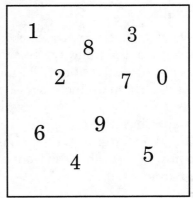

Fraction Flashcards

Have 15 flashcards for your child to answer. Write 15 as the denominator on the chalkboard. Show cards for 30 seconds, having child answer quickly. After the 30 seconds are up, count the number of cards that he answered correctly. Write the number as the numerator of the fraction. The child reads the fraction of the cards that were answered correctly.

Giant Step

Your child goes to the back of the room to be a giant. Show flashcards to your child. A giant gets to take a giant step each time he answers correctly. Continue until the giant gets to the front of the room.

Guess My Age

A. Clue: *My age is three times the number of feet in a yard.* **9**

B. Clue: *My age is double the number of quarts in a gallon.* **8**

C. Clue: *My age is half of the sum of 4 + 12.* **8**

D. Clue: *My age is four times the number of things in a half dozen.* **24**

E. Clue: *My age is nine times the number of sides in a triangle.* **27**

F. Clue: *My age is one fourth the number of sides in a square.* **1**

A variation is for the child to think of a clue for his age.

Moonwalk

Have your child go to the back of the room or other end of the hallway. Show the flashcard or call out combination. The moonwalker gets to take a step on the moon each time he answers correctly. The moonwalker takes large steps since the gravity on the moon is much less than the gravity on the earth. When the moonwalker reaches the front of the room he is a winner.

Name That Number

Call out the number of thousands, hundreds, tens, and ones in a number. Your child gives the correct number. A variation is to call out the number of tens, hundreds, thousands, and ones. Later, include millions.

Speedy Sam

Have your child stand in the back of the room. Call out a long combination. As you say each number, the child takes one step forward. After the last number is said, say *equals* so he knows the combination is finished. As soon as the *equals* is said, the child gives the answer. If he is correct he begins the next combination from that point. If the answer is incorrect he must start again from the back of the room. As soon as he reaches the front he is *Speedy Sam.*

Popcorn

Popcorn is a good game to get the wiggles out while he is reviewing. Call out numbers from 1 to 100. Have your child *pop up* if the number is even. He remains seated if the number is odd. Popcorn can be played to review a variety of concepts. For example, it can be used to review place value. Write a number on the chalkboard. Point to a digit. Have him *pop up* if the digit is in the one thousands' place. It can be used to review multiplication and division. Show a flashcard. If the answer is 9, have him *pop up*. Arrange the flashcards so many of them have an answer of 9. It can be used to review greater than and less than. Write a number on the chalkboard. Call out a number. Child should *pop up* if the number is greater than the number on the chalkboard.

Secret Code

Show 3 flashcards in a row. Your child is to determine the answers and remember them in order. After he has seen all 3 cards, call on him to give the secret code, which is the 3 an-swers in the proper or-der.

Three in a Row

The child answers combinations. When he answers correctly he puts up a finger. When a child has three fingers up, he is a winner. Repeat.

I Am a Calculator

Have your child answer ten flashcards in a row. If he answers the flashcards correctly and quickly, he is a calculator. If time permits, repeat.

Play Bills

(May be duplicated for use.)

Preparation

1.  Chalkboard

 A   3274621   8430907   431521   83240167

B
5,329 *science books*
7,314 *history books*
+ 13,589 *fiction books*
26,232 *books in all*

C
4,321	9,416	23,304
6,872	8,972	18,592
+ 5,899	+ 3,984	+ 3,871

2. *Arithmetic 4:* pp. 1–2
3. Visuals:
   - *Process Flashcards* for all 4 processes
     (Have 2–3 division table cards and 0–3 multiplication table cards.)
   - *Calculator* (chart 20) from Home School *Arithmetic 3–8 Charts (Arith Charts)*
   - *Tables and Facts Charts* 1–3
   - *Place Value (Arithmetic Charts* 1–2)
   - *Concept Cards* 1–15
   - 0 multiplication table

Note: Visuals listed in italics can be purchased from *A Beka Book.* Other visuals are supplied by parent.

0	0	0	0	0	0	0	0	0	0	0	0	0
x 0	x 1	x 2	x 3	x 4	x 5	x 6	x 7	x 8	x 9	x 10	x 11	x 12
0	0	0	0	0	0	0	0	0	0	0	0	0

Teaching Procedure

1. Oral review drills (12 min.)

Addition/Subtraction (6 min.)
- *Add./Subt. Cards* (in mixed order): Child answers.
- *Calculator:* Point to numbers. He adds numbers you say.
- **Oral combinations** (comb.): Call out combination. Child answers aloud.

6 + 3 + 5 = *14*	9 + 9 + 3 = *21*	8 + 7 + 9 = *24*
12 + 8 + 4 = *24*	7 + 5 + 8 = *20*	13 + 8 + 5 = *26*
3 + 9 + 9 = *21*	10 + 7 + 8 = *25*	16 + 7 + 5 = *28*
35 + 6 + 8 = *49*	12 + 12 + 9 = *33*	19 + 6 + 5 = *30*

Multiplication/Division (6 min.)
- *Tables/Facts Charts* **1–3:** Recite tables in this manner: *0 times 3 equals 0.* If you desire, cover division side of chart when child says multiplication table. If child understand that any number times 0 is 0 and that any number times 1 is that number, it is not necessary to drill charts 1 and 2 often.

Note: Tables/Facts Charts are on pages T15–T22 in the front of 5curriculum guide.

- **Mult./Div. Cards:** Expect quick responses.
- **Oral comb.**

4 + 6 = *10*	6 x 0 = *0*	11 + 5 = *16*
9 − 5 = *4*	8 + 9 = *17*	9 x 1 = *9*
3 + 8 = *11*	16 − 3 = *13*	6 x 2 = *12*
2 x 5 = *10*	21 − 2 = *19*	12 + 8 = *20*

2. **Introduce writing large numbers.** (9 min.)
- *Arith Chart* **1:** Briefly review ones' to thousands' places.
- *Arith Chart* **2:** Teach through millions' place.
- *Concept Cards* **1–15:** Child reads large numbers and gives values of circled digits. These cards are a great tool to use in comparing and ordering numbers.
- Instruct child to read **information box** at top of **p. 1.** He gives special attention to place value chart in box. Expect him to learn place values and periods.
- Child reads aloud **exercise (Ex.) 1, p. 1.** He names some numbers that include millions and when such numbers are used, such as population of large cities or number of hamburgers sold by a major fast food restaurant.
- **A** **Commas are used to separate periods. A full period has 3 digits. Only the last period to the left may not be a full period. We may use this simple rule when placing commas: 1 2 3 comma.** Child repeats rule and writes commas in correct places.
- Child answers **Ex. 2–3;** dictate these numbers for **Ex. 4:**

a. 3,271,313	**b.** 9,892,067	**c.** 2,478,309	**d.** 231,672
e. 932	**f.** 6,784	**g.** 9,431,678	**h.** 35,001

3. **Introduce story problems.** (9 min.)
- Teach these six questions as the procedure for solving story problems. Go through the questions several times with him.

> **What does the story problem tell us?**
>
> **What does the story problem ask us?**
>
> **Are there any clue words or rules that help us solve the problem?**
>
> **Are there any missing facts?**
>
> **Are there any unnecessary numbers that are not needed?**
>
> **What process should we use to solve this problem?**

- **B** Read story problem **5a.** Have child answer each of the six questions as the procedure for working the problem. Discuss setup given under **Ex. 5.** Use setup on ckbd to help with explanation.
- Child reads and works story problems **b–c.** Use six questions as the procedure for solving. Point out clue words *altogether* and *change.* Assist child when he needs help.

Note: Child uses his notebook paper for story problems. You may choose to let him use the same sheet for 1 week. In this case, he needs to be careful not to lose or misplace his story problem answer sheet.

4. Review addition with carrying. (6 min.)

- Work and explain concept of carrying. Child answers **Ex. 6.** Check child's work.

5. Homework: (Homework is optional for les. 1–5.) **Ex. 7–8**

Note: If homework (hwk) is not assigned 1st week, hwk section is optional practice. Train child to have hwk out to check immediately at beginning of arithmetic. Quickly call out all answers; child marks incorrect answers. Praise child if he missed 0 or 1.

Lesson

2

Preparation

1. Chalkboard:

     98
             73
           + 25

| B | 2 3 4 9 1 6 1 8

| C | 5,003,002   532

2. *Arithmetic 4:* pp. 3–4

3. *Lesson 2 Speed Drill: Student Tests and Speed Drills*

4. Visuals:
   - *Process Flashcards* for all 4 processes (Have 2–5 division table cards and 2–5 multiplication table cards.)
   - *1–100 Chart* (chart 23) from *Arith Charts*
   - *Tables/Facts Charts* 2–5
   - *Concept Cards* 1–16
   - *Place Value (Arith Chart* 2)

Teaching Procedure

1. Oral review drills (9 min.)

Addition/Subtraction (3 min.)
   - *Add./Subt. Cards* (in mixed order): Child answers.
   - **1–100 Chart:** Point to numbers, child adds or subtracts numbers that you say.
   - **Oral comb.**

$15 - 9 + 3 = 9$	$18 - 9 - 4 = 5$	$6 + 6 + 8 = 20$
$5 + 7 - 9 = 3$	$10 + 5 - 8 = 7$	$12 - 8 + 5 = 9$
$16 - 8 + 9 = 17$	$4 + 7 + 8 = 19$	$15 - 7 + 5 = 13$

Multiplication/Division (3 min.)
   - *Mult./Div. Cards:* Child answers.
   - *Tables/Facts Charts* **2–5:** Drill mult. tables 2–5.

Lesson 2
(cont.)

- **Oral comb.**

6 + 3 = 9	9 x 5 = *45*	6 − 5 = *1*	15 ÷ 5 = *3*
13 − 8 = *5*	8 x 3 = *24*	5 x 6 = *30*	12 ÷ 3 = *4*
18 − 9 = *9*	6 + 8 = *14*	23 − 5 = *18*	9 x 4 = *36*

Place value (3 min.)
- *Concept Cards* **1–15:** Child reads numbers and gives values of circled digits.
- Hand 3 cards to child. Have him put them in order from least to greatest. Repeat several times.

2. Written speed drill (4 min.)
- Speed drills are located in *Student Tests and Speed Drills.* They are given 4 days per week. The procedure for giving them is at front of *Teacher Tests and Speed Drills.* Distribute speed drills and time for 3 min. Scores are recorded once each week beginning the second week of school. The Curriculum/Lesson Plans denotes the graded ones.

3. Introduce addition. (9 min.)
- *Concept Card* **16:** Teach terminology.
- **A** Work problem for child explaining carrying process.
- Child reads **box at top of p. 3.** Be sure he understands what is in box each day. Sometimes he should explain information in own words. **Make it a daily practice to go over box material carefully.**
- Child does **Ex. 1.** Encourage him to work neatly in workbook or at ckbd.
- **A** Explain how to check. **To get the sum, add downward. To check, draw two lines over the top addend and then add upward. Both sums should agree if the problem has been worked correctly.**
- Child does **Ex. 2.**

4. Discuss story problems. (6 min.)
- Review 6 story problem questions and use as procedure to solve story problems. Child reads **Ex. 3a.** Help him find clue word *sum.* He works story problem *a* on a separate sheet of paper as noted in les. 1. Use setup as given in les. 1. Use same procedure for *b.*

5. Review reading and writing large numbers. (3 min.)
- *Arith Chart* **2:** Drill with child.
- **B** Child puts commas in correct places and reads number.
- **C** Use 2 numbers to show importance of 0. **There is a big difference between 5,003,002 and 532. Zeros are important as place holders. Also remember that each period should have 3 digits except the one to the far left which may have fewer than 3 digits.**
- Child does **Ex. 4–5.**

6. Review/Boardwork (6 min.) **Ex. 6–9**

Note: Review/Board-work is a daily part of each lesson. Child works independently in workbook while parent gives necessary help.

Preparation

1. Chalkboard:

    📱 3 dimes – 2 nickels + 12 pennies = _____

2. *Arithmetic 4:* pp. 5–6

3. *Lesson 3 Speed Drill: Student Tests and Speed Drills*

4. Visuals:
    - *Process Flashcards* for all 4 processes (Have 2–6 division table cards and 2–6 multiplication table cards.)
    - *1–100 Chart* from *Arith Charts* (chart 20)
    - *Concept Card* 16
    - *Tables/Facts Charts* 2–6
    - coins

Teaching Procedure

1. Oral review drills (9 min.)

   Addition/Subtraction (3 min.)
   - *Add./Subt. Cards* (in mixed order): Child answers.
   - *1–100 Chart:* Point to numbers, he adds or subtracts numbers that you say.
   - *Concept Card* **16:** Review terms.

   Multiplication/Division (6 min.)
   - *Mult./Div. Cards:* review
   - *Tables/Facts Charts* **2–6:** Drill mult. tables 2–6.
   - Oral comb.: Call out to child at a moderate speed. Child can answer. As he learns to be quicker, conduct drill at a faster pace. Encourage your child to build his arithmetic skills with these challenging drills. (Since these combinations are oral and not written, child does them in the order that he hears them, without regard to order of operations.)

$4 \times 3 + 2 - 5 \div 3 = 3$	$8 \times 4 - 5 \div 3 + 4 = 13$
$6 + 4 \div 2 \times 5 + 8 = 33$	$16 - 9 \times 3 + 4 \div 5 = 5$
$11 - 7 \times 5 + 2 \div 2 = 11$	$72 + 8 - 50 \div 3 = 10$
$20 \div 4 \times 6 - 2 = 28$	$27 \div 3 \times 4 + 4 - 3 = 37$

2. Written speed drill (4 min.) Time for 3 min.

3. Introduce money problems. (12 min.)
   - **Coins:** Review basic values of money. Call out these oral drills. Child should write answers on ckbd.

3 pennies = *3¢* or *$.03*	4 dimes = *40¢* or *$.40*
3 nickels = *15¢* or *$.15*	2 quarters = *50¢* or *$.50*

   - 📱 Work problem for him explaining how to solve money equations.

3 dimes – 2 nickels + 12 pennies = <u>*$.32*</u>

(3 x .10) – (2 x .05) + (12 x .01) = <u>*$.32*</u>

.30 – .10 + .12 = <u>*$.32*</u>

1. **Decide what each coin is worth and mult. the value by number of coins.**
2. **Draw parentheses around each mult. problem. Remind child that parentheses say, *Do me first*.**
3. **Solve each mult. problem.**
4. **Follow the signs and solve for the answer.**
5. **Put the answer in all 3 blanks.**
6. **Be sure to use the decimal point and dollar sign. The decimal point separates the cents from the dollars. It is essential that the decimal point is used correctly. If the decimal point is left out or put in the wrong place, the answer is wrong.**

- Read and discuss **box on p. 5.** Child does **Ex. 1–4.**
- **Coins:** If there is time, you can play store. Let your child be clerk and you are customer. Place a price such as $.59 on item being bought. Clerk counts back change from a dollar. He should say *.59, .60, .70, .75, $1.00* or *.59, .60, .65, .75, $1.00.*

4. **Discuss story problems.** (6 min.)
- Review six story problem questions and use as procedure to solve story problems. Child reads **Ex. 5a.** Help him find clue word *altogether.* Use same procedure for *b.*

5. **Review/Boardwork** (6 min.) **Ex. 6–8**

Lesson 4

Preparation

1. Chalkboard:

372	431
– 198	– 287

2. *Arithmetic 4:* pp. 7–8

3. *Lesson 4 Speed Drill*

4. Visuals:
- *Process Flashcards* (Have 2–6 division table cards and 2–6 multiplication table cards.)
- *Tables/Facts Charts* 2–6
- *Concept Cards* 16–17
- *Place Value (Arith Chart 2)*
- story problem clue words flashcards (optional) Prepare a set of flashcards using clue words found in workbook, p. 7, Ex. 2.

Add to set as new story problem clue words are introduced throughout year.
  • *Mixed Addition Facts (Arith 4, p.311)*

Teaching Procedure

1. Oral review drills (12 min.)

Addition/Subtraction (3 min.)
  • *Add./Subt. Cards* (in mixed order)
  • *Mixed Addition Facts:* Point to problems in order; child says sums. Encourage child to answer quickly.
  • *Concept Card* **16:** Review terms.

Place value (1 min.)
  • *Arith Chart* **2**

Multiplication/Division (5 min.)
  • *Mult./Div. Cards*
  • *Tables/Facts Charts* **2–6:** Drill mult. tables 2–6.
  • Oral comb.

$6 + 4 = 10$	$10 - 5 = 5$	$11 - 3 = 8$	$9 \times 7 = 63$
$36 \div 4 = 9$	$14 - 7 = 7$	$6 - 4 = 2$	$42 \div 6 = 7$

Story problems (3 min.)
  • Story problem clue words flashcards (optional): Drill clue words.

2. Written speed drill (4 min.) Time for 3 min.

3. Introduce subtraction. (9 min.)
  • *Concept Card* **17:** Teach terminology for subt. problem.

  • ▬ Work 1st problem for child explaining borrowing process.
    (a) Since 8 ones cannot be subtracted from 2 ones, borrow 1 ten from 7 tens. (Coins are useful when demonstrating borrowing. One dime contains 10 pennies as 1 ten contains 10 ones.)
    (b) After borrowing 1 ten, 6 tens are left.
    (c) Write borrowed ten next to 2 ones. 10 ones + 2 ones = 12 ones. Subtract 8 ones from 12 ones to get 4 ones.
    (d) Since 9 tens cannot be subtracted from 6 tens, borrow 1 hundred from 3 hundreds. (One dollar contains 10 dimes as 1 hundred contains 10 tens.)
    (e) After borrowing 1 hundred, 2 hundreds are left.
    (f) Write borrowed hundred next to 6 tens. 10 tens + 6 tens = 16 tens. Subtract 9 tens from 16 tens to get 7 tens.
    (g) Subtract 1 hundred from 2 hundreds to get 1 hundred. The final difference is 174.
    (h) To check, add subtrahend and difference together. The sum should be same number as minuend. Before adding, draw 2 lines under difference to indicate check.
    Work 2nd problem using same procedure.
  • Read and discuss **box on p. 7.** Child does **Ex. 1–2.**

4. Review/Boardwork (12 min.) **Ex. 3–8** (Ex. 7–8 can be assigned for hwk if hwk is given this week or used for optional practice.)

$$
\begin{array}{r}
\overset{2}{\cancel{3}}\ \overset{16}{\cancel{7}}\ \overset{1}{2} \\
-\ 1\ 9\ 8 \\
+\ \underline{1\ 7\ 4} \\
\hline
3\ 7\ 2
\end{array}
$$

Lesson

5

Preparation

1. Chalkboard:

   [chalkboard] 384   735
              x 6   x 4

2. *Arithmetic 4:* pp. 9–10

3. *Lesson 5 Speed Drill*

4. Visuals:
   - *Process Flashcards* (Have 2–6 division table cards and 2–6 multiplication table cards.)
   - *Concept Cards* 16–18
   - *Place Value (Arith Chart* 2)
   - *Tables/Facts Charts* 2–7
   - Story problem clue words flashcards (optional from les. 4)
   - *Mixed Subtraction Facts (Arith 4, p.316)*

Teaching Procedure

1. **Oral review drills** (10 min.)

   Addition/Subtraction (3 min.)
   - *Add./Subt. Cards:* Expect quick, accurate answers.
   - *Concept Cards* **16–17:** Review terms.
   - Oral comb.

   $12 - 9 + 7 - 5 = 5$ $8 + 9 - 6 - 4 = 7$ $25 - 7 - 8 + 7 = 17$

   $18 + 9 + 3 - 6 = 24$ $15 - 8 - 5 + 23 = 25$ $18 + 5 - 6 - 9 = 8$

   Place value (1 min.)
   - *Arith Chart* **2**

   Multiplication/Division (5 min.)
   - *Mult./Div. Cards*
   - *Tables/Facts Charts* **2–7:** Drill mult. tables 2–7.
   - *Mixed Subtraction Facts:* Point to problems in order; child says differences.

   Story problems (1 min.)
   - Story problem clue words flashcards

2. **Written speed drill** (4 min.) Time for 3 min.

3. **Introduce multiplication.** (9 min.)
   - ***Concept Card* 18:** Teach terminology for mult. problem.
   - [chalkboard] Remind him of importance of knowing mult. tables. If he does not know all facts, he must learn them. Explain how to do mult. problems on ckbd.
     (a) Multiply 4 times 6 to get 24. Put down 4 in ones' place of product and carry 2 because it is a tens' digit.

```
+5  +2
  3  8  4
  x     6
─────────────
2 , 3  0  4
```

(b) The 2 is a plus 2. Multiply 6 times 8 to get 48 and add the carrying 2 to get 50. Put down the 0 and carry the 5 because it is a hundreds' digit.

(c) The 5 that was carried is a plus 5. Multiply 6 times 3 to get 18 and add 5 to get 23. Put down the 23. Put a comma in the correct place, and the problem is finished.

Work 2nd problem using same procedure.

- Read and discuss **box on p. 9.** Child does **Ex. 1–2.**

4. Discuss story problems. (6 min.)

- **Story problem clue words flashcards:** Review clue words and story problem questions. Child does **Ex. 3–4.** Follow standard procedure of having problems read aloud, quickly discussed, and then worked by child. Gradually story problems require less discussion unless a new clue word is introduced.

5. Review/Boardwork (9 min.) **Ex. 5–9** (Ex. 9 can be assigned for hwk if hwk is given this week or used for optional practice.)

> **Note:** Child needs to stay busy at all times. If he finishes his work before time is called, have him work problems that are in Supplementary Exercises. Also, occasionally use a portion of this time to hear child recite his mult. tables. 4th graders should be able to say them quickly and accurately. If he is slow or unsure of his tables, give extra help. Begin immediately to work with him before he becomes discouraged. Supplementary Exercises are great practice for a child who is having trouble.

Lesson 6

Preparation

1. Chalkboard:

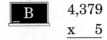
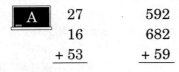

```
 A     27        592
       16        682
     + 53      + 59
```

```
 B    4,379     C    6,321      5,482
      x   5         − 4,829    − 2,691
```

2. *Arithmetic 4:* pp. 11–12

3. *Lesson 6 Speed Drill*

4. Visuals:

- *Process Flashcards* (Have 2–7 division table cards and 2–7 multiplication table cards.)
- *Place Value (Arith Chart 2)*
- *Tables/Facts Charts 2–7*

Lesson 6
(cont.)

• story problem clue words flashcards (optional from les. 4)
• *Mixed Multiplication Facts (Arith 4, p. 319)*

Teaching Procedure

1. Oral review drills (9 min.)

Addition/Subtraction (3 min.)

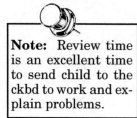

Note: Drill time is an excellent time to have good math games. See the front of this Curriculum/ Lesson Plans for math games.

• *Add./Subt. Cards:* Review quickly—Child adds 9 to each sum. A good way to add 9 is to add 10 and subtract 1.
• **A** He adds downward as you point to each addend. He checks by adding upward as you point to each addend.
• Call out these addends; he gives 3rd addend to make sum of 10. Child should *Pop-up* when he knows correct addend.

4, 5 **1**   3, 3 **4**   5, 2 **3**   4, 3 **3**

Place value (1 min.)

• *Arith Chart* **2**

Multiplication/Division (4 min.)

• *Mult./Div. Cards*
• *Tables/Facts Charts* **2–7:** Drill mult. tables 2–7.
• *Mixed Multiplication Facts:* Point to problems in order; child says products.
• Oral comb.

$4 \times 4 + 4 \div 2 \times 5 = 50$	$2 \times 2 + 2 \div 2 - 2 = 1$
$11 - 6 \times 3 + 7 \div 2 = 11$	$11 \times 7 \times 0 + 5 - 3 = 2$
$37 - 5 \div 4 + 2 = 10$	$18 \div 3 \times 5 + 3 - 8 = 25$
$9 + 3 \times 4 + 2 = 50$	$7 + 5 - 6 \times 7 + 3 = 45$

Story problems (1 min.)

• Story problem clue words flashcards

2. Written speed drill (4 min.) Time for 3 min.

3. Review the processes. (12 min.)

Note: Review time is an excellent time to send child to the ckbd to work and explain problems.

• **B** Work mult. problem on ckbd as child watches. He does **Ex. 1, p. 11.** Give needed assistance. Sometimes use your pen to give a ✓ or X to a particular problem. When an X is given, expect child to rework problem until it is correct. Occasionally give a sticker or a reward when child has neat and accurate worksheet. This encourages him to work harder.
• **C** Work 1st subt. problem for him. He explains as you work 2nd subt. problem. Child does **Ex. 2–3.**

4. Discuss story problems. (6 min.)

• **Story problem clue words flashcards:** Review clue words and story problem questions. Child does **Ex. 4.** Use standard procedure. Since not all story problems have clue words, it is important to teach child to think before solving word problems.

5. Review/Boardwork (6 min.) **Ex. 5**

6. Homework Ex. 6–7

Preparation

1. Chalkboard:

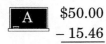 $50.00
   – 15.46

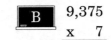 9,375
   x   7

2. *Arithmetic 4:* pp. 13–14

3. *Lesson 7 Quiz: Student Tests and Speed Drills*

4. Visuals:
   - *Process Flashcards* (Have 2–7 division table cards and 2–7 multiplication table cards.)
   - *Calculator (Arith Chart 20)*
   - *Place Value (Arith Chart 2)*
   - *Concept Cards 1–15*
   - *Tables/Facts Charts 2–7*
   - *1–100 Chart (Arith Chart 23)*
   - coins

Teaching Procedure

1. Oral review drills (9 min.)

Homework check

Addition/Subtraction (3 min.)
   - *Add./Subt. Cards:* Let child answer. Praise child if he answers quickly.
   - **A** Child explains borrowing process.
   - *Calculator:* He adds 8 to number you push.

Place value (1 min.)
   - *Arith Chart* 2
   - *Concept Cards* **1–15:** He reads numbers and gives value of circled digits.

Multiplication/Division (3 min.)
   - *Mult./Div. Cards*
   - *Tables/Facts Charts* **2–7:** Drill mult. tables 2–7.
   - *1–100 Chart:* Point to numbers 1–12, child mult. by 7 and adds 3. Repeat for other combinations.

Money (2 min.)
   - Coins: Show coin and tell how many you have of that coin; he gives value.
   - Call out these money problems; child writes values on ckbd.

   7 dimes = *$.70*   8 nickels = *$.40*   11 dollars = *$11*

2. Quiz 1 (9 min.)
   - Quizzes are located in *Student Tests and Speed Drills.* See front of this *Curriculum/Lesson Plans* for instructions on averaging quiz and test grades.

Note: Train child to take hwk out immediately at beginning of class. Have child get out a pen to check his hwk. Quickly call out all answers; child marks incorrect answers. Praise child if he missed 0 or 1.

Note: A quiz is given bi-weekly on Tuesdays (or any day other than Monday to suit your schedule). The procedure for giving a quiz is at the front of the *Teacher Tests and Speed Drills.* The grading scale is in the *Teacher Tests and Speed Drills.*

3. Review multiplication. (6 min.)

- ▇ B Work mult. problem on ckbd as child watches. Child does **Ex. 1–3, p. 13.**

4. Discuss story problem. (3 min.)

- Child does **Ex. 4.**

5. Review place values and combinations. (2 min.)

- Call out these numbers for **Ex. 5.**
  - **a.** 432,000,600
  - **b.** 9,132,020
  - **c.** 70,050,106
  - **d.** 250,003,300
- Call out these combinations for **Ex. 6.**
  - **a.** $7 \times 4 + 3 =$
  - **b.** $19 - 7 + 5 =$
  - **c.** $6 \times 3 - 9 =$
  - **d.** $5 \times 6 - 4 =$
  - **e.** $8 + 3 =$
  - **f.** $2 \times 6 - 3 =$

6. Review/Boardwork (7 min.) **Ex. 7–10**

Lesson 8

Preparation

1. Chalkboard:

9,376	25	78	49	19
x 7	x 46	x 43	x 73	x 87

2. *Arithmetic 4:* pp. 15–16

3. *Lesson 8 Speed Drill*

4. Visuals:

- *Process Flashcards* (Have 2–7 division table cards and 2–7 multiplication table cards.)
- *Tables/Facts Charts* 2–7
- *Calculator (Arith Chart 20)*
- story problem clue words flashcards (optional from les. 4)

Teaching Procedure

1. Oral review drills (9 min.)

Addition/Subtraction (3 min.)

- *Flashcards:* Mix add. and subt. cards; class, rows, and individuals give answers.
- Oral comb.

$5 + 6 - 4 = 7$	$12 - 7 + 8 = 13$	$15 - 9 + 6 = 12$	$13 - 7 = 6$
$5 + 2 + 8 = 15$	$14 - 8 - 6 = 0$	$11 + 4 - 7 = 8$	$17 - 9 = 8$
$13 - 4 + 9 = 18$	$9 + 5 - 6 = 8$	$7 + 9 + 4 = 20$	$8 + 9 = 17$
$12 - 6 = 6$	$5 + 4 = 9$	$6 + 8 = 14$	$12 - 4 - 2 = 6$
$5 + 6 = 11$	$9 + 7 = 16$	$10 - 8 = 2$	$21 - 3 = 18$

Multiplication/Division (5 min.)
- *Mult./Div. Cards*
- *Tables/Facts Charts* **2–7:** Drill mult. tables 2–7.
- *Calculator:* Point to numbers, child mult. by 4 and adds 7. Repeat for other combinations.
- Oral comb.

  9 x 4 = *36*   6 x 8 = *48*   4 + 7 = *11*   20 ÷ 2 = *10*

  13 – 6 = *7*   12 + 7 = *19*   3 x 9 = *27*   6 x 7 = *42*

Story problems (1 min.)
- Story problem clue words flashcards

2. Written speed drill (3 min.) Time for 1 min. 30 sec.

3. Introduce two-digit multiplication. (12 min.)
- Work 1st problem as he explains. Child does **Ex. 1 *a–e*.**

- Work 2nd problem as you explain how to multiply by a 2-digit factor.
  - (a) Cover 4 in 46. Multiply 6 times 5 and 6 times 2 as usual, remembering to carry when necessary.
  - (b) Cover 6 in 46. Multiply 4 times 5 and 4 times 2. The 0 in the product of 4 times 5 must be in the tens' place. When we multiply by the 4, we are really multiplying by 40 since it is in the tens' place. If a child has trouble remembering to begin the 2nd partial product in the tens' place, have him put a 0 in the ones' place of the 2nd partial product.
  - (c) Explain that the two products are partial products and must be added to get the product.

  Work other problems on ckbd step by step as child follows along.
- Read and discuss **box on p. 15.** Child does remaining problems in **Ex. 1** and problems in **Ex. 2–3.** You may need to work some mult. problems on ckbd as he works in text.

```
     2
     8
    2 5
  x 4 6
  -------
    1 5 0
+ 1 0 0 0
  -------
  1,1 5 0
```

4. Discuss story problems. (6 min.)
- Child does **Ex. 4.** Explain that *per* in story problem *b* is a clue word for mult.

5. Review/Boardwork (6 min.) **Ex. 5–8** (Notice that Ex. 8 is Extra Practice and is therefore optional.)

Preparation

Lesson 9

1. Chalkboard:

```
   43        55
 x 76      x 82
```

2. *Arithmetic 4:* pp. 17–18

Lesson 9
(cont.)

3. *Lesson 9 Speed Drill*
4. Visuals:
   - *Process Flashcards* (Have 2–7 division table cards and 2–7 multiplication table cards.)
   - *Concept Cards* 16–18 and 111
   - *Place Value (Arith Chart* 2)
   - *Tables/Facts Charts* 2–7
   - *1–100 Chart (Arith Chart* 20)
   - story problem clue words flashcards (optional from les. 4)

Teaching Procedure

1. **Oral review drills** (7 min.)

   Addition/Subtraction (2 min.)
   - *Flashcards:* Let child answer.
   - Oral comb. (Call out long combinations slowly at 1st to get child thinking.)

     $5 + 5 - 3 - 2 + 8 + 2 - 4 = 11$

     $12 - 7 + 5 + 3 - 6 - 3 + 8 + 3 = 15$

     $9 + 9 + 2 - 10 - 4 + 6 + 3 + 7 + 0 + 3 = 25$

     $11 - 8 - 2 + 6 + 3 - 7 + 5 - 6 + 4 + 5 = 11$

     $8 + 5 + 7 + 5 - 10 - 10 + 6 + 4 + 6 = 21$

     $3 + 3 + 3 + 3 - 3 + 3 - 3 - 3 + 3 + 3 + 3 - 3 = 12$
   - *Concept Cards* **16–17:** Review terms.

   Place value (1 min.)
   - *Arith Chart* **2**

   Multiplication/Division (3 min.)
   - *Mult./Div. Cards*
   - *Tables/Facts Charts* **2–7:** Drill mult. tables 2–7.
   - *1–100 Chart:* Point to numbers 1–12, child mult. by 6 and adds 9. Repeat for other combinations.
   - *Concept Cards* **18** and **111:** Review terms.

   Story problems (1 min.)
   - Story problem clue words flashcards

2. **Written speed drill** (6 min.) Time for 5 min.
   - Grade and record as a speed drill/quiz grade. Count off 10 points for each incorrect answer.

3. **Introduce checking multiplication.** (9 min.)
   - ▮▮▮ Work 1st problem for child. Be sure to emphasize where to begin 2nd partial product. Also emphasize importance of knowing mult. tables very well. Explain how to check mult. by reversing factors. Just as we can change the order of addends and get the same sum, we can change the order of factors and get the same product.

$$
\begin{array}{r}
43 \\
\times\ 76 \\
\hline
258 \\
+\ 301 \\
\hline
3{,}268
\end{array}
\qquad
\begin{array}{r}
76 \\
\times\ 43 \\
\hline
228 \\
+\ 304 \\
\hline
3{,}268
\end{array}
$$

Work and check 2nd problem as he explains.

- Read and discuss **box on p. 17.** Child does **Ex. 1.**

4. Discuss story problems. (6 min.)

- Child does **Ex. 2.** Be sure he is quickly finding clue words if there are any clue words in problems.

5. Review/Boardwork (9 min.) **Ex. 3–8**

6. Homework Ex. 9–10

Mon

Lesson

10

Preparation

1. Chalkboard:

 $2\overline{)6}$ $\qquad$ $4\overline{)8}$

2. *Arithmetic 4:* pp. 19–20

3. *Lesson 10 Speed Drill*

4. Visuals:
   - *Process Flashcards* (Have 2–7 division table cards and 2–7 multiplication table cards.)
   - *Place Value (Arith Chart 2)*
   - *Division Steps (Arith Chart 3)*
   - *Table/Facts Charts 2–7*
   - story problem clue words flashcards (optional from les. 4)
   - *Concept Card 19*
   - *Mixed Divison Facts (Arith 4, p. 322)*

Teaching Procedure

1. Oral review drills (9 min.)

Homework check

Addition/Subtraction (3 min.)

- *Flashcards:* Let child answer.

Place value (1 min.)

- *Arith Chart* **2**

Multiplication/Division (4 min.)

- *Mult./Div. Cards*
- *Tables/Facts Charts* **2–7:** Drill mult. tables 2–7.
- *Tables/Facts Charts* **2–4:** Drill div. tables 2–4.
- *Mixed Division Facts:* Point to problems in order; child gives quotients.

Lesson 10
(cont.)

Story problems (1 min.)
- Story problem clue words flashcards

2. **Written speed drill** (4 min.) Time for 3 min.

3. **Introduce division.** (9 min.)
- *Arith Chart* **3:** Teach 5 steps of division. Show how each step was used to find quotient. Child stands and says 5 steps of div. in order several times. He needs to memorize steps.
- *Concept Card* **19:** Introduce terms in div. problem.
- 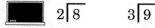 Work 1st problem for child. Emphasize 5 steps in div.

$$\begin{array}{r} x\,3 \\ 2\overline{)\ 6} \\ -\,6 \\ \hline 0 \end{array}$$

Step 1: Divide 2 into 6. Say, *How many 2s are in 6?* or *What number times 2 equals 6?* Write quotient of 3 above 6. (Help child see that div. is opposite of mult. When he div., he is finding missing factor.)

Step 2: Mult. the number last put in quotient (3) times divisor 2. Place product 6 below dividend 6.

Step 3: Subt. 6 from 6 to get 0.

Step 4: Compare difference 0 with divisor 2. The difference must be less than divisor. If difference is the same number or greater than divisor, quotient is wrong.

Step 5: Bring down next number in dividend. Since there is nothing to bring down, problem is finished.

Work 2nd problem for child again emphasizing 5 steps.
- Read and discuss **box on p. 19.** Child does **Ex. 1–2.** You may need to work a few problems on ckbd as child works in text.

4. **Discuss story problems.** (6 min.)
- Child does **Ex. 3.**

5. **Review/Boardwork** (9 min.) **Ex. 4–7**

6. **Homework Ex. 8–9**

Lesson 11

Preparation

1. Chalkboard:

2⟌8   3⟌9

2. *Arithmetic 4:* pp. 21–22

3. *Lesson 11 Speed Drill*

4. Visuals:
- *Place Value (Arith Chart* 2)
- *Division Steps (Arith Chart* 3)
- *Process Flashcards* (Have 2–7 division table cards and 2–7 multiplication table cards)
- *Tables/Facts Charts* 2–6
- *1–100 Chart (Arith Chart* 23)
- story problem clue words flashcards (optional from les. 4)

Teaching Procedure

1. **Oral review drills** (9 min.)

    Homework check

    Place value (2 min.)
    - *Arith Chart* **2**
    - Call out these numbers; students write on ckbd or paper.

1,321,678	231,642,879	67,497,877
14,390,487	2,301,002	192,001,307

    Multiplication/Division (3 min.)
    - *Mult./Div. Cards*
    - *Tables/Facts Charts* **2–6:** Drill mult. tables 2–6. Most children should be able to say tables without benefit of charts.
    - *Tables/Facts Charts* **2–4:** Drill div. tables 2–4.
    - *1–100 Chart:* Point to even numbers from 2 to 24, child div. by 2 and then mult. by 6.

    Addition/Subtraction (3 min.)
    - *Flashcards:* Let child answer and then play *Beat the Clock.* Let your child answer 20 cards as quickly as possible. Time him to see how long it takes. Record time. Make it a goal to beat record each time game is played.

    Story problems (1 min.)
    - Story problem clue words flashcards

2. **Written speed drill** (4 min.) Time for 3 min.

3. **Review division.** (9 min.)
    - *Arith Chart* **3:** Review 5 steps.
    - Work 1st problem for child. Emphasize 5 steps in div. He explains as you work 2nd problem.
    - Child does **Ex. 1–2 p. 21.**

4. **Discuss story problems.** (6 min.)
    - Child does **Ex. 3** together. Be sure he is quick to pick up clue words and can determine correct process to use.

5. **Review/Boardwork** (9 min.) **Ex. 4–8**

6. **Homework Ex. 9–10**

wed

Preparation

Test 1, pp. 9–10 from *Student Tests and Speed Drills.* Directions for giving test and a suggested grading scale are located in *Teacher Tests and Speed Drills.*

Teaching Procedure

1. **Homework check**

Lesson 12
(cont.)

2. Administer test.

- Child takes out 2 sharpened pencils with erasers and 1 sheet of paper for a check sheet. Notice that space has been allowed on this test for child to work story problems.

- Give child test. Parent always grades tests and records grades.

Lesson 13

Thurs

Preparation

1. Chalkboard:

 A

7	25	6	32
x 30	x 400	x 50	x 300

B   3⟌18   5⟌15   4⟌12

2. *Arithmetic 4:* pp. 23–24

3. *Lesson 13 Speed Drill*

4. Visuals:
   - *Process Flashcards* (Have 2–8 division table cards and 2–8 multiplication table cards)
   - *Tables/Facts Charts* 2–8
   - *Calculator (Arith Chart 20)*
   - *Division Steps Arith Chart* 3

Teaching Procedure

1. Oral review drills (6 min.)

Addition/Subtraction (2 min.)
- *Flashcards:* Encourage child to answer quickly.

Multiplication/Division (4 min.)
- *Mult./Div. Cards*
- *Tables/Facts Charts* **2–8:** Drill mult. tables 2–8. Practice tables that are most difficult for child.
- *Tables/Facts Charts* **2–6:** Drill div. tables 2–6.
- *Calculator:* Child mult. by 8, 7, 5, and 3. For variety, have him mult. and then add a number.

2. Written speed drill (4 min.) Time for 3 min.

3. Introduce multiplying by 10 and 100 (10 min.)
- **When mult. by 10 and 100, you can use a short-cut method. If mult. by 10, simply write a 0 after the number being mult. If mult. by 100, simply write 2 zeros after the number being mult. Also we can use a short cut with multiples of 10 and 100.**

- **A** Explain problems step by step on ckbd.

  Step 1: Since this number is a multiple of 10, there is a 0 at the end of it. We can hang the 0 off the problem and write it in our product directly below where it is in the 2nd factor.

  Step 2: Use regular procedure to mult. by 3.

$$
\begin{array}{r}
7 \\
\times\ 3\ 0 \\
\hline
2\ 1\ 0
\end{array}
$$

  Step 1: Since 400 is a multiple of 100, there are 2 zeros at the end of it. We can hang both 0s off the problem and write them in our product directly below where they are in the 2nd factor.

  Step 2: Use regular procedure to mult. by 4.

$$
\begin{array}{r}
2\ 5 \\
\times\ 4\ 0\ 0 \\
\hline
1\ 0,0\ 0\ 0
\end{array}
$$

  Use same steps to work other mult. problems on ckbd.

- Read and discuss **box on p. 23.** Child does **Ex. 1.**

4. Introduce two-step story problems. (9 min.)

- Explain that some story problems have a hidden question. This question must be answered before the one given in story problem. Child must learn to think and to find hidden questions. Do **Ex. 2a** together. Help him find hidden question *How many bugs did Kevin collect?* Do **b** together. Help him find hidden question *How much does 3 yards of material cost?*

5. Review division. (6 min.)

- *Arith Chart* 3: Review 5 steps.

- **B** Work 1st div. problem for him.

  Step 1: 3 cannot be divided into 1 so we divide 3 into 18. Place the quotient 6 above the 8.
  Step 2: Mult. 6 times 3 to get 18.
  Step 3: Subt. 18 from 18 to get 0.
  Step 4: Compare 0 with the divisor 3. It is less.
  Step 5: Bring down. There is nothing to bring down; therefore problem is finished.

$$
\begin{array}{r}
\overset{\times\ 6}{} \\
3\,\overline{\smash{)}\,18} \\
-\,18 \\
\hline
0
\end{array}
$$

  Use same steps to do 2nd div. problem. Child explains as you do 3rd problem on ckbd.

- Child does **Ex. 3.**

6. Review/Boardwork (6 min.) **Ex. 4–8** (Notice that Ex. 8 is Extra Practice and is therefore optional.)

Preparation

1. Chalkboard:

   A
$$
\begin{array}{r}
306 \\
274 \\
328 \\
749 \\
+\ 632 \\
\end{array}
$$

   B $3\,\overline{)\,21}$ $2\,\overline{)\,16}$ $4\,\overline{)\,24}$

Lesson 14
(cont.)

2. *Arithmetic 4:* pp. 25–26
3. *Lesson 14 Speed Drill*
4. Visuals:
   - *Process Flashcards* (2–8 division table cards and 2–8 multiplication table cards)
   - *Division Steps (Arith Chart 3)*
   - *Tables/Facts Charts 2–8*

Teaching Procedure

1. Oral review drills (7 min.)

Addition/Subtraction (4 min.)
- *Flashcards:* Play *Around the World.* Choose a path around the room with a certain number of places to stop. (The number of stops will vary with the number of flashcards your child has learned.) Show him a flashcard; count silently to three; if he answers within that time he moves to the next stop. If he cannot answer in the allotted time, have him repeat the combination with the answer three times. The object of the game is to travel all the way around the "world." You could have the same number of flashcards as stops to make the game a greater challenge.
  Variation: Let your child take one step around the room for every correct answer.

- **A** Fast oral addition: Add column addition orally together. Point to each digit in ones' column beginning with top number. Child says aloud first digit and then says only sum as you move down column. When you finish a column, write sum in proper place and write carrying number at top of next column. Continue in same manner with tens' column, hundreds' column, etc., having child say sums orally. When you finish a problem, use same procedure to check, adding upward. This fast oral addition teaches your child to add numbers quickly in his head. It should be a quick, *mental* exercise. It should take no more than **one minute** of Oral Review Drill. Aim toward a steady, rhythmic speed, with no pauses. The rhythmic speed should increase by daily practice.

Multiplication/Division (3 min.)
- *Mult./Div. Cards*
- *Arith Chart* **3:** Drill steps in division.
- *Tables/Facts Charts* **2–8:** Drill mult. tables 2–8. Practice tables that are most difficult for child.
- *Tables/Facts Charts* **2–6:** Drill div. tables 2–6.

2. Written speed drill (6 min.) Time for 5 min.
- Grade. Record as a speed drill/quiz grade. Count off 6 points for each incorrect answer.

3. Introduce checking division. (6 min.)

- 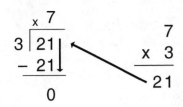 Work 1st problem step by step, referring often to 5 steps of div. Use problem to show how to check div.

$$3 \overline{)21} \quad \overset{\times 7}{} \quad -21 \quad 0$$

$$\begin{array}{r} 7 \\ \times\ 3 \\ \hline 21 \end{array}$$

Mult. the quotient by the divisor. The product should be the same as the dividend. If not, a mistake has been made, and the problem and checking should be done again.

Use same steps to work and check other div. problems on ckbd.

- Read and discuss **box on p. 25.** Child does **Ex. 1.**

4. Review two-step story problems. (9 min.)

(a) In a two-step story problem, you have two problems to work in order to answer the written question.

(b) The 1st question must be answered before finding the answer to the written question.

(c) The answer to the 1st question is used to answer the written question.

(d) The 1st question is not usually written into the story problem. It is referred to as the "hidden question."

(e) Ask *What must I know before I can find the answer to the written question?*

Guide child as he does **Ex. 2.**

5. Review/Boardwork (9 min.) **Ex. 3–6**

6. Homework Ex. 7–8

pres

Preparation

1. Chalkboard:

A 234
456
785
932
+ 341

B $3 \overline{)672}$ $4 \overline{)892}$ $5 \overline{)705}$

2. *Arithmetic 4:* pp. 27–28

3. *Lesson 15 Speed Drill*

4. Visuals:
- *Process Flashcards* (Have 2–8 division table cards and 2–8 multiplication table cards)
- *Tables/Facts Charts* 2–8
- *Division Steps (Arith Chart* 3)

- *Calculator (Arith Chart 20)*
- story problem clue words flashcards (optional from les. 4)
- *Mixed Subtraction Facts (Arith 4, p. 316)*

Teaching Procedure

1. **Oral review drills** (9 min.)

Homework check

Addition/Subtraction (4 min.)

- *Flashcards:* Child answers.
- A Use procedure given in les. 14 to do the fast oral addition.
- *Mixed Subtraction Facts*

Multiplication/Division (4 min.)

- *Mult./Div. Cards*
- *Arith Chart* **3:** Drill steps in division.
- *Tables/Facts Charts* **2–8:** Drill mult. tables 2–8. Practice tables that are most difficult for child.
- *Tables/Facts Charts* **2–7:** Drill div. tables 2–7.
- *Calculator:* Child mult. by 7 or 8 and then subt. a number from product.
- Oral comb.: Play *Moon Walk.* Have your child go to the back of the room. Call out a combination. The moonwalker gets to take a giant step on the moon each time he answers correctly. The moonwalker takes large steps since the gravity on the moon is much less than the gravity on earth. When he reaches the front of the room he is a winner.

3 x 7 – 2 = *19*	6 ÷ 2 – 3 = *0*	7 + 3 x 0 = *0*
4 x 9 – 5 = *31*	6 + 5 x 4 = *44*	9 – 7 x 9 = *18*
12 – 5 x 8 = *56*	3 + 8 + 5 = *16*	5 x 8 ÷ 2 = *20*

Story problems (1 min.)

- story problem clue words flashcards

2. **Written speed drill** (4 min.) Time for 3 min.

3. **Introduce division with three numbers in the dividend.** (9 min.)

- B Work 1st problem step by step, referring often to 5 steps of div. Point out that problems are not harder, just longer. We must use steps of div. 3 times.

```
  x 2 2 4
   ______
 3 | 6 7 2
   - 6
     0 7
   - 6
       1 2
     - 1 2
         0
```

Step 1: Div. 3 into 6 to get 2.
Step 2: Mult. 2 times 3 to get 6.
Step 3: Subt. 6 from 6 to get 0.
Step 4: Compare 0 with 3. It is less.
Step 5: Bring down 7. (Only 1 number can be brought down at a time.)
Step 6: Div. 3 into 7 to get 2. 3 does not go evenly into 7 so we decide as closely as possible how many 3s are in 7. We cannot choose 3 because 3 times 3 is 9 which is greater than 7. We cannot choose 1 because 3 times 1 is

3 and we get 4 when we subt. Therefore 2 is the correct answer because 6 is not greater than 7 and there are no more groups of 3 in 7.

$$\begin{array}{r} 2\ 2\ 4 \\ \times\quad 3 \\ \hline 6\ 7\ 2 \end{array}$$

Step 7: Mult. 2 times 3 to get 6.
Step 8: Subt. 6 from 7 to get 1.
Step 9: Compare 1 with 3. It is less.
Step 10: Bring down 2.
Step 11: Div. 3 into 12 to get 4.
Step 12: Mult. 4 times 3 to get 12.
Step 13: Subt. 12 from 12 to get 0.
Step 14: Compare 0 with 3. It is less.
Step 15: Bring down. Since there is nothing to bring down, the problem is finished. Check the problem by mult. the quotient 224 by the divisor 3. The product is the same as the dividend.

Explain 2nd problem, using same steps. Child explains as you work 3rd problem on ckbd.
- Read and discuss **box on p. 27.** Child does **Ex. 1.** You may need to work on ckbd as child works in text.

4. Discuss story problems. (6 min.)
- Child does **Ex. 2.** Use standard procedure. Help him if having trouble finding hidden question.

5. Review/Boardwork (9 min.) **Ex. 3–7** Encourage child to make good use of his time so he can finish all problems assigned on his workbook page.

6. Homework Ex. 8–9

Lesson 16

Preparation

1. Chalkboard:

A	B	C	D
327	832	3,201	3 ⟌ 788
659	× 3	− 2,783	
842			
726			
+ 388			

2. *Arithmetic 4:* pp. 29–30

3. *Lesson 16 Speed Drill*

4. Visuals:
- *Process Flashcards* (Have 2–8 division table cards and 2–9 multiplication table cards.)
- *Tables/Facts Charts* 2–9
- *Division Steps (Arith Chart* 3)
- *Mixed Addition Facts (Arith 4, p.311)*

Teaching Procedure

1. **Oral review drills** (7 min.)

   Homework check

   Addition/Subtraction (3 min.)

   - *Flashcards:* For variety, have child mult. difference by 2 and stand to say answer.
   - ▮ A ▮ Use standard procedure to do fast oral addition.
   - *Mixed Addition Facts:* Point to problems in order.

   Multiplication/Division (4 min.)

   - *Arith Chart* **3:** Drill steps in division.
   - *Tables/Facts Charts* **2–9:** Drill mult. tables 2–9. Practice tables that child most needs to practice.
   - *Tables/Facts Charts* **2–8:** Drill div. tables 2–8.
   - *Mult./Div. Cards:* Play *Four Corners.* Have your child stand in one corner. Show card. When he answers correctly he gets to move up to next corner. Goal is to go around room and get back to his original corner. Repeat.
   - Oral comb.: Call out combinations.

$5 \times 8 - 7 = 33$	$24 \div 4 + 11 = 17$	$42 \div 6 - 1 = 6$
$2 + 7 \times 5 = 45$	$7 \times 2 \div 7 = 2$	$13 + 7 \div 4 = 5$
$11 - 5 + 7 = 13$	$17 - 9 \times 4 = 32$	$32 \div 4 + 4 = 12$

2. **Written speed drill** (6 min.) Time for 5 min.

   - Grade. Record as a speed drill/quiz grade. Count off 2 points for each incorrect answer.

3. **Discuss story problems.** (6 min.)

   - Child does **Ex. 1, p. 29.** Use standard procedure. Encourage child to think on his own and figure out steps and answers.

4. **Review multiplication.** (6 min.)

   - ▮ B ▮ Work for child. Remind him to be careful to write all digits in correct places. Also remind him of importance of mastering mult. tables.
   - Child does **Ex. 2.**

5. **Review subtraction.** (3 min.)

   - ▮ C ▮ Work and check. Emphasize borrowing process.
   - Child does **Ex. 3.**

6. **Review division.** (6 min.)

   - ▮ D ▮ Explain step by step. Point out that problem is not finished until there are no more digits in dividend to bring down. Check.
   - Child does **Ex. 4.**

7. **Review/Boardwork** (3 min.) **Ex. 5–7**

8. **Homework Ex. 8–9**

Preparation

1. Chalkboard:

A	593	B	5,000	C	$7\overline{)238}$	$6\overline{)504}$
	876		$-\,2{,}678$			
	295					
	838					
	$+\,965$					

2. *Arithmetic 4:* pp. 31–32

3. *Lesson 17 Quiz* (*Student Tests and Speed Drills* p. 13)

4. Visuals:
   - *Calculator (Arith Chart 20)*
   - *Process Flashcards* (Have 2–8 division table cards and 2–9 multiplication table cards.)
   - *Place Value (Arith Chart 2)*
   - *Concept Cards* 1–15
   - *Tables/Facts Charts* 2–9
   - coins

Teaching Procedure

1. **Oral review drills** (9 min.)

   Homework check

   Addition/Subtraction (3 min.)
   - A Do fast oral addition.
   - B Child explains borrowing process.
   - *Calculator:* He adds 8 to number you push.
   - *Add./Subt. Cards:* Play *Capture the Card.* Show a card to child. If he answers correctly he gets card. If he cannot capture the card set it aside for later. After game is over practice the cards that were not captured.

   Place value (1 min.)
   - *Arith Chart* **2**
   - *Concept Cards* **1–15:** Child reads numbers and gives value of circled digits.

   Multiplication/Division (3 min.)
   - *Mult./Div. Cards*
   - *Tables/Facts Charts* **2–9:** Drill mult. tables 2–9.
   - *Tables/Facts Charts* **2–8:** Drill div. tables 2–8.

   Money (3 min.)
   - Coins: Show coin and tell how many you have of that coin; child gives value.
   - Call out these money problems; he writes values on ckbd.

     4 dimes = *$.40*   12 nickels = *$.60*   15 dollars = *$15*

2. Quiz 2 (9 min.)

3. Review division. (9 min.)

- Work and check div. problems on ckbd as child watches. Child does **Ex. 1–3, p. 31.** Story problems all involve div.

4. Review/Boardwork (9 min.) **Ex. 4–8**

Lesson 18

Preparation

1. Chalkboard:

3,246
7,829
3,875
+ 4,996

4 feet   24 feet

___ inches   ___ yards

2. *Arithmetic 4:* pp. 33–34

3. *Lesson 18 Speed Drill*

4. Visuals:
   - *Process Flashcards* (Have 2–8 division table cards and 2–9 multiplication table cards.)
   - *Tables/Facts Charts* 2–9
   - story problem clue words flashcards (optional from les. 4)
   - *Place Value (Arith Charts* 2)
   - *English Linear Measures (Arith Chart* 5)
   - *Concept Cards* 32–36

Teaching Procedure

1. Oral review drills (9 min.)

Processes (7 min.)

- Paper drill—Call out these combinations; child writes answers. Check after every 4 answers. Praise child when he misses 0.

6 + 7 = *13*	15 − 9 = *6*	12 − 7 = *5*	13 − 7 + 8 = *14*
8 + 8 = *16*	5 + 4 = *9*	11 − 8 = *3*	5 + 16 = *21*
5 + 3 − 7 = *1*	15 − 8 − 3 = *4*	9 + 3 − 6 = *6*	11 − 9 = *2*

- Use standard procedure to do fast oral addition.
- *Process Cards:* Mix add., subt., and mult. cards together. This makes child look not only at numbers but also process sign.
- *Process Cards:* Play *Giant Step.* Child goes to back of his row to be a giant. Show card to child. When he answers correctly he gets to take a giant step toward front of room. When giant reaches front of room he is a winner.
- *Tables/Facts Charts* **2–9:** Drill mult. tables 2–9. Practice tables that child most needs to practice.

- *Tables/Facts Charts* **2–8:** Drill div. tables 2–8.
- Oral comb.

5 x 9 + 3 ÷ 4 = *12*	29 − 7 ÷ 2 x 4 = *44*	35 ÷ 7 + 6 − 7 = *4*
7 + 4 x 3 − 4 = *29*	10 x 9 − 8 + 5 = *87*	8 + 7 x 0 + 13 = *13*
18 ÷ 2 + 8 − 2 = *15*	17 + 7 ÷ 3 x 7 = *56*	65 − 1 ÷ 8 x 6 = *48*

Story problems (1 min.)

- story problem clue words flashcards

Place value (1 min.)

- *Arith Chart* **2**

2. Written speed drill (5 min.) Time for 4 min.

3. Introduce English linear measures. (8 min.)

- *Arith Chart* **5:** Introduce linear measures. Show approximate length with hands and have child show approximate lengths. (To show approximate size of mile, child puts hands as far apart as possible.)
- *Concept Cards* **32–36:** Review linear measures. As he gives answer to card 32, he should show approximate size of foot and inch. Repeat for other cards.
- Introduce 2 measurement rules.
  - **(a) When converting measures from larger to smaller, multiply.**
  - **(b) When converting measures from smaller to larger, divide.**

  Drill these rules and expect him to memorize them. His hands can be used to demonstrate rules. If measure is yards to inches, have hands go from far apart to close together to represent yards to inches. Let hands finally cross to represent mult. sign, since mult. is process used here. If measure is inches to yards, have hands go from close together to far apart to represent inches to yards. Let hands make 2 points to represent dots in div. problem, since div. is process used here.

- [B] Work 1st problem step by step.

  4 feet

  48 inches
  ⎯⎯⎯⎯⎯

  1. x
  2. s ⑫
  3. 12
     x 4
     ⎯⎯
     48

  Step 1: Which rule is being used? We are going from feet to inches, larger to smaller, so mult. Write times sign beside step 1.

  Step 2: What is our special number? The special number is obtained by knowing how many of the smaller measures are in just one of the larger measures. There are 12 inches in 1 foot.

  Step 3: Mult. the special number 12 by the given number 4 which is in our problem. The answer is 48 inches.

  Use same 3 steps to work 2nd problem. Child should notice that he must div. since he is going from a smaller to larger unit. He should check each answer to make sure it makes sense. If he chooses wrong process, answer will not make sense.

- Read and discuss **box on p. 33.** Child does **Ex. 1–2.**

4. Discuss story problems. (6 min.)

- Child does **Ex. 3.** Guide him as he does **a.** It is a measurement problem and should be set up as a measurement problem and worked as explained in today's lesson.

5. Review/Boardwork (9 min.) **Ex. 4–8** Notice that Ex. 7–8 are Extra Practice and are therefore optional.

Lesson 19

Preparation

1. Chalkboard:

A

$$9,786$$
$$3,592$$
$$7,849$$
$$+ \ 6,375$$

B   12 feet = ___ yards   3 yards = ___ inches

C

329	489
x 47	x 25

D   6⟌396   5⟌435

2. *Arithmetic 4:* pp. 35–36

3. *Lesson 19 Speed Drill*

4. Visuals:
   - *Process Flashcards* (Have 2–8 division table cards and 2–9 multiplication table cards.)
   - *Tables/Facts Charts* 2–9
   - *Concept Cards* 32–36
   - *English Linear Measures (Arith Chart 5)*
   - *Mixed Multiplication Facts (Arith 4, p. 319)*

Teaching Procedure

1. Oral review drills (6 min.)

Processes (4 min.)

- *Flashcards:* Child adds 5 to each answer.
- **A** Use standard procedure to do fast oral addition.
- *Tables/Facts Charts* **2–9:** Drill mult. tables 2–9. Practice tables that child most needs to practice.
- *Tables/Facts Charts* **2–8:** Drill div. tables 2–8. Practice tables that he most needs to practice.
- *Mixed Multiplication Facts:* Point to problems in order.

Measures (2 min.)

- *Concept Cards* **32–36:** Praise child if he knows linear measures already. He cannot do well on measurement problems if he has not memorized tables of measures.

• Drill 2 measurement rules.

2. Written speed drill (4 min.) Time for 3 min.

3. Introduce simple measurement problems. (9 min.)

  • *Chart* **5:** Review linear measures and 2 measurement rules. For variety, use hand motions.

  • [B] Work 1st problem step by step.

Step 1: What measure are you looking for? (yard)
Write ___ yards = ___ yards.

| 12 feet | = _4_ yards |
| 4 yards | = _4_ yards |

Step 2: Draw a box around 12 feet

___ yards.

1. ÷

2. s ③

Step 3: Work as a simple measurement problem, using 3 steps taught in les. 18.

3. x 4

3⟌12
−12↓

Step 4: Put answer in all 3 blanks.

Use same steps to work 2nd problem.

  • Read and discuss **box on p. 35.** Child does **Ex. 1.**

4. Review multiplication and division. (9 min.)

  • [C/D] Have your child work problems on ckbd and explain. Child recites tables.

  • Child does **Ex. 2–3.**

5. Discuss story problem. (3 min.)

  • Child does **Ex. 4.** Follow standard procedure.

6. Review/Boardwork (6 min.) **Ex. 5–7**

7. Homework Ex. 8–9

Preparation

Lesson 20

1. Chalkboard:

[A] 7,824
6,387
4,938
7,965
+ 7,858

[B] 3 ft. + 6 in. = ___ in.   5 yd. − 6 ft. = ___ yd.

2. *Arithmetic 4:* pp. 37–38

3. *Lesson 20 Speed Drill*

4. Visuals:

  • *Tables/Facts Charts* 2–9
  • *Process Flashcards* (Have 2–9 division table cards and 2–9 multiplication table cards.)
  • story problem clue words flashcards (optional from les. 4)
  • *Concept Cards* 32–36

Teaching Procedure

1. Oral review drills (9 min.)

Homework check

Processes (7 min.)

- *Tables/Facts Charts* **2–9**: Drill mult./div. tables. Practice tables that child most needs to practice.
- *Flashcards:* Let him answer and then play *Four Corners*.
- ▮ A ▮ Use standard procedure to do fast oral addition.

Story problems (1 min.)

- story problem clue words flashcards

Measures (1 min.)

- *Concept Cards* **32–36**
- Drill 2 measurement rules.

2. Written speed drill (3 min.) Time for 2 min. 30 sec.

3. Introduce addition and subtraction of measures. (9 min.)

- Teach and drill 5 steps used in adding and subtracting unlike units of measure.

  1: What are we looking for?
  2: Find the two that are the same and write that number down.
  3: Find the two that are different.
  4: Box the different ones and work the box problem.
  5: Add or subtract.

- ▮ B ▮ Work 1st problem using 5 steps.

  Step 1: What are we looking for? (inches)

  Write ___ in. + ___ in. = ___ in. Be sure to keep problem lined up correctly.

  Step 2: Find the two that are the same and write that number down. (in. and in.; Write down the 6.)

  Step 3: Find the two that are different. (ft. and in.)

  Step 4: Box the different ones and work the box problem. Use the same steps as taught in les. 18. Write the answer only in the box.

  Step 5: Add or subtract. This problem tells us to add. Write the sum in both blanks.

$$\boxed{3\ \text{ft.}} + \underline{6}\ \text{in.} = \underline{42}\ \text{in.}$$
$$\boxed{36\ \text{in.}} + \underline{6}\ \text{in.} = \underline{42}\ \text{in.}$$

1. x
2. s ⑫
3. 12
   $$\begin{array}{r} 12 \\ \times\,3 \\ \hline 36 \end{array}$$

Use same steps to work 2nd problem. Drill steps several times. Include 5 steps in oral review of measures until child has . them memorized.

- Read and discuss **box on p. 37.** Child does **Ex. 1.**

4. Discuss story problem. (6 min.)

- Child does **Ex. 2.** Follow standard procedure.

5. Review/Boardwork (9 min.) **Ex. 3–5**

6. Homework Ex. 6–8

Preparation

1. Chalkboard:

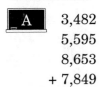 **A**   3,482
              5,595
              8,653
            + 7,849

B quart ___ gallon   pint ____ cup   fluid ounce ___ cup

C 24 quarts = ___ gallons

2. *Arithmetic 4:* pp. 39–40

3. *Lesson 21 Speed Drill*

4. Visuals:
   - *Process Flashcards*
   - *1–100 Chart (Arith Chart 23)*
   - *Concept Cards 32–36, 38–40, 112, and 21–23*
   - *English Measures of Capacity (Arith Chart 11)*

Teaching Procedure

Note: Do not allow child to use charts as a crutch. Mult/Div. facts need to be memorized.

1. Oral review drills (9 min.)

   Homework check

   Processes (7 min.)
   - **A**   Use standard procedure to do fast oral addition.
   - *Add./Subt. Cards:* Play *Secret Code.* Show 3 flashcards in a row. Your child is to determine answers and remember them in order. After he has seen all 3 cards, call on him to give secret code, which is 3 answers in proper order.
   - *Mult./Div. Tables:* Drill tables that child most needs to practice. Continue to use charts only if child still needs them. You may want to keep charts handy so child who is having trouble can see them to write them.
   - *1–100 Chart:* Point to even numbers 2–24, child div. by 2 and then mult. by 9.
   - *Mult./Div. Cards:* Play *Giant Step.*

   Measures (2 min.)
   - *Concept Cards* **32–36**
   - Review 5 measurement problem steps.

2. Written speed drill (4 min.) Time for 3 min.

3. Introduce liquid measures. (9 min.)
   - *Arith Chart* **11:** Teach liquid measures of capacity, except teaspoons and tablespoons. Keep measures charts displayed so he can study during any free time.

Lesson 21
(cont.)

- *Concept Cards* **38–40** and **112:** Drill liquid measures.
- *Concept Cards* **21–23:** Introduce symbols for greater than and less than. Review symbol for equals.
- **B** Child writes correct symbols in blanks. You may want to tell him that open "mouth" is always open toward greater amount.
- **C** Work problem step by step for child. Be sure he understands how to determine if he mult. or div. and how to know what to mult. or div. by.
- Read and discuss **box on p. 39.** Child does **Ex. 1–2.**

4. Discuss story problems. (6 min.)

- Child does **Ex. 3.** Use standard procedure.

5. Review/Boardwork (9 min.) **Ex. 4–7**

6. Homework Ex. 8–9

Lesson 22

Preparation

Test 2, pp. 17–18 from *Student Tests and Speed Drills*. Directions for giving test and a suggested grading scale are located in *Teacher Tests and Speed Drills*.

Teaching Procedure

1. Homework check

2. Administer test.

- Child takes out 2 sharpened pencils with erasers and a sheet of paper to be used as a check sheet. Notice that space has been allowed on this test for child to work story problems.

- Give child test. Parent always grades test and records grade.

Lesson 23

Preparation

1. Chalkboard:

A
   7,326
   5,987
   2,829
   7,384
+ 5,993

B 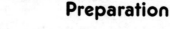 4 pounds – 17 ounces = ___ ounces

2. *Arithmetic 4:* pp. 41–42

3. *Lesson 23 Speed Drill*

4. Visuals:
   - *Process Flashcards* (Child should be ready to answer any process flashcard now.)
   - *Concept Cards* 32–36, 38–40, 112, and 43–44
   - *English Measures of Weight (Arith Chart 7)*

Teaching Procedure

1. **Oral review drills** (9 min.)

   Processes (7 min.)
   - *Add./Subt./Mult./Div. Cards:* Train child to give prompt answers. If he does not know answer, parent answers. Return to card missed to repeat correct answer.
   - Paper drill: Call out these comb. Check answers after every 4.

$12 - 6 = 6$	$7 + 8 = 15$	$16 - 9 = 7$	$11 - 7 + 6 = 10$
$4 + 8 = 12$	$11 - 6 = 5$	$5 + 8 = 13$	$16 - 8 = 8$
$13 - 9 = 4$	$5 + 3 - 2 = 6$	$12 - 7 + 6 = 11$	$15 - 7 = 8$

   - Mult./Div. Tables
   - **A** Use standard procedure to do fast oral addition.
   - Oral comb.

$2 \times 8 \div 8 \times 3 \div 2 = 3$	$9 + 3 \div 2 - 1 = 5$
$8 \times 8 \div 8 + 4 - 3 = 9$	$8 + 3 + 2 - 2 = 11$
$2 + 2 \div 2 \times 8 - 3 - 1 \div 6 = 2$	$2 \times 8 \div 2 + 5 - 3 = 10$
$2 + 2 + 10 \div 2 - 1 = 6$	$5 \times 5 \div 5 + 10 - 5 = 10$
$5 \times 3 \div 5 + 5 \times 9 = 72$	$18 \div 3 \times 3 \div 2 \times 2 = 18$

   Measures (2 min.)
   - *Concept Cards* **32–36, 38–40,** and **112**

2. **Written speed drill** (4 min.) Time for 3 min.

3. **Introduce English table of weight measures.** (9 min.)
   - *Arith Chart* **7**: Introduce ounces, pounds, and tons. Be sure to point out abbreviations of ounces and pounds, since they are difficult for some children.
   - *Concept Cards* **43–44**: Drill measures of weight.
   - **B** Drill measurement rules and steps in working a measurement equation. Explain problem step by step on ckbd.
   - Read and discuss **box on p. 41.** Child does **Ex. 1–2.**

4. **Discuss story problem.** (3 min.)
   - Child does **Ex. 3.** Use standard procedure.

5. **Review/Boardwork** (12 min.) **Ex. 4–11**

Lesson
24

wed

Preparation

1. Chalkboard:

   A   73,246
             29,783
             46,903
         + 77,899

   B $3\overline{)29}$ $5\overline{)42}$

2. *Arithmetic 4:* pp. 43–44

3. *Lesson 24 Speed Drill*

4. Visuals:
   - *Process Flashcards*
   - *Division Steps (Arith Chart* 3*)*
   - *Calculator (Arith Chart* 20*)*
   - *Concept Cards* 32–36, 38–40, 112, and 43–44

Teaching Procedure

1. **Oral review drills** (9 min.)

   Processes (6 min.)
   - Mult./Div. Tables
   - *Flashcards:* Play *Around the World.*
   - **A** Use standard procedure to do fast oral addition.
   - *Arith Chart* **3:** Drill steps in division.
   - *Calculator:* Child mult. by 8 and div. product by 2.
   - Oral comb. Play *Moonwalk.*

$18 \div 3 \times 3 \div 2 = 9$	$8 + 2 + 1 + 9 \div 5 = 4$
$10 + 11 \div 3 - 5 \times 2 = 4$	$3 + 7 + 5 \div 5 = 3$
$12 \div 6 \times 9 + 2 \div 5 = 4$	$10 + 9 + 2 \div 7 = 3$
$10 + 2 \div 6 + 4 - 2 \div 2 = 2$	$3 \times 7 + 8 + 1 \div 5 = 6$
$3 \times 5 \div 3 + 8 = 13$	$2 \times 8 \div 2 + 5 = 13$

   Measures (3 min.)
   - *Concept Cards* **32–36, 38–40, 112,** and **43–44:** Go through all cards once with child and then play *Four Corners.* It is very important that your child memorizes his tables of measures.
   - Review 5 measurement problem steps.

2. **Written speed drill** (3 min.) Time for 2 min.

3. **Introduce checking division with a remainder.** (9 min.)
   - **B** Work 1st problem step by step, referring often to 5 steps of div. Use problem to show how to check div. **Mult. the quotient by the divisor and add the remainder. The sum should be the same as the dividend. If not, a mistake has been made, and the problem and checking should be done again.**

Note: It is better not to play games if child is struggling with facts. Use the time to drill the facts instead.

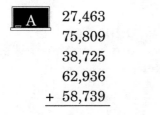

Step 1: Div. 3 into 29 to get 9.
Step 2: Mult. 9 times 3 to get 27.
Step 3: Subt. 27 from 29 to get 2.
Step 4: Compare 2 with 3. It is less.
Step 5: Bring down. There is nothing to bring down so problem is finished. 2 is the remainder. Be sure the remainder is also put in the quotient.

Checking:
Step 1: Mult. quotient 9 by divisor 3 to get 27.
Step 2: Add remainder 2 to product to get 29. Sum is same as dividend so problem is correct.

Use same steps to work other div. problems on ckbd.
- Read and discuss **box on p. 43.** Child does **Ex. 1–2.**

4. Discuss story problems. (6 min.)
- Child does **Ex. 3.** Use standard procedure.

5. Review/Boardwork (9 min.) **Ex. 4–6** Be sure child is working neatly in workbook and at ckbd.

6. Homework Ex. 7–8

Lesson 25

Preparation

1. Chalkboard:

A		B	C
27,463		6⟌47	$2.47
75,809			x 93
38,725			
62,936			
+ 58,739			

2. *Arithmetic 4:* pp. 45–46

3. *Lesson 25 Speed Drill*

4. Visuals:
   - *Process Flashcards*
   - *Place Value (Arith Chart 2)*
   - *Concept Cards* 1–15, 32–36, 38–40, 112, and 43–44
   - story problem clue words flashcards (optional from les. 4)
   - *Division Steps (Arith Chart 3)*

Teaching Procedure

1. Oral review drills (7 min.)

   Homework check

   Processes (4 min.)

Lesson 25
(cont.)

- Mult./Div. Tables
- *Flashcards:* Have child answer. Be sure to use cards that child needs to practice.
- Use standard procedure to do fast oral addition.
- *Arith Chart* **3:** Drill steps in division.

Measures (2 min.)

- *Concept Cards* **32–36, 38–40, 112,** and **43–44:** Go through all cards once with child and then play *Giant Step.*

Place value (1 min.)

- *Chart* **2**
- *Concept Cards* **1–15**

2. **Written speed drill** (6 min.) Time for 5 min.
   - Grade. Record as a speed drill/quiz grade. Count off 3 points for each incorrect answer.

3. **Review division with a remainder.** (6 min.)
   - Work and check step by step with him.
   - Child does **Ex. 1–2, p. 45.**

4. **Review multiplication.** (6 min.)
   - **C** Work problem, emphasizing placing digits in correct position and carrying. Point out that product needs to be in terms of money. There must be 2 decimal places to show cents, and there needs to be a dollar sign. Show him where to put decimal point and dollar sign. He reads product aloud.
   - Child does **Ex. 3.** Make sure he puts decimal point in correct place in 3*a*.

> **Note:** Make sure child understands that if decimal point is missing or in the wrong place, the entire answer is wrong. He should include dollar sign, but it is not as crucial as decimal point.

5. **Discuss story problems.** (6 min.)
   - Story problem clue words flashcards: Drill with child.
   - Child does **Ex. 4.** Use standard procedure. Continue to help if he is having trouble finding hidden question.

6. **Review/Boardwork** (6 min.) **Ex. 5–8**

7. **Homework** **Ex. 9–10**

Lesson 26

Preparation

1. Chalkboard:

   A
   ```
     3,825
     9,936
     8,723
     2,399
   + 8,903
   ```

B $48 \div 8 =$ ___ $25 \div 5 =$ ___ $32 \div 4 =$ ___

$56 \div 7 =$ ___ $63 \div 9 =$ ___ $72 \div 12 =$ ___

C $6\overline{)789}$ $5\overline{)431}$

D
$$\begin{array}{r} 274 \\ \times 65 \\ \hline \end{array}$$

E 4 ft. + 5 in. = ___ in.

2. *Arithmetic 4:* pp. 47–48

3. *Lesson 26 Speed Drill*

4. Visuals:
   - *Process Flashcards*
   - *Concept Cards* 32–36, 38–40, 112, and 43–44

Teaching Procedure

1. Oral review drills (9 min.)

Homework check

Processes (9 min.)
   - *Flashcards:* Have child answer a few cards to get warmed-up and then play *Rithmetic Rhythm*. Using the "clap, clap, snap, snap" of the regular Rhythm game, the parent calls out a multiplication fact on the "snap, snap" such as *three fives*. The child responds with the answer on the next "snap, snap" *(fifteen)*. The parent then calls another multiplication fact, etc. Try to go as far as possible without breaking the rhythm. Be sure the rhythm is well started and child is ready before calling out any number facts.
   - Mult./Div. Tables
   - **A** Use standard procedure to do fast oral addition.
   - **B** Point to div. problems and call on child to give quotients.

2. Written speed drill (4 min.) Time for 3 min.

3. Introduce division with a larger dividend and a remainder. (6 min.)
   - **C** Work and check problems as child listens. These problems are no harder; they are just longer.
   - Child does **Ex. 1, p. 47.**

4. Review multiplication. (6 min.)
   - **D** Work for child. Stress importance of accuracy. Mult. is easy and enjoyable for children who know tables. Give special attention if your child is still weak with tables.
   - Child does **Ex. 2.**

5. Review measurement equations. (3 min.)
   - *Concept Cards 32–36, 38–40, 112,* and *43–44:* Conduct a brisk review of measures. Praise child who knows them all.

Lesson 26
(cont.)

- [E] Work step by step for child.
- Child does **Ex. 3–4.**

6. Discuss story problems. (6 min.)
- Child does **Ex. 5.**

7. Review/Boardwork (3 min.) **Ex. 6–7**

8. Homework Ex. 8–10 Child needs to have a ruler in arithmetic tomorrow.

Mon

Lesson 27

Preparation

1. Chalkboard:

[A]
```
   8,793
   5,326
   7,849
   8,975
 + 4,326
 -------
```

[B] 24 ÷ 8 = ___ 36 ÷ 6 = ___ 14 ÷ 7 = ___
90 ÷ 10 = ___ 84 ÷ 12 = ___ 54 ÷ 6 = ____

[C] 8 qt. + 3 gal. = ___ gal.

[D] Use *Rolling Ruler* (*Arith Chart* 24) to draw lines that are 7 in. and 11 in.

2. *Arithmetic 4:* pp. 49–50
3. *Lesson 27 Quiz*
4. Visuals:
   - *Process Flashcards*
   - *Calculator (Arith Chart 20)*
   - *Place Value (Arith Chart 2)*
   - *Concept Cards* 1–15, 32–36, 38–40, 112, and 43–44
   - coins
   - *Rolling Ruler* (in.) *(Arith Chart* 24)
   - ruler

Teaching Procedure

1. Oral review drills (9 min.)

Homework check

Processes (6 min.)
- *Flashcards:* Expect quick, accurate answers.
- [A] Use standard procedure to do fast oral addition.
- *Calculator:* Child adds 13 to number you push.
- [B] Call on him to give quotients as you point to problems. Point to them in random order.
- Mult./Div. Tables: Have him recite tables. Sometimes you may want to have child write a table in a given amount of time.

Place value (1 min.)
- *Arith Chart* **2**
- *Concept Cards* **1–15:** Child reads numbers and gives value of circled digits.

Money (2 min.)
- Coins: Show coin and tell how many you have of that coin; child gives value.
- Call out these money problems; child writes values on ckbd.

    13 dimes = *$1.30*   20 nickels = *$1.00*   7 quarters = *$1.75*

2. Quiz 3 (9 min.)

3. Review measures. (6 min.)
- *Concept Cards* **32–36, 38–40, 112,** and **43–44:** Review briefly.
- ▓ **C** ▓ Child explains how to work as you work on ckbd.
- ▓ **D** ▓ *Rolling Ruler:* Explain to him that *Rolling Ruler* is enlarged so it can be seen easily. Show him how to measure 7 in. line to nearest inch. Zero inches needs to be put at beginning of line. Ruler should be aligned with line. Point where line ends on ruler gives number of in. Allow child to measure 11 in. line, using *Rolling Ruler*.
- **rulers:** Child needs to get out his ruler and find side marked inches. Have him find 0 in. on ruler. For some rulers that is simply beginning of ruler. Other rulers have a mark near beginning of ruler to show 0 in.
- Child does **Ex. 1–5, p. 49.** Be sure he understands that he is measuring to nearest in. String of beads may be a little longer or shorter than a whole inch. He should write number of inches that it is closest to.

4. Discuss story problems. (6 min.)
- Child does **Ex. 6.** Work problems together.

5. Review/Boardwork (6 min.) **Ex. 7–9**

Tues

Preparation

1. Chalkboard:

    ▓ **A** ▓

        5,439
        7,884
        5,563
        7,089
      + 9,316

    ▓ **B** ▓   7)438   3)$2.36

2. *Arithmetic 4:* pp. 51–52

3. *Lesson 28 Speed Drill*
4. Visuals:
   - *1–100 Chart*
   - *Process Flashcards*
   - *Place Value (Arith Chart 2)*
   - *Division Steps (Arith Chart 3)*

Teaching Procedure

1. Oral review drills (7 min.)

    Processes (6 min.)
   - Mult./Div. Tables
   - *1–100 Chart:* Have your child point to all numbers in order that are products when we mult. by 7. Have him say these numbers.
   - Paper drill—Call out these combinations. Check after every 4 answers. Praise child who improves each time.

9 x 7 = *63*	5 x 8 = *40*	12 x 7 = *84*	48 ÷ 6 + 8 = *16*
64 ÷ 8 = *8*	12 x 4 = *48*	11 x 11 = *121*	6 x 9 – 8 = *46*
12 x 3 ÷ 6 = *6*	15 – 8 – 3 = *4*	9 ÷ 3 x 6 = *18*	11 x 9 = *99*

   - **A** Use standard procedure to do fast oral addition.
   - *Flashcards:* Show a flashcard. Child writes correct answer. Check after every four cards.
   - *Arith Chart* **3**: Drill 5 steps of div.
   - Oral comb.

5 + 2 – 6 x 3 x 7 = *21*	13 + 1 + 5 + 4 + 6 = *29*
4 x 3 x 6 – 2 = *70*	5 + 5 – 4 + 2 = *8*
4 + 6 + 2 – 7 = *5*	2 + 7 – 4 + 6 = *11*
2 + 7 + 9 + 4 + 3 = *25*	5 + 6 + 3 + 7 + 2 = *23*
4 + 2 + 7 + 3 + 2 = *18*	16 + 3 + 4 + 6 + 2 = *31*

    Place value (1 min.)
   - *Arith Chart* **2**
   - Call out these numbers for child to write on paper or ckbd.

      30,006,780   234,000,003   17,004,010

2. Written speed drill (6 min.) Time for 5 min.
   - Grade. Record as a speed drill/quiz grade. Count off 5 points for each incorrect answer.

3. Introduce division with money. (9 min.)
   - **B** Child explains how to work 1st problem. Show how 2nd problem is like 1st except dividend is in dollars and cents. Quotient must be given in dollars and cents. All we do is write decimal point in quotient directly above decimal point in dividend. Write dollar sign in quotient directly above dollar sign in dividend. Then we proceed as we normally would.

- Read and discuss **box on p. 51.** Child does **Ex. 1.** You may want to have him put decimal points and dollar signs immediately in quotients of *d–f.*

4. Discuss story problems. (6 min.)

- Child does **Ex. 2.** He may need help with ***a.*** He needs to set up as a div. problem with a money dividend. Again he must be careful to write decimal point and dollar sign in quotient 1st.

5. Review/Boardwork (9 min.) **Ex. 3–7** Praise child who works quickly in his text.

wed

Preparation

1. Chalkboard:

A
7,326
9,587
4,599
3,288
+ 9,562

B

23	87
78	95
49	96
57	78
63	93
	91

C $4\overline{)3,201}$

2. *Arithmetic 4:* pp. 53–54

3. *Lesson 29 Speed Drill*

4. Visuals:
   - *Process Flashcards*
   - *1–100 Chart*
   - *Concept Cards 32–36, 38–40, 112, and 43–44*
   - *Averaging Numbers (Arith Chart 6)*
   - *Division Steps (Arith Chart 3)*

Teaching Procedure

1. Oral review drills (9 min.)

Processes (7 min.)

- *Flashcards:* Child adds 5 to each answer.
- **A** Use standard procedure to do fast oral addition.
- Mult./Div. Tables

Lesson 29
(cont.)

- *1–100 Chart:* Have child point to numbers in order that are products when we mult. by 8. Child recites numbers.
- Call out these div. problems. He includes remainder in quotient.

$13 \div 6 = 2r.1$	$15 \div 4 = 3r.3$	$19 \div 3 = 6r.1$	$37 \div 5 = 7r.2$
$52 \div 6 = 8r.4$	$8 \div 3 = 2r.2$	$19 \div 5 = 3r.4$	$22 \div 7 = 3r.1$
$33 \div 6 = 5r.3$	$13 \div 2 = 6r.1$	$55 \div 9 = 6r.1$	$50 \div 8 = 6r.2$

Measures (2 min.)

- *Concept Cards* **32–36, 38–40, 112,** and **43–44:** Play *Beat the Clock.*

2. Written speed drill (3 min.) Time for 2 min.

3. Introduce number averaging. (6 min.)

- *Arith Chart* **6:** Discuss that when several numbers such as grades are given that we sometimes want to know an average of the numbers. The average number is somewhere between the least and greatest numbers in the group. Show 2 easy steps used to find average—addition and division.

- **B** Work 1st problem step by step.

  Step 1: Add addends to find sum.

  Step 2: Div. sum by number of addends. The carrying number is not an addend. The average is 54. Have child notice that 54 is between least number 23 and greatest number 78. (You may prefer to have him div. into sum without making a separate problem as in $5\overline{\smash{)}270}\,\boxed{54}$.)

  $$
  \begin{array}{r}
  23 \\
  78 \\
  49 \\
  57 \\
  + 63 \\
  \hline
  270
  \end{array}
  \qquad
  \begin{array}{r}
  \times\,54 \\
  5\overline{)270} \\
  -25 \\
  \hline
  20 \\
  -20 \\
  \hline
  0
  \end{array}
  $$

  Use same steps to work 2nd problem.
- Read and discuss **box on p. 53.** Child does **Ex. 1.**

4. Review division. (6 min.)

- *Arith Chart* **3:** Review 5 steps of div.
- Call out these div. problems for quick oral answers.

$12 \div 6 = 2$	$25 \div 5 = 5$	$28 \div 4 = 7$	$21 \div 7 = 3$
$27 \div 3 = 9$	$22 \div 2 = 11$	$45 \div 5 = 9$	$36 \div 6 = 6$

- **C** Child explains how to work and check problem as you work on ckbd.
- Child does **Ex. 2.**

5. Discuss story problems. (6 min.)

- Child does **Ex. 3.** Have him notice clue word *average* in **b.** He should follow 2 steps learned in today's lesson.

6. Review/Boardwork (6 min.) **Ex. 4–6**

7. Homework **Ex. 7–8**

Thur

Preparation

1. Chalkboard:

| A | 4,938 | B | 85 | C | 4) $32.21 |

A   4,938   B   85   C   4) $32.21
       2,657   97
       7,899   93
       8,431   88
    + 9,056

2. *Arithmetic 4:* pp. 55–56

3. *Lesson 30 Speed Drill*

4. Visuals:
   - *Process Flashcards*
   - *Averaging Numbers (Arith Chart 6)*
   - *1–100 Chart (Arith Chart 23)*
   - *Concept Cards 32–36, 38–40, 112, and 43–44*

Teaching Procedure

1. **Oral review drills** (9 min.)

   Homework check

   Processes (7 min.)
   - *Flashcards:* Let child answer and then play *Four Corners.*
   - *Arith Chart* **6:** Review 2 steps to find number average.
   - Mult./Div. Tables
   - *1–100 Chart:* Point to numbers that are divisible by 6; child div. by 6 and gives quotient. Repeat by pointing to numbers that are not divisible by 6; he div. by 6 and includes remainder in quotient.
   - **A** Use standard procedure to do fast oral addition.
   - Oral comb.

4 + 9 = *13*	7 + 6 = *13*	3 + 9 = *12*	8 x 5 = *40*
6 x 9 = *54*	16 ÷ 4 = *4*	12 ÷ 2 = *6*	40 ÷ 6 = *6r.4*

   Measures (2 min.)
   - *Concept Cards* **32–36, 38–40, 112,** and **43–44:** Play a favorite game.
   - Drill 2 measurement rules.

2. **Written speed drill** (4 min.) Time for 3 min.

3. **Review number averaging.** (6 min.)
   - ***Arith Chart* 6:** Review 2 steps for averaging numbers.
   - **B** Average numbers as child watches.
   - Child does **Ex. 1, p. 55.**

4. **Review division with a money dividend.** (6 min.)
   - **C** Remind him that decimal point and dollar sign go directly above in quotient.

- Child does **Ex. 2.**
5. Discuss story problem. (6 min.)
- Child does **Ex. 3.**
6. Review/Boardwork (6 min.) **Ex. 4–6**
7. Homework Ex. 7–8

Lesson

31

Preparation

1. Chalkboard:

A	4,678	B	8⟌1,432	C	$9.32
	6,789				$6.49
	5,902				$8.38
	9,439	D	497		
	+ 3,772		x 82		

2. *Arithmetic 4:* pp. 57–58

3. *Lesson 31 Speed Drill*

4. Visuals:
   - *Process Flashcards*
   - *1–100 Chart (Arith Chart 23)*
   - *Averaging Numbers (Arith Chart 6)*
   - story problem clue words flashcards (optional from les. 4)

Teaching Procedure

1. Oral review drills (9 min.)

Homework check

Processes (7 min.)

- *Flashcards:* Have child answer and then play *Beat the Clock.*
- **A** Use standard procedure to do fast oral addition.
- Mult./Div. Tables: Drill tables that he most needs to practice. Continue to use charts only if he still needs them.
- *1–100 Chart:* Point to numbers that are divisible by 9; child div. by 9 and gives quotients. Repeat for numbers that are not divisible by 9; he includes remainder in quotient.
- *Arith Chart* **6:** He gives 2 steps used in averaging numbers.
- Oral comb.

$4 \times 8 + 3 \div 7 + 5 = 10$	$8 \times 9 + 6 - 3 = 75$
$17 - 2 + 5 - 7 = 13$	$5 \times 9 + 5 - 4 = 46$
$8 \times 6 + 2 \div 5 + 5 = 15$	$100 \div 10 \times 3 + 4 = 34$
$7 + 3 \times 4 = 40$	$2 \times 6 \div 2 + 1 = 7$
$10 - 2 + 1 \times 4 = 36$	$9 \times 7 + 6 - 6 = 63$

Measures (1 min.)
- Review 3 steps in a measurement problem and when to mult. or div.
- Use hands signals for measures; child tells if mult. or div. when changing from one measure to another.

Story problems (1 min.)
- story problem clue words flashcards

2. **Written speed drill** (4 min.) Time for 3 min.

3. **Review division.** (6 min.)
- **B** Child explains how to work and check as you do on ckbd. He should have a good knowledge of division with a 1-digit divisor.
- Child does **Ex. 1, p. 57.**

4. **Review number averaging.** (6 min.)
- *Chart* 6: Review 2 steps.
- **C** Child explains how to average amounts as you work on ckbd.
- He does **Ex. 2.**

5. **Review multiplication.** (3 min.)
- **D** He explains how to work problem. Stress keeping numbers in proper place. He must know mult. tables very well to do well with mult.
- Child does **Ex. 3.**

6. **Discuss story problems.** (6 min.)
- Child does **Ex. 4.** Use standard procedure.

7. **Review/Boardwork** (3 min.) **Ex. 5–8**

8. **Homework Ex. 9**

Mon

Lesson 32

Preparation

Test 3, pp. 25–26 from *Student Tests and Speed Drills.*

Teaching Procedure

1. **Homework check**

2. **Administer test.**

Notice that space has been allowed on this test for child to work story problems.

Lesson

33

Preparation

1. Chalkboard:

   A 6,435
      9,768
      8,396
      4,892
    + 5,902

   B   476
      x 53

   C   832   437
      x 142   x 321

2. *Arithmetic 4:* pp. 59–60

3. *Lesson 33 Speed Drill*

4. Visuals:
   - *Process Flashcards*
   - *Concept Cards 32–36, 38–40, 112, 43–44, and 111*
   - *Place Value (Arith Chart 2)*
   - story problems clue words flashcards (optional from les. 4)

Teaching Procedure

1. Oral review drills (9 min.)

   Processes (6 min.)
   - *Flashcards:* Expect accurate responses
   - Paper drill with *Flashcards:* Child gets out paper and number to 4. Show card, count silently to 5, and show next card. Repeat until all 4 cards are shown. Call out 4 answers; he checks work. Repeat with 4 more cards.
   - A Use standard procedure.
   - Mult./Div. Tables
   - Oral comb.

   $4 \div 2 \times 2 + 1 - 4 = 1$ $\quad$ $24 \div 2 \times 3 \div 4 = 9$ $\quad$ $12 \div 3 \times 4 + 2 \div 3 = 6$

   $10 \div 2 \times 6 + 1 = 31$ $\quad$ $5 + 8 + 1 \div 2 = 7$ $\quad$ $9 \times 3 + 12 - 4 = 35$

   $9 \times 6 + 2 - 1 = 55$ $\quad$ $4 + 4 \div 2 + 3 = 7$ $\quad$ $9 - 5 \times 9 + 6 \div 7 = 6$

   $5 \times 5 + 2 \div 3 + 3 = 12$ $\quad$ $16 \div 4 \times 3 \div 2 = 6$ $\quad$ $10 - 9 + 1 + 3 = 5$

   $6 \times 4 + 8 \div 4 \times 2 = 16$ $\quad$ $8 \times 3 + 1 - 3 + 2 = 24$ $\quad$ $12 - 2 \times 5 + 9 = 59$

   Measures (2 min.)
   - *Concept Cards* **32–36, 38–40, 112,** and **43–44**
   - Call out these measures and have child decide if he should mult. or div. to change from one to another.

     ft. to yd. *div.* $\qquad$ gal. to qt. *mult.* $\qquad$ t. to lb. *mult.*

     oz. to lb. *div.* $\qquad$ fl. oz. to c. *div.* $\qquad$ mi. to yd. *mult.*

Place value (1 min.)
- *Arith Chart* **2**

2. Written speed drill (3 min.) Time for 2 min.

3. Introduce multiplication with a 3-digit factor. (9 min.)
- *Concept Card* **111:** Review problem terminology. Show him that if he mult. by a 2-digit factor that he has 2 partial products.
- [B] Work problem on ckbd as he explains what to do.
- [C] Point to 1st problem. Have him tell how many partial products they think problem will have. Point out that problem will not be harder, just longer. Work problem step by step.

$$\begin{array}{r} 832 \\ \times\ 142 \\ \hline 1664 \\ 3328 \\ +832 \\ \hline 118{,}144 \end{array}$$

Step 1: Mult. 2 times 2, 2 times 3, and 2 times 8 as usual.

Step 2: Mult. 4 times 2, 4 times 3, and 4 times 8, being careful to start partial product in tens' place. The ones' place should be empty or have a 0 in it.

Step 3: Mult. 1 times 2, 1 times 3, 1 times 8, being careful to start partial product in hundreds' place. The ones' and tens' places should be empty or have 0s in them. Last digit in each line should make a diagonal line if a line were drawn through digits.

Step 4: Add all 3 partial products.

Step 5: Check over problem to make sure no careless mistakes were made.

Point to 2nd problem; child tells how many partial products. Work step by step for him.
- Read and discuss **box on p. 59.** Child does **Ex. 1.**

4. Discuss story problems. (6 min.)
- Story problem clue words flashcards: Review briefly with him.
- Child does **Ex. 2.** Use standard procedure.

5. Review/Boardwork (9 min.) **Ex. 3–7** Notice that Ex. 7 is Extra Practice and is therefore optional.

Preparation

Wed

1. Chalkboard:

[A]
$$\begin{array}{r} 7{,}902 \\ 8{,}235 \\ 9{,}783 \\ 1{,}895 \\ +4{,}318 \\ \hline \end{array}$$

[B]
$$\begin{array}{r} 478 \\ \times\ 231 \\ \hline \end{array}$$

Lesson 34
(cont.)

2. *Arithmetic 4:* pp. 61–62
3. *Lesson 34 Speed Drill*
4. Visuals:
   - *Division Flashcards*
   - *Concept Cards* 20 and 63–71
   - *Averaging Numbers (Arith Chart* 6)
   - *Fractions (Arith Char 8)*
   - story problem clue words flashcards (optional from les. 4)
   - Fractional Circles

Teaching Procedure

1. **Oral review drills** (4 min.)

   Processes (3 min.)
   - [A] Use standard procedure.
   - *Div. Cards:* Play *Around the World.*
   - *Concept Card* **20:** Review 5 steps in div.
   - *Arith Chart* **6:** Child gives 2 steps to find average.
   - Oral comb. Play *Moonwalk.*

   $10 + 4 \div 2 \times 7 = 49$ $4 \times 3 - 5 \times 7 = 49$

   $7 \times 4 - 4 \div 6 - 2 + 1 + 1 = 4$ $3 \times 9 + 5 - 4 + 3 = 31$

   $6 \times 3 - 2 \div 2 - 5 \times 6 \div 3 + 4 = 10$ $2 \times 3 - 6 + 5 \times 5 - 5 = 20$

   $6 \times 6 \div 6 + 9 - 3 = 12$ $6 \times 3 \div 2 \times 9 - 1 \div 10 - 1 = 7$

   $2 + 4 + 6 - 5 \times 5 = 35$ $3 \times 12 - 2 = 34$

   Story problems (1 min.)
   - Story problem clue words flashcards

2. **Written speed drill** (6 min.) Time for 5 min.
   - Grade. Record as a speed drill/quiz grade. Count off 8 points for each incorrect answer.

3. **Introduce fractions** (12 min.)
   - Use a common situation such as sharing a candy bar to introduce fractions.
   - *Arith Chart* **8:** Introduce definition of fraction and 2 parts of fraction. Explain that numerator is top term and gives the number of equal parts used or taken. The denominator is bottom term and gives number of equal parts in all. Explain that if we divide candy bar into 3 equal parts that 3 is denominator since that is number of equal parts. If we give 2 parts to a friend, the 2 is numerator since that is number of equal parts given away. We say that the friend has $\frac{2}{3}$ of candy bar.
   Show on chart that a fraction can be part of an object such as a candy bar or part of a group such as girls in class. As you explain each fraction on chart, be sure to stress jobs of numerator and denominator.
   - *Concept Card* **63:** Review terms in fraction.
   - Call out these fractions; child gives denominators: $\frac{3}{4}$, $\frac{6}{7}$, $\frac{1}{3}$, and $\frac{2}{5}$. Tell him this clue: **The denominator is down under-**

neath the line; denominator and down both start with
d. You may want to tell him that line is called a fraction bar.

- *Concept Cards* **64–71:** Show fronts of cards; child read fractions. Show backs so they can see that he reads correctly. Explain that in ⅓, 3 is denominator because there are 3 parts. 1 is numerator because 1 part is colored. He explains why 1 is numerator and 6 is denominator in ⅙. Repeat explanations for other cards.
- **Fractional Circles:** Give 3 thirds to child. He shows ⅔. Repeat with him showing ¾ with fourths. If time permits, allow him to work with other circles proving his understanding of fractions.
- Read and discuss **box on p. 61.** Child does **Ex. 1–2.**

4. Review multiplication with a 3-digit factor. (10 min.)

- **B** Work problem on ckbd as child watches. Stress putting digits in correct places.
- Child does **Ex. 3.**

5. Review/Boardwork (15 min.) **Ex. 4–6**

6. Homework Ex. 7–8

Lesson
35

Preparation

1. Chalkboard:

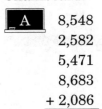

   A 8,548
   2,582
   5,471
   8,683
   + 2,086

   B 64 ÷ 8 = ___   27 ÷ 5 = ___   41 ÷ 4 = ___
   49 ÷ 7 = ___   72 ÷ 9 = ___   38 ÷ 12 = ___

2. *Arithmetic 4:* pp. 63–64

3. *Lesson 35 Speed Drill*

4. Visuals:
   - *Process Flashcards*
   - *Mixed Multiplication Facts (Arith 4, p.319)*
   - *Concept Cards* 32–36, 38–40, 112, 43–44, and 63–78
   - *Fractions (Arith Chart* 8)
   - Fractional Circles

Lesson 35
(cont.)

Teaching Procedure

1. **Oral review drills** (9 min.)

   Homework check

   Processes (5 min.)
   - Mult./Div. Tables
   - *Flashcards:* Have child answer. Be sure to use cards that child needs to practice.
   - **A** Use standard procedure.
   - **B** Point to in random order; child gives quotients.
   - *Mixed Multiplication Facts*

   Measures (2 min.)
   - *Concept Cards* **32–36, 38–40, 112,** and **43–44:** Go through all cards once with child and then play a game.

   Fractions (2 min.)
   - *Arith Chart* **8:** Review concept of fractions.
   - *Concept Card* **63:** Drill jobs of numerator and denominator.
   - *Concept Cards* **64–78:** He reads fractions. Cover fractions; child writes fractions on ckbd.

2. **Written speed drill** (3 min.) Time for 2 min.

3. **Review fractions.** (9 min.)
   - **Fractional Circles:** Child demonstrates fractions.
   - Child does **Ex. 1–3, p. 63.**

4. **Discuss story problems.** (6 min.)
   - Child does **Ex. 4.** Use standard procedure.

5. **Review/Boardwork** (9 min.) **Ex. 5–7**

6. **Homework** **Ex. 8–9**

Lesson 36

Preparation

1. Chalkboard:

   A 9,994 / 7,520 / 8,285 / 4,669 / + 8,483

   B $\frac{1}{2}$ of 6 dogs $\frac{1}{7}$ of 21 cookies

   C 432 x 284

2. *Arithmetic 4:* pp. 65–66

3. *Lesson 36 Speed Drill*

4. Visuals:
   - *Process Flashcards*
   - *Averaging Numbers (Arith Chart 6)*
   - *Fractions (Arith Chart 8)*
   - *Mixed Addition Facts (Arith 4, p.311)*
   - *Concept Cards 63–78*
   - coins

Teaching Procedure

1. Oral review drills (9 min.)

Homework check

Processes (6 min.)
- *Flashcards:* Let child practice and then play a game.
- ☐ A ☐ Use standard procedure.
- Mult./Div. Tables
- *Arith Chart* **6:** Child gives 2 steps to find average.
- *Mixed Addition Facts*
- Oral comb.

6 x 6 ÷ 3 + 4 − 8 x 3 = *24*	24 ÷ 6 + 4 x 3 = *24*
12 + 8 x 2 ÷ 8 x 3 + 2 = *17*	11 − 3 + 8 ÷ 4 x 9 ÷ 3 = *12*
7 x 9 + 3 ÷ 2 − 1 ÷ 4 = *8*	7 x 5 + 5 − 10 ÷ 6 x 9 = *45*
6 x 9 + 2 ÷ 7 + 2 = *10*	8 x 3 + 1 x 2 x 2 x 9 = *900*
7 x 4 − 1 ÷ 9 x 6 = *18*	27 − 2 ÷ 5 x 8 + 8 ÷ 6 = *8*
8 x 7 − 2 ÷ 6 x 7 − 3 ÷ 5 = *12*	7 x 12 + 1 − 10 − 3 ÷ 12 = *6*

Fractions (3 min.)
- *Arith Chart* **8:** Review fractions.
- *Concept Card* **63:** Review numerator and denominator.
- *Concept Cards* **63–78:** Child practices reading fractions. Cover fractions on fronts; he looks at illustration and gives correct fraction.
- *Concept Cards* **63–70:** Show fronts of 2 cards; he decides which fraction is greater. You may want to tell him that when a fraction has a numerator of 1, it is a unit fraction. When you compare unit fractions, one with smaller denominator is greater. That makes sense if you think of a pizza being cut into more pieces. The more pieces, the smaller each piece.

2. Written speed drill (3 min.) Time for 2 min.

3. Introduce finding a fractional part of a group. (6 min.)
- Have 6 pennies one desk or table. Child tells how many are in one half of group. Write ½ of 6 = 3 on ckbd. Tell him that he found a fractional part of a group. **To find a fractional part of a group when the numerator is 1, we just divide the whole number by the denominator.**
- *Arith Chart* **8:** Discuss 5 pieces of fruit and what part the oranges are of whole group. Repeat for apples.
- ☐ B ☐ Point to 1st problem. Child gives whole number and fraction. Ask him if numerator is 1. Tell him that since it is 1 that we can just divide whole number by denominator to find fractional part. Repeat for 2nd problem.
- Read and discuss **box on p. 65.** Child does **Ex. 1.**

4. Introduce how to check a mult. problem with a 3-digit factor. (10 min.)

- ☐ C ☐ Work problem step by step.
  - Step 1: Work problem, being careful to put all digits in proper places.

Lesson 36
(cont.)

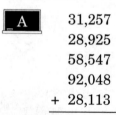

```
    432
  x 284            284
  1728           x 432
  3456             568
+ 864              852
─────          
122,688        + 1136
               ────────
                122,688
```

Step 2: Remind child that factors can be switched without changing product. Switch factors and work problem, still being careful to keep all digits in proper places. The products should be the same unless a mistake was made.

  • Child does **Ex. 2.**

5. Discuss story problems. (6 min.)

  • Child does **Ex. 3.**

6. Review/Boardwork (6 min.) **Ex. 4–6**

7. Homework Ex. 7 Child needs to have a ruler in arithmetic tomorrow.

mon

Lesson 37

Preparation

1. Chalkboard:

A
```
  31,257
  28,925
  58,547
  92,048
+ 28,113
────────
```

B $48 \div 8 =$ ___ $56 \div 6 =$ ___ $13 \div 7 =$ ___

  $80 \div 10 =$ ___ $45 \div 9 =$ ___ $38 \div 6 =$ ___

C $\frac{1}{5}$ of 35 $\frac{1}{8}$ of 56

D Use *Rolling Ruler* (*Arith Chart* 24) to draw lines that are 7 ½ in. and 11 ½ in.

2. *Arithmetic 4:* pp. 67–68

3. *Lesson 37 Quiz*

4. Visuals:

  • *Process Flashcards*
  • *Calculator (Arith Chart* 20)
  • *Place Value (Arith Chart* 2)
  • *Concept Cards* 1–15 and 63–70
  • coins
  • *Rolling Ruler* (in.)(*Arith Chart* 24)
  • ruler

Teaching Procedure

1. Oral review drills (9 min.)

  Homework check

  Processes (6 min.)

- *Flashcards:* Have child answer a few to get warmed up then play *Rithmetic Rhythm*.
- **A** Use standard procedure.
- *Calculator:* Child mult. number you push by 7.
- **B** Child gives quotients as you point to problems. Point to them in random order.
- Mult./Div. Tables: Have him recite tables.

Place value (1 min.)

- *Arith Chart* **2**
- *Concept Cards* **1–15:** He gives numbers that are 100 more or 1,000 more.

Money (2 min.)

- Coins: Have child make change from $1.00. Tell price of item such as 53¢. He uses coins to count back change.

2. **Quiz 4** (9 min.)

3. **Review fractions.** (6 min.)

- *Concept Cards* **63–70:** Show 2 cards; child gives greater amount.
- **C** He finds fractional part by div. whole number by denominator.
- **D** *Rolling Ruler:* Remind him that *Rolling Ruler* is enlarged so it can be seen easily. Show him how to measure 7½ in. line to nearest half inch. Point to several half-inch marks on *Rolling Ruler*. Have him measure 11½ in. line, using *Rolling Ruler*. If he seems weak with half inches, let him come to *Rolling Ruler* and point to half-inch lines.
- **rulers:** Child needs to get out his ruler and point to 3½ inches and 8½ inches. Be sure he points to half inches and not quarter or eighth inches.
- Child does **Ex. 1–7, p. 67.**

4. **Discuss story problems.** (6 min.)

- Child does **Ex. 8.** Work problems together. You may want to illustrate time lapse in *b* on demonstration clock.

5. **Review/Boardwork** (6 min.) **Ex. 9–11**

Tues

Preparation

1. Chalkboard:

A
$$\begin{array}{r} 38,492 \\ 46,678 \\ 83,239 \\ 29,511 \\ + \ 56,893 \\ \hline \end{array}$$

B	$\frac{1}{6}$ of 24	$\frac{1}{9}$ of 81	$\frac{1}{7}$ of 28
C	20)48	20)61	40)87

2. *Arithmetic 4:* pp. 69–70

3. *Lesson 38 Speed Drill*

4. Visuals:
   - *Process Flashcards*
   - *1–100 Chart (Arith Chart 23)*
   - *Averaging Numbers (Arith Chart 6)*
   - *Fractions (Arith Chart 8)*
   - *Concept Cards 32–36, 38–40, 112, 43–44, and 63–78*

Teaching Procedure

1. **Oral review drills** (9 min.)

   Processes (4 min.)
   - Mult./Div. Tables
   - **A** Use standard procedure. Review quickly then play *Capture the Card.*
   - *Flashcards:* Show a flashcard to your child. If he answers correctly within three seconds, he captures the card. If he cannot capture the card, set it aside for later. After the game is over, practice the cards that were not captured.
   - *1–100 Chart:* Point to numbers that are divisible by 6; child gives quotients. Point to numbers that are not divisible by 6; he includes remainders in quotients.
   - *Arith Chart* **6:** He gives 2 steps used to find an average.

   Fractions (3 min.)
   - *Arith Chart* **8:** Review fractions.
   - **B** Child gives fractional parts and rule for finding fractional part when numerator is 1. Remind him that fractions with numerators of 1 are unit fractions.
   - *Concept Card* **63:** Review jobs of numerator and denominator. Call out several fractions for him to write on ckbd.
   - *Concept Cards* **63–78:** Cover fractions on several cards; he gives fractions.

   Measures (2 min.)
   - *Concept Cards* **32–36, 38–40, 112,** and **43–44:** Have child answer.

2. **Written speed drill** (3 min.) Time for 2 min.

3. **Introduce division with 2-digit divisor.** (9 min.)

   - **C** Child looks at 1st problem and see what is different from div. problems that he has been working. Ask him if we know a 20 div. table. Explain 1st problem step by step.

$$\begin{array}{r} 2 \text{ r.8} \\ 20\overline{)48} \\ -40 \\ \hline 8 \end{array}$$

   Step 1: Since we have a 2-digit divisor, we must div. into 2 digits in dividend. We div. 20 into 48. Since we do not have a 20 div. table, we say *How many 2s are in 4?* Write 2 over 8.

Step 2: Mult. quotient 2 times divisor 20 to get 40.

Step 3: Subt. 40 from 48 to get 8.

Step 4: Compare 8 with 20. It is less.

Step 5: Bring down. Since there is nothing to bring down, problem is finished. 8 is the remainder.

Follow same steps when explaining 2nd and 3rd problems.

- Read and discuss **box on p. 69.** Child does **Ex. 1.**

4. Discuss story problems. (6 min.)

- Child does **Ex. 2.** He may need help with *b*. He needs to div. by a 2-digit divisor.

5. Review/Boardwork (9 min.) **Ex. 3–8** Notice that Ex. 6–8 are Extra Practice and therefore are optional. Child needs to have a ruler in arithmetic tomorrow.

Wed

Lesson 39

Preparation

1. Chalkboard:

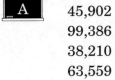

   A   45,902
        99,386
        38,210
        63,559
      + 57,683

   B   6⟌23   5⟌27   4⟌18

   C   30⟌71   40⟌87

2. *Arithmetic 4:* pp. 71–72

3. *Lesson 39 Speed Drill*

4. Visuals:
   - *Process Flashcards*
   - *Concept Cards* 20 and 63–78
   - *Mixed Division Facts (Arith 4, p. 322)*
   - *1–100 Chart (Arith Chart 23)*

Teaching Procedure

1. Oral review drills (7 min.)

   Processes (4 min.)

   - *Flashcards:* Let child answer. After he gets warmed up, have him add 7 to each answer.
   - *Concept Card* **20:** Review 5 steps in div.
   - A Use standard procedure.

- Mult./Div. Tables
- *Mixed Division Facts*
- *1–100 Chart:* Let child point to numbers in order that are products when we mult. by 4. He recites numbers.

Fractions (3 min.)
- *Concept Card* **63:** Review terms.
- *Concept Cards* **63–70:** Show 2 cards; he gives greater.
- *Concept Cards* **71–78:** Tell him that these are not unit fractions because numerators are not 1. Have child tell you what is same on all of these fractions. He should notice that denominators are all 9. **To compare fractions with the same denominators, we look at the numerators. The fraction with the greater numerator is the greater fraction.** Show 2 cards; he gives greater.

2. **Written speed drill** (6 min.) Time for 5 min.
- Grade. Record as a speed drill/quiz grade. Count off 4 points for each incorrect answer.

3. **Introduce writing a remainder as a fraction.** (6 min.)
- **B** Work 1st problem step by step for child.

$$\times \ 3\tfrac{5}{6}$$

$$6\overline{)23}$$
$$\underline{-18}\downarrow$$
$$5$$

Step 1: Div. as usual. The quotient is 3 with a remainder of 5.

Step 2: Tell him that a remainder is a fraction of the divisor. To write the remainder as a fraction, write the remainder as the numerator and the divisor as the denominator.

Use same steps to work 2nd and 3rd problems.
- Read and discuss **box on p. 71.** Child does **Ex. 1.**

4. **Review division with a 2-digit divisor.** (6 min.)
- **C** Work 1st problem for him. Explain that we check same way by mult. quotient by divisor and adding the remainder. **Since the divisor is a 2-digit number and the quotient is a 1-digit number, it is best to write the divisor as the top factor and the quotient as the bottom factor. This is fine to do since we know that the factors can be changed without changing the product.** Have him explain 2nd problem as you work.
- Child does **Ex. 2.**

5. **Discuss story problems.** (6 min.)
- Child does **Ex. 3.**

6. **Review/Boardwork** (6 min.) **Ex. 4–6**

7. **Homework Ex. 7–8**

Lesson

40

Preparation

1. Chalkboard:

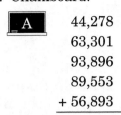

        44,278
        63,301
        93,896
        89,553
     + 56,893

B $\frac{1}{3}$ of 27 $\frac{1}{7}$ of 35 $\frac{1}{6}$ of 24 $\frac{1}{9}$ of 54 $\frac{1}{8}$ of 56

C $41\overline{)168}$

D $5\overline{)39}$

2. *Arithmetic 4:* pp. 73–74

3. *Lesson 40 Speed Drill*

4. Visuals:
   - *Process Flashcards*
   - *1–100 Chart (Arith Chart 23)*
   - *Concept Cards 63–78*
   - story problem clue words flashcards (optional from les. 4)
   - *Division Steps (Arith Chart 4)*

Teaching Procedure

1. **Oral review drills** (9 min.)

   Homework check

   Processes (6 min.)
   - *Flashcards:* Let him answer and then play *Four Corners.*
   - **A** Use standard procedure.
   - Mult./Div. Tables
   - *1–100 Chart:* Point to several large numbers; child adds 7 to each. If he is adding 7 to 12, he adds ones' places and keeps tens' place since there was no carrying. If he adds 7 to 15, he adds ones' places and adds 1 to tens' place since there was carrying. Repeat with 4.
   - Oral comb.

$4 \times 7 + 2 - 4 \times 0 = 0$	$16 + 4 + 4 \times 2 \div 4 = 12$
$4 \times 3 + 4 \div 4 + 4 = 8$	$165 + 5 + 5 - 10 = 165$
$6 \times 7 + 5 + 3 = 50$	$3 \times 7 + 4 - 4 + 9 = 30$
$80 + 10 + 5 - 2 = 93$	$2 \times 9 + 4 \times 4 = 88$

   Fractions (2 min.)
   - **B** Child gives answers.

Lesson 40
(cont.)

- *Concept Cards* **63–70:** Show 2 cards; child compares.
- *Concept Cards* **70–78:** Show 2 cards; he compares.

Story problems (1 min.)
- Story problem clue words flashcards

2. Written speed drill (4 min.) Time for 3 min. 30 sec.

3. Introduce estimating divisors. (6 min.)
- *Arith Chart* **4:** Explain that we cannot div. mentally by 2-digit divisor. We must estimate our quotient. **If a 2-digit divisor ends in the digits 0, 1, 2, 3, or 4, divide by the first digit in divisor.** Show that we have added 1 step to our 5 steps of div. Show how 2 was divided into 17 and that 8 did not work. **Estimation does not always work. We must often use trial and error to find the correct quotient.**

- **C** Work problem as child watches.

$$41 \overline{)\,168\,}$$
x 4 r.4
− 164
4

41
x 4
164
+ 4
168

Step 1: Estimate the divisor. Since the divisor ends in 1, we divide by 4.
Step 2: Div. 4 into 16 to get 4. Write 4 above 8.
Step 3: Mult. 4 by 1 and put under 8 and mult. 4 by 4 and put under 16.
Step 4: Subt. 164 from 168 to get 4.
Step 5: Compare 4 with 41. It is less.
Step 6: Bring down. Since there is nothing to bring down, problem is finished.
Check as usual.

- Read and discuss **box on p. 73.** Child does **Ex. 1.**

4. Review writing remainders as fractions. (3 min.)

- **D** Work problem for him. Have a him explain how to write remainder as fraction.
- Child does **Ex. 2.**

5. Discuss story problems. (6 min.)
- Child does **Ex. 3.**

6. Review/Boardwork (9 min.) **Ex. 4–6**

7. Homework Ex. 7–9

Fri

Lesson
41

Preparation

1. Chalkboard:

A
99,378
75,427
24,678
53,458
+ 57,890

B 31$\overline{)\,47\,}$

C 6$\overline{)\,46\,}$

| D | 21 ft. = ___ yd. | 3 lb. – 12 oz. = ___ oz. |

2. *Arithmetic 4:* pp. 75–76

3. *Lesson 41 Speed Drill*

4. Visuals:
   - *Process Flashcards*
   - *1–100 Chart (Arith Chart 23)*
   - *Averaging Numbers (Arith Chart 6)*
   - *Concept Cards* 63 and 70–78
   - story problem clue words flashcards (optional from les. 4)

Teaching Procedure

1. Oral review drills (9 min.)

Homework check

Processes (6 min.)
- Mult./Div. Tables
- *Flashcards:* Play *Secret Code.* Show your child 3 flashcards in a row. Your child is to determine the answers and remember them in order. After he as seen all 3 cards, call on him to give the secret code, which is the 3 answers in the proper order.
- | A | Use standard procedure.
- *1–100 Chart:* Point to numbers that are divisible by 4; child div. by 4 and gives quotients. Repeat for numbers that are not divisible by 4; he includes remainder in quotient.
- *Arith Chart* **6:** He gives 2 steps used in averaging numbers.

Fractions (2 min.)
- Call out these fraction problems.

  $\frac{1}{3}$ of 12 = *4* $\frac{1}{7}$ of 56 = *8* $\frac{1}{11}$ of 22 = *2*

  $\frac{1}{9}$ of 54 = *6* $\frac{1}{12}$ of 144 = *12* $\frac{1}{5}$ of 40 = *8*
- *Concept Card* **63:** Review terms.
- *Concept Cards* **70–78:** Cover fractions; child gives fractions for colored portion.

Story problems (1 min.)
- story problem clue words flashcards

2. Written speed drill (4 min.) Time for 3 min.

3. Review division. (9 min.)
- | B | Child explains how to work and check as you do on ckbd.
- Child does **Ex. 1, p. 75.**
- | C | Child explains how to div. and write remainder as fraction.
- Child does **Ex. 2.**

4. Review measurement equations. (6 min.)
- | D | Child works on paper as you work on ckbd.
- Child does **Ex. 3.**

5. Review/Boardwork (9 min.) **Ex. 4–6**

Lesson 41
(cont.)

6. Homework Ex. 7–9 Ex. 7 is a story problem. You may want to discuss briefly and get him started in right direction. Since test has a similar problem, you may want to discuss problem before test tomorrow to make sure he did it correctly and is ready to work a similar one on test.

Monday

Lesson 42

Preparation

Test 4, pp. 33–34 from *Student Tests and Speed Drills*.

Teaching Procedure

1. Homework check

2. Administer test.

Notice that space has been allowed on this test for child to work story problems.

Tues

Lesson 43

Preparation

1. Chalkboard:

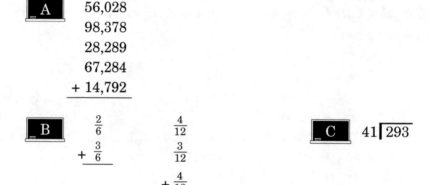

2. *Arithmetic 4:* pp. 77–78

3. *Lesson 43 Speed Drill*

4. Visuals:
   - *Process Flashcards*
   - *Division Steps (Arith Chart 4)*
   - *Mixed Subtraction Facts (Arith 4, p. 316)*
   - *Concept Cards 32–36, 38–40, 112, 43–44, and 1–15*
   - Fractional Circles

Teaching Procedure

1. Oral review drills (9 min.)

Processes (6 min.)

- *Flashcards:* Drill and then play a game.

- ▪A▪ Use standard procedure.
- Paper drill with *Flashcards:* Child gets out paper and number to 4. Show card, count silently to 5, and show next card. Repeat until all 4 cards are shown. Call out 4 answers; he checks work. Repeat with 4 more cards.
- Mult./Div. Tables
- *Arith Chart* **4:** Review 6 steps of div. when divisor is more than 1 digit.
- *Mixed Subtraction Facts*
- Oral comb.

$6 \times 6 + 8 + 3 + 1 \div 8 = 6$	$5 \times 4 + 2 - 2 + 4 \div 4 = 6$
$4 + 6 \times 5 \div 5 \times 10 = 100$	$4 \times 4 - 4 + 4 = 16$
$5 \times 5 + 5 \times 3 + 50 = 140$	$5 \times 4 + 20 - 10 \div 5 + 4 = 10$
$4 \times 8 + 6 = 38$	$4 \times 5 + 5 \div 5 = 5$
$6 \times 2 - 2 + 3 + 4 + 1 \div 6 = 3$	$8 \times 9 \div 6 + 1 - 2 = 11$

Measures (2 min.)
- *Concept Cards* **32–36, 38–40, 112,** and **43–44**
- Call out these measures and have child decide if he should mult. or div. to change from one to other.

yd. to mi. *div.*	lb. to oz. *mult.*	qt. to pt. *mult.*
c. to pt. *div.*	in. to ft. *div.*	gal. to fl. oz. *mult.*

Place value (1 min.)
- *Concept Cards* **1–15:** Child subt. 100 or 1,000 from each number.

2. **Written speed drill** (3 min.) Time for 2 min.

3. **Introduce adding fractions with a common denominator.** (6 min.)
   - **Fractional Circles:** Use this story problem to introduce. *Mrs. Oler made a pizza and cut it into 6 parts. She gave her son 1 slice.* Display $\frac{1}{6}$. *She gave her daughter 1 slice.* Display another $\frac{1}{6}$. *Since she gave away $\frac{1}{6}$ and $\frac{1}{6}$ of the pizza, how much of the pizza did she give away?* Write $\frac{1}{6} + \frac{1}{6} = \frac{2}{6}$ on ckbd. Have child notice that denominators are same. **When we add fractions with a common denominator, we add the numerators and keep the common denominator.** You can illustrate rule by saying, *If we add 2 **apples** and 2 **apples**, we get 4 **apples**. If we add 2 **inches** and 2 **inches**, we get 4 **inches**. If we add 2 **tenths** and 2 **tenths**, we get 4 **tenths**.* Write $\frac{2}{10} + \frac{2}{10} = \frac{4}{10}$ on ckbd. Use Fractional Circles to demonstrate other adding of fraction problems.
   - ▪B▪ Work 1st problem step by step.

     Step 1: Write down denominator 6.
     Step 2: Add the numerators.

$$\begin{array}{r} \frac{2}{6} \\ \frac{3}{6} \\ + \phantom{\frac{3}{6}} \\ \hline \frac{5}{6} \end{array}$$

Lesson 43
(cont.)

Follow same procedure to work 2nd problem.
- Read and discuss **box on p. 77.** Child does **Ex. 1.**

4. Review division with a 2-digit divisor. (6 min.)

- Work and check problem on ckbd as he explains.
- Child does **Ex. 2.**

5. Discuss story problems. (6 min.)
- Child does **Ex. 3.**

6. Review/Boardwork (6 min.) **Ex. 4–9** Notice that Ex. 9 is Extra Practice and is therefore optional.

Lesson 44

Preparation

1. Chalkboard:

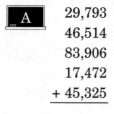   29,793
46,514
83,906
17,472
+ 45,325

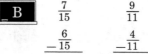 $\frac{7}{15}$ $\frac{9}{11}$ 31⟌874   7⟌239
$-\frac{6}{15}$ $-\frac{4}{11}$

2. *Arithmetic 4:* pp. 79–80

3. *Lesson 44 Speed Drill*

4. Visuals:
- *Process Flashcards*
- *Calculator (Arith Chart 20)*
- story problem clue words flashcards (optional from les. 4)
- *Concept Cards* 32–36, 38–40, 112, 43–44, 70–74, and 63
- Fractional Circles

Teaching Procedure

1. Oral review drills (7 min.)

Processes (4 min.)
- *Flashcards:* Play *Around the World.*
- Mult./Div. Tables
- **A** Use standard procedure.
- *Calculator:* Child mult. each number you point to by 8 or other factor.
- Oral comb. Play *Speedy Sam.*

5 x 10 + 10 – 9 + 1 + 8 ÷ 6 = *10*

10 x 10 + 100 + 100 – 100 + 400 = *600*

7 x 10 + 3 – 1 = *72*

22 ÷ 2 x 9 + 1 = *100*

6 x 10 + 10 + 30 = *100*

7 x 2 + 6 + 1 + 10 + 1 = *32*

4 x 4 + 1 + 3 = *20*

6 x 5 x 2 ÷ 6 = *10*

4 x 5 x 2 x 2 + 10 = *90*

10 x 9 + 10 – 10 + 20 = *110*

8 x 12 + 6 + 2 = *104*

5 x 5 x 2 – 1 ÷ 7 = *7*

Story problems (1 min.)

- Story problem clue words flashcards

Measures (1 min.)

- *Concept Cards* **32–36, 38–40, 112,** and **43–44:** Have each child answer.

Fractions (1 min.)

- *Concept Cards* **70–74:** Show fronts of 2 cards; child adds 2 fractions. Make sure he notices that they have common denominators. He keeps common denominators and adds numerator. Repeat with 2 other cards.

2. **Written speed drill** (6 min.) Time for 5 min.

- Grade. Record as a speed drill/quiz grade. Count off 8 points for each incorrect answer.

3. **Introduce subtracting fractions with a common denominator.** (6 min.)

- **Fractional Circles:** Show $^5/_5$. Take $^1/_5$ away and write $^5/_5 - ^1/_5 = ^4/_5$ on ckbd. Child should notice that denominators are same. **To subtract fractions with a common denominator, keep the common denominator and subtract the numerators.** Use Fractional Circles to illustrate other subtracting problems.

- **▌B▐** Work 2 problems step by step for child.

- *Concept Card* **63:** Review terms in fraction.

- Read and discuss **box on p. 79.** Child does **Ex. 1.**

4. **Review division.** (6 min.)

- **▌C▐** Work and check problems on ckbd as he works on paper. He should write remainder in 2nd problem as a fraction. Check problems with remainder written as fraction as usual. The remainder, not the fraction, is added.

- Child does **Ex. 2–3.**

5. **Discuss story problems.** (6 min.)

- Students do **Ex. 4.**

6. **Review/Boardwork** (6 min.) **Ex. 5–7**

7. **Homework Ex. 8–9** Child needs ruler for les. 45.

Preparation

1. Chalkboard:

   A
   $$48,893$$
   $$24,782$$
   $$13,980$$
   $$55,389$$
   $$+\ 71,105$$

   B $\frac{1}{3}$ of 22 = ___ $\frac{1}{5}$ of 37 = ___

   C
   $$\frac{6}{7} \qquad\qquad \frac{2}{9}$$
   $$-\ \frac{3}{7} \qquad\qquad +\ \frac{2}{9}$$

2. *Arithmetic 4:* pp. 81–82

3. *Lesson 45 Speed Drill*

4. Visuals:
   - *Process Flashcards*
   - *Calculator (Arith Chart 20)*
   - *Concept Cards 32–36, 38–40, 112, 43–44, 79, and 133–139*
   - Fractional Circles

Teaching Procedure

1. **Oral review drills** (9 min.)

   Homework check

   Processes (7 min.)
   - *Flashcards:* Have child answer. Be sure to use cards that he needs to practice.
   - Mult./Div. Tables: Play *Just the Facts* with mult. table 6. Put the answers to multiplication facts on flashcards, the chalkboard, or call them out from a list. Have the child write or call out the multipication fact that fits that answer. If game goes well, practice other tables, using same game.
   - *Calculator:* Child points to even numbers and mult. by 6. *Is the product odd or even when an even number is mult. by an even number?* **even** He points to odd numbers and mult. by 3. *Is the product odd or even when an odd number is mult. by an odd number?* **odd**
   - **A** Use standard procedure.

   Measures (2 min.)
   - *Concept Cards* **32–36, 38–40, 112,** and **43–44**

2. **Written speed drill** (3 min.) Time for 2 min.

3. **Introduce mixed numbers.** (9 min.)
   - **Fractional Circles:** Use Fractional Circles to demonstrate

story problem. *Brandon was very hungry. He ate a whole pizza and ⅓ of another pizza.* Show child how this number has 2 parts. Point to 1. He should recognize as a whole number. Point to ⅓. He knows this is a fraction. **A mixed number has a whole number and a fraction.**
- *Concept Card* **79:** Show mixed number to child. Have him distinguish 2 parts.
- *Concept Cards* **133–139:** Show backs of cards; child reads mixed numbers.
- Call out several mixed numbers and send child to ckbd to write them.
- Read and discuss **box on p. 81.** Child does **Ex. 1–3.**

4. Review fractions. (6 min.)
- Call out these problems.

  $\frac{1}{5}$ of 25 = *25* $\frac{1}{7}$ of 49 = *7* $\frac{1}{11}$ of 55 = *5*

  $\frac{1}{6}$ of 48 = *8* $\frac{1}{9}$ of 81 = *9* $\frac{1}{12}$ of 48 = *4*

- Do 1st problem for him showing how to write remainder as a fraction. Child does other problem.
- Review rules for adding and subtracting fractions with common denominators. Do problems together.
- Child does **Ex. 4.**

5. Review/Boardwork (9 min.) **Ex. 5–7**

6. Homework Ex. 8

Preparation

1. Chalkboard:

   A   48,029
   72,586
   68,218
   19,729
   + 58,830
   _____

   B $12\frac{5}{8}$ $25\frac{4}{11}$
   $+\ 7\frac{1}{8}$ $-\ 17\frac{2}{11}$

   C  $31\overline{)478}$

2. *Arithmetic 4:* pp. 83–84

3. *Lesson 46 Speed Drill*

4. Visuals:
   - Place flashcards with answers of 4, 12, 20, 25, 42, and 54 and a few additional cards around room. Have side without answer showing. Place cards in places that are easy to see.

- Write these comb. on individual strips of paper.

  $6 \times 8 + 6 =$ $4 \times 4 + 4 =$

  $6 \times 8 - 6 =$ $10 \div 5 \times 6 =$

  $2 \times 6 - 8 =$ $20 \div 4 \times 5 =$

- story problem clue words flashcards
- *Place Value (Arith Chart 2)*

Teaching Procedure

1. **Oral review drills** (9 min.)

   Homework check

   Processes (7 min.)
   - Mult./Div. Tables
   - Placed flashcards and comb. strips: Play *Fast Thinker*. Have your child be a *Thinker*. Let him know that you have placed several flashcards around room. Point to a few of them. *When we are ready to begin this game, I will give you a comb. strip. You must figure the answer and then look around the room for a flashcard that has the same answer. When you find it you are a* Fast Thinker. Repeat with other strips. Have thinker read comb. and show flashcard to check if thinker is correct.
   - **A** Use standard procedure.
   - Oral comb.

$6 + 7 = 13$	$8 + 7 = 15$	$13 - 6 = 7$	$27 - 17 = 10$
$9 + 5 = 14$	$9 + 4 = 13$	$19 - 11 = 8$	$16 - 9 = 7$
$4 \times 8 = 32$	$5 \times 8 = 40$	$72 \div 6 = 12$	$24 \div 3 = 8$
$6 \times 9 = 54$	$12 \times 12 = 144$	$56 \div 7 = 8$	$48 \div 6 = 8$

   Story problems (1 min.)
   - Story problem clue words flashcards

   Place value (1 min.)
   - *Arith Chart* **2**

2. **Written speed drill** (2 min.) Time for 1 min.

3. **Introduce addition and subtraction of mixed numbers.** (9 min.)
   - **B** Point to 1st problem. Child reads 2 addends. Remind him that addends are mixed numbers and that mixed numbers have 2 parts. Since they have 2 parts, there will be 2 steps to problem. 1st, we add fractions. Child should notice that fractions have common denominator. 2nd, we add whole numbers. Of course, he could add whole numbers 1st with equal success. Choose Have him read sum. Child explains 2nd problem as you work on ckbd.
   - Read and discuss **box on p. 83.** Child does **Ex. 1–3.**

4. **Review division.** (6 min.)

- Work and check problem step by step.
- Child does **Ex. 4.**

5. Review/Boardwork (9 min.) **Ex. 5–7**

6. Homework Ex. 8 He needs to have a ruler in arithmetic tomorrow.

mon

Lesson

47

Preparation

1. Chalkboard:

A   31,257
28,925
58,547
92,048
+ 28,113

B 5 $\frac{2}{3}$ $4\frac{1}{2}$ $7\frac{3}{4}$ 11 $5\frac{8}{9}$

C $\frac{1}{5}$ of 37 $\frac{1}{8}$ of 19

D Use *Rolling Ruler* (*Arith Chart* 24) to draw lines that are 7¼ in. and 11¾ in.

2. *Arithmetic 4:* pp. 85–86

3. *Lesson 47 Quiz*

4. Visuals:
   - *Process Flashcards*
   - *Concept Cards* 63–70 and 133–139
   - Fractional Circles
   - coins
   - play bills (Make or buy some play bills. Many children's games have play money. Sample $1, $5, $10, and $20 bills are in the front of this *Curriculum / Lesson Plans*. You may reproduce them.)
   - *Rolling Ruler* (in.) (*Arith Chart* 24)

Teaching Procedure

1. Oral review drills (9 min.)

Homework check

Processes (5 min.)
   - *Flashcards:* Play *Baking a Cake*. *To bake a cake we need several ingredients. You are going to get the needed ingredients by answering a flashcard correctly.* Show card to your child. When he answers correctly he gets card. Repeat with other cards. When he gets at least 10 cards he can *Bake a Cake.* You might want to have miniature cookie treats for your child.

- Child answers these questions. *The product is 35. One factor is 7. What is the other factor?* **5** *The product is 42. One factor is 7. What is the other factor?* **6** *Give 2 factors that equal 15.* **1 and 15** or **3 and 5** *Give 2 factors that equal 36.* **1 and 36, 2 and 18, 3 and 12,** or **4 and 9**

- **A** Use standard procedure.

- Mult./Div. Tables: Have him recite tables.

Fractions (2 min.)

- **B** Point to each number; he stands and reads if mixed number. He remain seated and read if not a mixed number.

- *Concept Cards* **63–70:** Child reads fractions.

- Fractional Circles: He demonstrates number of parts needed to make whole for these fraction.

  $\frac{1}{3}$ **3** $\frac{1}{5}$ **5** $\frac{1}{2}$ **2**

  What whole number is $\frac{3}{3}$ equal to? **1** *What whole number is any fraction with the same number for the numerator and denominator equal to?* **1**

Money (2 min.)

- *Coins/play bills:* Have your child make change from $5.00. Tell price of item such as $2.50. He uses coins and play bills to count back change.

2. Quiz 5 (9 min.)

3. Review fractions. (12 min.)

- *Concept Cards* **133–139:** Show backs of cards; he reads mixed numbers.

- **C** Child finds fractional part by div. whole number by denominator. He gives remainder as fraction.

- **D** *Rolling Ruler:* Remind him that *Rolling Ruler* is enlarged so it can be seen easily. Show him how to measure $7\frac{1}{4}$ in. line to nearest quarter inch. Point to several quarter-inch marks on *Rolling Ruler*. Be sure he understands that $\frac{1}{2}$ in. is $\frac{2}{4}$ in. He should also be able to find $\frac{3}{4}$ on ruler. Let child measure $11\frac{3}{4}$ in. line, using *Rolling Ruler*. If he seems weak with quarter inches, have him come to *Rolling Ruler* and point to quarter-inch lines.

- **rulers:** Child needs to get out his ruler and point to $3\frac{1}{4}$ inches and $8\frac{3}{4}$ inches.

- Child does **Ex. 1–7, p. 85.**

4. Discuss story problems. (3 min.)

- Child does **Ex. 8.** Work problems together.

5. Review/Boardwork (3 min.) **Ex. 9–12** Child needs ruler with metric marking for les. 48.

Preparation

1. Chalkboard:

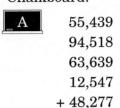   55,439
94,518
63,639
12,547
+ 48,277

B 20⟌876

2. *Arithmetic 4:* pp. 87–88

3. *Lesson 48 Speed Drill*

4. Visuals:
   - *Process Flashcards*
   - *1–100 Chart (Arith Chart 23)*
   - *Place Value (Arith Chart 2)*
   - *Metric Units of Length (Arith Chart 17)*
   - *Concept Cards 32–36, 38–40, 112, 43–44, 118–129*
   - story problem clue words flashcards (optional from les. 4)
   - meter stick
   - yardstick
   - *Rolling Ruler* (cm) *(Arith Chart 26)*
   - ruler

Teaching Procedure

1. Oral review drills (8 min.)

Processes (4 min.)
   - Mult./Div. Tables
   - *Flashcards:* Have child answer quickly and accurately.
   - **A** Use standard procedure.
   - *1–100 Chart:* Point to numbers that are divisible by 3; child gives quotients. Point to numbers that are not divisible by 3, he includes remainders in quotients.
   - Oral comb.

$12 \times 4 \div 8 \times 12 \div 9 \times 8 = 64$ $6 \times 8 + 2 \times 2 \times 2 \div 10 = 20$

$10 + 1 - 5 + 6 \times 2 \div 6 \times 4 = 16$ $0 \times 21 + 1{,}000 - 900 = 100$

$7 + 3 \div 5 + 5 \times 3 = 21$ $5 \times 9 + 6 = 51$

$6 + 6 \times 2 + 3 - 1 + 6 - 4 \div 7 = 4$ $5 \times 9 + 6 - 1 \times 2 + 99 + 6 = 205$

$5 + 2 - 4 \times 3 \times 4 + 4 = 40$ $5 \times 2 - 8 \times 5 \times 4 + 6 - 3 = 43$

$6 + 8 - 8 + 4 - 6 = 4$ $3 + 10 - 4 + 4 = 13$

Place value (1 min.)
   - *Arith Chart* **2**

Measures (2 min.)
- *Concept Cards* **32–36, 38–40, 112,** and **43–44:** Have child answer.

Story problems (1 min.)
- Story problem clue words flashcards

2. **Written speed drill** (6 min.) Time for 5 min.
   - Grade. Record as a speed drill/quiz grade. Count off 3 points for each incorrect answer.

3. **Introduce metric units of length.** (12 min.)
   - **Meter stick/yardstick:** Show yardstick and review yards, inches, and feet. Discuss relative lengths. Show meter stick and tell him that meter is basic linear unit in another system of measure, the metric system. Put yardstick on meter stick to compare lengths. He can see that meter is a little longer distance than yard.
   - *Rolling Ruler:* Discuss that meters are made up of decimeters, centimeters, and millimeters. Remind him that *Rolling Ruler* is enlarged. **1 meter has 10 decimeters.** A decimeter is about width of palm. **1 meter has 100 centimeters.** A centimeter is about width of little finger. **1 meter has 1,000 millimeters.** Child puts thumb and index finger as close together as possible without touching. That distance is about 1 millimeter.
   - **Rulers:** He gets out ruler and finds side with centimeters. Discuss that a cm is a shorter distance than in. It takes about $2\frac{1}{2}$ cm to make in. He finds millimeters. **1 centimeter has 10 millimeters.** He finds decimeter. **10 centimeters equals 1 decimeter.**
   - *Arith Chart* **17:** Discuss. Especially note units that are longer than meter and discuss about how long they are. Discuss that a kilometer is a shorter distance than mile. A kilometer is a little longer than $\frac{1}{2}$ mile.
   - *Concept Cards* **118–123:** Briefly review each unit. These are new to most children and will take a while for him to master.
   - *Concept Cards* **124–129:** Briefly look at prefixes. **Deci means $\frac{1}{10}$ because a decimeter is $\frac{1}{10}$ of meter. Kilo means 1,000 because a kilometer is 1,000 meters.**
   - Read and discuss **box on p. 87.** Child does **Ex. 1–3.**

4. **Review division.** (6 min.)
   - **B** Work and check as he explains. Child should have a good knowledge of div. by now.
   - Child does **Ex. 4.**

5. **Review/Boardwork** (6 min.) **Ex. 5–7**

Preparation

1. Chalkboard:

A
47,250
58,235
17,890
45,734
+ 92,893

B

kilometer	meter	centimeter
100 meters	kilometer	3 hectometers
2,000 meters	kilometer	10 hectometers

C 42) 894

Note: You will need to make a Mixed Fact Chart to use throughout the year. Here is the example.

Mixed Facts			
18 − 9	18 ÷ 9	9 × 6	17 − 9
8 + 3	64 ÷ 8	16 − 7	9 × 8
28 ÷ 4	13 − 8	6 × 3	8 + 5
4 × 4	8 × 8	7 + 4	32 ÷ 8
5 + 7	12 − 6	42 ÷ 7	7 + 7
12 − 8	7 × 6	40 ÷ 8	15 − 6
3 + 9	7 + 8	12 × 9	8 + 7
45 ÷ 5	8 × 6	48 ÷ 6	9 + 5
9 + 8	24 ÷ 6	15 − 8	63 ÷ 9
5 × 8	16 − 9	7 × 8	11 − 3
8 + 9	7 + 5	15 − 9	54 ÷ 6
13 − 7	63 ÷ 7	9 + 6	9 × 3

2. *Arithmetic 4:* pp. 89–90

3. *Lesson 49 Speed Drill*

4. Visuals:
   - *Process Flashcards*
   - *Averaging Numbers (Arith Chart 6)*
   - *1–100 Chart (Arith Chart 23)*
   - *Metric Units of Length (Arith Chart 17)*
   - *Mixed Fact Chart*
   - *Concept Cards 63, 70–78, and 118–129*

Teaching Procedure

1. **Oral review drills** (9 min.)

Processes (7 min.)
   - *Flashcards:* Let child answer. After he gets warmed up, let him play a game.
   - 11–12 Mult./Div. Tables
   - **A** Use standard procedure.
   - *Arith Chart* **6:** He gives 2 steps to average numbers.
   - *1–100 Chart:* He adds 7 to several large numbers.
   - Mixed Fact Chart: Point to problems, child responds.
   - Oral comb.

6 x 9 ÷ 6 x 9 = *81*	16 ÷ 4 x 4 − 16 = *0*
6 x 9 ÷ 6 x 8 + 1 = *73*	6 ÷ 2 x 5 + 6 = *21*
63 ÷ 9 x 8 ÷ 8 = *7*	25 ÷ 5 + 10 x 3 + 3 = *48*
62 − 62 x 7 + 1 + 3 ÷ 4 x 1 = *1*	3 + 7 + 5 ÷ 5 = *3*
5 x 3 ÷ 5 + 5 x 9 = *72*	3 x 5 ÷ 3 + 8 = *13*

Fractions (2 min.)
   - *Concept Card* **63:** Review terms.
   - *Concept Cards* **70–78:** Show 2 cards; child adds or subt.

Lesson 49
(cont.)

 • Call out several fractions, whole numbers, and mixed numbers. He stands when you say a mixed number.

2. Written speed drill (4 min.) Time for 3 min.

3. Review metric units of length. (9 min.)
 • *Arith Chart* **17:** Review units and relative size with him.
 • *Concept Cards* **118–123:** Drill units.
 • *Concept Cards* **124–129:** Drill metric prefixes. Be sure he understands relationships such as a decameter is 10 meters. That explains why prefix means 10.
 • Child chooses longer in each row.
 • Child does **Ex. 1–2, p. 89.**

4. Review division. (6 min.)
 • Work and check as he explains. Encourage him to work these problems quickly.
 • Child does **Ex. 3.**

5. Discuss story problem. (6 min.)
 • Child does **Ex. 4.**

6. Review/Boardwork (3 min.) **Ex. 5–6**

7. Homework Ex. 7–8

Lesson 50

Preparation

1. Chalkboard:

```
   74,325
   39,411
   16,895
   49,339
 + 62,256
```

 250 meters + 3 kilometers = ___ meters

2. *Arithmetic 4:* pp. 91–92

3. *Lesson 50 Speed Drill*

4. Visuals:
 • *Process Flashcards*
 • *Mixed Addition Facts (Arith 4, p.311)*
 • *1–100 Chart (Arith Chart 23)*
 • *Concept Cards 32–36, 38–40, 112, 43–44, and 118–129*
 • story problem clue words flashcards (optional from les. 4)
 • *Metric Units of Length (Arith Chart 17)*

Teaching Procedure

1. Oral review drills (9 min.)

 Homework check

Processes (7 min.)

- *Flashcards:* Let child answer and then play *Four Corners*.
- ▮ A ▮ Use standard procedure.
- Mult./Div. Tables
- *Mixed Addition Facts*
- *1–100 Chart:* Point to several large numbers; child subt 7 from each. Repeat with 4.

Measures (1 min.)

- *Concept Cards* **32–36, 38–40, 112,** and **43–44**

Story problems (1 min.)

- Story problem clue words flashcards

2. Written speed drill (4 min.) Time for 3 min.

3. Review metric units of length. (9 min.)

- *Arith Chart* **17:** Look at briefly with child. Leave chart displayed so he can study measures when he has free time.
- *Concept Cards* **118–123:** Review with him. Each day he should become more comfortable with metric units.
- *Concept Cards* **124–129:** Review with him.
- Call out 1,000, $\frac{1}{100}$, 100, $\frac{1}{1,000}$, 10, and $\frac{1}{10}$. Child responds with correct prefix.
- Call out 2 metric units of length; he choose longer.
- Child does **Ex. 1–3, p. 91.**

4. Review measurement equations. (6 min.)

- ▮ B ▮ Work problem step by step.

250 meters + ⎰ 3 kilometers ⎱ = 3,250 meters   Step 1: Write all measures as meters.

250 meters + ⎰ 3,000 meters ⎱ = 3,250 meters

Step 2: Bring down 250 meters.

    1. ×

    2. s ⟨1,000⟩

Step 3: Box kilometers and meters and work.

    3. 1,000
      × 3
     ─────
     3,000

Step 4: Add.

- Child does **Ex. 4.**

5. Discuss story problems. (6 min.)

- Child does **Ex. 5.**

6. Review/Boardwork (3 min.) **Ex. 6–7**

7. Homework Ex. 8

Lesson

51

Preparation

1. Chalkboard:

   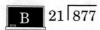 **A** 5 kilometers – 3 meters = ___ meters

   B $21\overline{)877}$

2. *Arithmetic 4:* pp. 93–94

3. *Lesson 51 Speed Drill*

4. Visuals:

   - *Process Flashcards*
   - *1–100 Chart (Arith 23)*
   - *Concept Cards* 63, 32–36, 38–40, 112, 43–44, and 118–129

Teaching Procedure

1. **Oral review drills** (7 min.)

   Homework check

   Processes (5 min.)
   - *Flashcards:* Have child answer and then play a game.
   - Mult./Div. Tables
   - Paper drill: He writes answers to oral comb. Check after every 3 answers.

$63 \div 7 + 3 = 12$	$5 \times 9 + 5 = 50$	$24 \div 4 \times 3 = 18$
$9 \times 4 - 8 = 28$	$5 \times 3 - 6 = 9$	$18 \div 2 \times 4 = 36$
$77 \div 7 \times 5 = 55$	$28 \div 4 + 6 = 13$	$9 \times 6 = 54$

   - *1–100 Chart:* Point to numbers; he adds 9. Repeat for 7.
   - Oral comb.

$5 \times 8 + 8 \div 6 = 8$	$8 \div 2 \times 5 + 4 \div 8 = 3$
$40 + 8 \div 6 \times 6 + 2 = 50$	$10 \times 5 + 4 \div 9 - 6 = 0$
$7 + 5 \times 6 \div 9 = 8$	$8 + 2 \times 3 - 4 \times 10 = 260$
$10 \times 5 + 5 \div 5 + 11 = 22$	$30 \times 3 + 1 + 9 = 100$

   Fractions (1 min.)
   - *Concept Card* **63:** Review terms.

   Measures (1 min.)
   - *Concept Cards* **32–36, 38–40, 112,** and **43–44**

2. **Written speed drill** (6 min.) Time for 5 min.
   - Grade. Record as a speed drill/quiz grade. Count off 3 points for each incorrect answer.

3. **Review metric units of length.** (9 min.)
   - *Concept Cards* **118–129:** Let child answer.
   - Call out 2 measures, such as km and cm; he chooses shorter.
   - **A** Work problem as he explains.

- Child does **Ex. 1–2, p. 93.**

4. Review division. (6 min.)

- ▮▬B▬ He works on paper as you work on ckbd.
- Child does **Ex. 3.**

5. Review/Boardwork (9 min.) **Ex. 4–6**

6. Homework Ex. 7–8

Lesson 52

Preparation

Test 5, pp. 41–42 from *Student Tests and Speed Drills.*

Teaching Procedure

1. Homework check.

2. Administer test.
Notice that space has been allowed on this test for child to work story problems.

Lesson 53

Preparation

1. Chalkboard:

   ▮▬▬   8   9   6   12

2. *Arithmetic 4:* pp. 95–96

3. *Lesson 53 Speed Drill*

4. Visuals:
   - *Calculator (Arith Chart 20)*
   - *Process Flashcards*
   - *Averaging Numbers (Arith Chart 6)*
   - *Concept Cards* 32–36, 38–40, 112, 43–44, and 118–129
   - story problem clue words flashcards (optional from les. 4)

Teaching Procedure

1. Oral review drills (9 min.)

   Processes (7 min.)
   - *Calculator:* Point to number. Child mult. by 7.
   - *Flashcards:* Expect quick, accurate answers.
   - Tables: Mult. 6/Div. 7
   - *Arith Chart* **6:** Review 2 steps for averaging.
   - *Mult. Cards:* Play *Fraction Fun.* Count out 15 cards. *I have a total of 15 cards. When I say* Go, *you have 30 seconds to*

answer as many cards as possible. We will write a fraction that expresses how many of the whole group you could answer in 30 seconds. What will be the denominator of the fraction? **15** *What will be the numerator?* **the number answered in 30 seconds** Show cards to child; he answers as fast as he can. If he does well, play again, giving fewer seconds. If he does poorly, increase time.

    Measures (2 min.)

- *Concept Cards* **32–36, 38–40, 112,** and **43–44**
- *Concept Cards* **118–123:** Review metric linear measures.
- *Concept Cards* **124–129:** Review metric prefixes.
- Call out these measures and have him decide if he should mult. or div. to change from one to other.

m to km *div.*	m to cm *mult.*	ft. to in. *mult.*
hm to km *div.*	qt. to gal. *div.*	mi. to yd. *mult.*

2. **Written speed drill** (4 min.) Time for 3 min.

3. **Introduce factoring.** (15 min.)

- *Calculator:* Point to 4. Tell child that 4 can be product. If it is a product, there must be 2 factors that we can mult. together to get 4. Of course, we can mult. 1 times 4 to get 4. Have him name 2 other factors that give 4. (2 x 2 = 4) He should now realize that there are no other pairs of factors that give 4. Have him notice that 1, 2, and 4 all div. into 4 without a remainder.

- Point to 8. Have child think of 8 as a product and name 2 pairs of factors that make 8. (1 x 8 and 2 x 4) Write factors on ckbd. Be sure he understands that 1, 2, 4, and 8 all div. evenly into 8. Write 1, 2, 4, 8 on ckbd. Tell him that these are factors of 8 written in numerical order.

  Point to 9. Child lists pairs of factors and then gives factors in numerical order. Repeat for 6 and 12.

- Read and discuss **box on p. 95.** Explain factoring chart; child finds factors of several numbers, using chart. He does **Ex. 1–2.** It may be necessary to work with him to get him thinking in right direction.

4. **Discuss story problems.** (6 min.)

- **Story problem clue words flashcards:** Review briefly.
- Child does **Ex. 3.**

5. **Review/Boardwork** (3 min.) **Ex. 4–6** Notice that Ex. 6 is Extra Practice and is therefore optional.

Lesson 54

Preparation

1. Chalkboard:

8   12   16   25   28

2. *Arithmetic 4:* pp. 97–98

3. *Lesson 54 Speed Drill*

4. Visuals:
  - *Process Flashcards*
  - coins
  - Concept Cards 124–129

Teaching Procedure

1. Oral review drills (9 min.)

  Processes (8 min.)
  - *Flashcards:* Let child answer.
  - Coins: Show 1 nickel. *What is the value of 7 nickels?* **35¢** Write 7n = 35¢ on ckbd. *This means 7 times 5¢ equals 35¢.*
    Show 1 dime. *What is the value of 12 dimes?* **$1.20** Write 12d = $1.20 on ckbd. *This means 12 times 10¢ equals $1.20.*
    Show 1 quarter. *What is the value of 6 quarters?* **$1.50** Write 6q = $1.50 on ckbd. *This means 6 times 25¢ equals $1.50.*
  - Mult./Div. Tables
  - Oral comb. Play *Speedy Sam.*

$5 \times 9 \div 5 + 3 + 9 \div 3 + 7 = 14$ $9 \times 8 \div 6 - 7 + 1 \div 3 \times 9 = 18$

$2 \times 9 + 2 \div 4 \times 5 + 5 \div 6 = 5$ $9 \times 9 - 1 \div 2 \times 2 = 80$

$3 \times 9 + 1 \div 7 - 3 \times 10 \times 100 = 1,000$ $48 \div 6 \times 2 + 12 = 28$

$3 \times 5 - 3 \times 9 = 108$ $2 \times 10 \div 10 \times 10 = 20$

$7 \times 9 - 3 \div 5 + 40 - 10 + 20 - 1 = 61$ $9 \times 9 \div 9 \times 3 + 1 = 28$

$3 \times 9 + 3 \times 3 - 9 \div 9 \times 7 + 1 \div 8 \times 2 + 2 = 18$

  Metric prefixes (1 min.)
  - *Concept Cards* **124–129**

2. Written speed drill (3 min.) Time for 2 min.

3. Review factoring. (15 min.)
  -  Find pairs of factors and list in numerical order for a couple of numbers. He comes to ckbd and factor remaining numbers.
  - Child does **Ex. 1–3, p. 97.**

4. Review/Boardwork (9 min.) **Ex. 4–7**

5. Homework Ex. 8–9

Preparation

Lesson
55

1. Chalkboard:

  $20\overline{)492}$

2. *Arithmetic 4:* pp. 99–100

3. *Lesson 55 Speed Drill*

4. Visuals:

   - *Process Flashcards*
   - *Mixed Addition Facts (Arith 4, p. 311)*
   - *Concept Cards* 32–36, 38–40, 112, 43–44, 118–129, 24–31, and 113–116
   - coins
   - *Measures of Time (Arith Chart 15)*

Teaching Procedure

1. **Oral review drills** (9 min.)

   Homework check

   Processes (6 min.)

   - *Flashcards:* Have child answer a few cards and then play *Giant Step.*
   - Mult./Div. Tables: Play *Just the Facts.*
   - *Mixed Addition Facts*

   Fractions (1 min.)

   - Coins: Show 1 dime. *What fraction of a dollar is 1 dime?* $\frac{1}{10}$ *The denominator is 10 because there are 10 dimes in 1 dollar. The numerator is 1 because we are using 1 dime.*

     Show 1 quarter. *What fraction of a dollar is 1 quarter?* $\frac{1}{4}$ *The denominator is 4 because it takes 4 quarters to make a dollar. The numerator is 1 because we are using 1 quarter.*

     Show 1 nickel. *What fraction of a dollar is 1 nickel?* $\frac{1}{20}$ *The numerator is 20 because it takes 20 nickels to make 1 dollar. The numerator is 1 because we are using 1 nickel.*

   Measures (2 min.)

   - *Concept Cards* **32–36, 38–40, 112, 43–44,** and **118–129**

2. **Written speed drill** (4 min.) Time for 3 min.

3. **Introduce table of time.** (6 min.)

   - *Arith Chart* **15:** Discuss that a year is divided into 12 months, 365 days, and about 52 weeks. Discuss that there are 7 days in each week and 24 hours in each day. Each hour is made up of 60 minutes which are made up of 60 seconds. Discuss longer units of time (decade, century, and millennium). If time permits, discuss number of days in each month.
   - *Concept Cards* **24–31** and **113–116:** Look at each card and review units.
   - Read and discuss **box on p. 99.** Child does **Ex. 1.**

4. **Review factoring.** (6 min.)

   - Call out numbers, such as 8, 10 and 12. Child writes factors in numerical order. If he can do without writing pairs of factors, allow him to do so.
   - Child does **Ex. 2.**

5. **Review division.** (6 min.)

   - ▮ He explains as you work on ckbd.

- Child does **Ex. 3–4.**

6. Review/Boardwork (6 min.) **Ex. 5–6**

7. Homework Ex. 7–8

wed ¹¹⁄₃₀

Lesson

56

Preparation

1. Chalkboard:

	8	9
	12	6
		12

2. *Arithmetic 4:* pp. 101–102

3. *Lesson 56 Speed Drill*

4. Visuals:
   - story problem clue words flashcards
   - *Rolling Ruler* (in.) *(Arith Chart 24)*
   - *Concept Cards* 24–40, 43–44, 112–116, and 63–70

Teaching Procedure

1. Oral review drills (9 min.)

   Homework check

   Processes (5 min.)
   - Mult./Div. 11–12 Tables
   - Have child stand. *I am going to read you a statement. If the statement is sensible, face the front. If the statement is silly, face the back.*

   We go to school about 1,000 days per year.

   10 times 100 is 1,000.

   If we took 1,000 steps, we would travel about 1 mile.

   1,000 pennies is 10 dollars.

   A penny roll holds 50 pennies. 20 penny rolls hold 1,000 pennies.

   We could answer 1,000 combinations in 1 minute.

   1,000 dollars is more than enough to buy a new car.

   10,000 divided by 10 is 1,000.

   We could put 1,000 books in our desk.

   Our best friend weighs about 1,000 pounds.

• Oral comb.

12 x 5 + 3 + 4 = *67*	2 + 2 ÷ 2 x 8 − 3 − 1 ÷ 6 = *2*
12 ÷ 6 x 9 + 2 − 6 ÷ 7 = *2*	22 − 6 ÷ 8 x 100 + 6 = *206*
1 + 1 + 1 x 3 x 4 ÷ 3 = *12*	5 + 3 − 7 + 9 − 6 + 20 = *24*
· 3 + 3 + 3 + 3 ÷ 6 x 2 + 6 x 5 = *50*	6 + 10 ÷ 4 x 2 − 1 − 1 + 5 = *11*
2 + 2 + 6 x 5 + 4 ÷ 6 x 12 = *108*	5 x 6 + 2 − 4 ÷ 7 x 5 = *20*

Story problems (1 min.)
- Story problem clue words flashcards

Measures (2 min.)
- *Rolling Ruler:* Child shows where to stop when drawing line segments of these lengths:
  $5\frac{3}{4}$ in. $8\frac{1}{2}$ in. $3\frac{1}{4}$ in. $10\frac{2}{4}$ in.
- *Concept Cards* **24–40, 43–44,** and **112–116**

Fractions (1 min.)
- *Concept Card* **63:** Review terms.
- *Concept Cards* **63–70:** Cover fractions; he gives fractions by looking at circles.

2. **Written speed drill** (4 min.) Time for 3 min.

3. **Introduce finding common factors.** (12 min.)

- █████ Child give factors of 8. If necessary, he list pairs of factors 1st and then gives in numerical order. He lists factors of 12. He looks at both groups of factors to see if any factor is found in both lists. Circle factors that are in both lists. **A common factor is a factor that belongs to two or more numbers.** Repeat with 9, 6, and 12.
- Read and discuss **box on p. 101.** Child does **Ex. 1–2.**

4. **Review division.** (3 min.)
- Give him 3 min. to do **Ex. 3.** Call out answers for him to check his work.

5. **Review/Boardwork** (9 min.) **Ex. 4–6**

6. **Homework Ex. 7–8** Child needs to have a ruler with metric markings in arithmetic tomorrow.

Thurs

Lesson 57

Preparation

1. Chalkboard:

| █ A | 8 | $\frac{5}{9}$ | $12\frac{1}{2}$ | $7\frac{2}{3}$ | 201 | $6\frac{1}{11}$ |

| █ B | $\frac{1}{12}$ of 49 | $\frac{1}{10}$ of 53 |

 C Use *Rolling Ruler (Arith Chart 26)* to draw lines that are 17 cm and 25 cm.

2. *Arithmetic 4:* pp. 103–106

3. *Lesson 57 Quiz*

4. Visuals:
   - *Process Flashcards*
   - *Mixed Facts Chart (refer to lesson 49)*
   - *Concept Cards* 63–70 and 118–129
   - Fractional Circles
   - coins
   - play bills
   - *Rolling Ruler* (cm) *(Arith Chart* 26)
   - ruler

Teaching Procedure

1. **Oral review drills** (9 min.)

   Homework check

   Processes (5 min.)
   - *Flashcards:* Play a game after child is warmed up.
   - Child answers these questions. *The product is 99. One factor is 9. What is the other factor?* **11** *The product is 56. One factor is 7. What is the other factor?* **8** *Give 2 factors that equal 9.* **1 and 9** or **3 and 3** *Give 2 factors that equal 36.* **1 and 36, 2 and 18, 3 and 12,** or **4 and 9**
   - Mult./Div. Tables: Have him recite tables.
   - Mixed Facts Chart

   Fractions (2 min.)
   - **A** Point to each number; child stands and reads if mixed number. He remains seated and reads if not a mixed number.
   - *Concept Cards* **63–70:** He reads fractions.
   - Fractional Circles: He demonstrates number of parts needed to make whole for these fractions.

     $\frac{1}{2}$ **2** $\frac{1}{6}$ **6** $\frac{1}{5}$ **5**

     What whole number is $\frac{5}{5}$ equal to? **1** *What whole number is any fraction with the same number for the numerator and denominator equal to?* **1**
   - **B** He gives remainders as fractions.

   Money (2 min.)
   - Coins/play bills: Have child make change from $10. Tell price of item such as $6.53. He uses coins and play bills to count back change.

2. **Quiz 6** (9 min.)

3. **Review metric system.** (6 min.)
   - *Concept Cards* **118–129:** Review linear measures and metric prefixes.
   - **C** */Rolling Ruler* (cm): Remind him that *Rolling Ruler* is enlarged so it can be seen easily. Show him how to measure line, using centimeters. Ask him if he thinks line is at least 17 in. long. He should understand that since a centimeter is a shorter distance than an inch, line is much shorter than

Lesson 57
(cont.)

17 in. Have child measure 2nd line, using cm side of *Rolling Ruler.*
- **rulers:** He needs to get out his ruler and point to 21 cm and 15 cm.
- Read and discuss **box on p. 103.** Child does **Ex. 1–2.**

4. Review common factors. (3 min.)
- Work **Ex. 3** together.

5. Discuss story problems. (3 min.)
- Child does **Ex. 4, pp. 104–105.** Work problems together.

6. Review/Boardwork (6 min.) **Ex. 5–10, p. 106.**

Lesson 58

Preparation

1. Chalkboard:

$$19\frac{5}{7}$$
$$+8\frac{1}{7}$$

2. *Arithmetic 4:* pp. 107–108

3. *Lesson 58 Speed Drill*

4. Visuals:
- *Process Flashcards*
- *1–100 Chart (Arith Chart 23)*
- *Concept Cards* 16–19, 111, 24–40, 43–44, 112–116, and 118–129
- story problem clue words flashcards (optional from les. 4)

Teaching Procedure

1. Oral review drills (11 min.)

Processes (7 min.)
- Mult./Div. Tables
- *Flashcards:* Have child answer and then play game.
- *1–100 Chart:* Point to numbers; students add 11.
- *Concept Cards* **16–19** and **111:** Review terms.

Measures (3 min.)
- *Concept Cards* **24–40, 43–44, 112–116,** and **118–129:** Have child answer and then play *Beat the Clock.*

Story problems (1 min.)
- Story problem clue words flashcards

2. Written speed drill (6 min.) Time for 5 min.
- Grade. Record as a speed drill/quiz grade. Count off 6 points for each incorrect answer.

3. Review common factors. (9 min.)

- Call out these numbers; child gives factors in numerical order.
  5   8   10   12   15   18   20
- Work **Ex. 1a, p. 107** together. He completes **Ex. 1** and work **Ex. 2.**

4. Review adding fractions with common denominators. (10 min.)

- 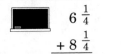 Work as he explains.
- Child does **Ex. 3.**

5. Review/Boardwork (9 min.) **Ex. 4–8**

Lesson 59

Preparation

1. Chalkboard:

$$6\frac{1}{4}$$
$$+8\frac{1}{4}$$

$$5\frac{9}{10}$$
$$-3\frac{7}{10}$$

2. *Arithmetic 4:* pp. 109–110

3. *Lesson 59 Speed Drill*

4. Visuals:
   - *Process Flashcards*
   - *Averaging Numbers (Arith Chart 6)*
   - *1–100 Chart (Arith Chart 23)*
   - *Concept Cards 63 and 70–78*

Teaching Procedure

1. Oral review drills (9 min.)

Processes (7 min.)
- *Flashcards:* Let child answer. After he gets warmed up, let him play a game.
- Mult./Div. 7–9 Tables
- *Arith Chart* **6:** Child gives 2 steps to average numbers.
- *1–100 Chart:* He adds 12 to several large numbers.
- Oral comb.

  9 x 4 ÷ 6 x 5 x 3 + 10 x 8 = *800*   18 ÷ 9 x 12 + 5 = *29*

  7 x 7 + 1 x 3 + 50 x 3 = *600*   7 x 4 – 5 + 6 = *29*

  9 x 5 – 3 + 8 = *50*   20 + 5 + 8 – 3 = *30*

  11 x 4 + 4 – 3 = *45*   8 x 5 + 8 = *48*

  6 x 4 + 9 – 3 = *30*   18 ÷ 9 x 9 + 5 = *23*

  18 ÷ 2 x 5 + 3 = *48*   18 ÷ 9 x 12 + 5 = *29*

Fractions (2 min.)
- *Concept Card* **63:** Review terms.
- *Concept Cards* **70–78:** Show 2 cards; he adds or subt.
- Call out several fractions, whole numbers, and mixed numbers. He stands when you say a mixed number.

Lesson 59
(cont.)

2. **Written speed drill** (3 min.) Time for 2 min. 30 sec.

3. **Introduce greatest common factor.** (12 min.)
   - Call out these numbers for child to factor.
     4   6   7   9   12
   - Write 12 and 15 on ckbd. He lists factors and circles common factors. He looks at circled factors and tells which one is greatest common factor. **The greatest common factor is the largest factor any two or more numbers have in common.** Write *g.c.f.* on ckbd and explain that it is abbreviation for greatest common factor.
   - Read and discuss **box on p. 109.** Child does **Ex. 1.**

4. **Review adding and subtracting fractions.** (6 min.)

   - Work 2 problems as he explains. Encourage him to work these problems quickly.
   - Child does **Ex. 2–3.**

5. **Review/Boardwork** (6 min.) **Ex. 4–6**

6. **Homework Ex. 7–9**

Lesson
60

Preparation

1. Chalkboard:

   5;15   3;6   4;10

2. *Arithmetic 4:* pp. 111–112

3. *Lesson 60 Speed Drill*

4. Visuals:
   - *Process Flashcards*
   - *Mixed Division facts (Arith 4, p. 322)*
   - *Concept Cards* 1–15, 24–40, 43–44, 112–116, and 118–129
   - *Place Value (Arith Chart* 2)

Teaching Procedure

1. **Oral review drills** (9 min.)

   Homework check

   Processes (5 min.)
   - *Flashcards:* Let child answer and then play *Four Corners.*
   - Mult./Div. Tables
   - *Mixed Division Facts*
   - Oral comb.

     $5 \times 3 \div 5 \times 3 - 1 = 8$ $10 \times 5 \div 5 \times 10 + 2 = 102$

     $2 + 1 \div 3 - 1 + 200 - 199 = 1$ $4 + 6 \times 10 - 50 + 2 = 52$

$2 \times 4 \div 8 \times 9 \times 8 = 72$ $7 \times 9 + 7 + 30 = 100$

$4 \times 4 + 1 + 1 \div 9 \times 3 = 6$ $5 \times 4 + 80 - 10 = 90$

Measures (3 min.)

- *Concept Cards* **24–40, 43–44, 112–116,** and **118–129:** Review. Play a game if he does well.

Place value (1 min.)

- *Arith Chart* **2**
- *Concept Cards* **1–15:** Child adds 10,000 to each number.

2. Written speed drill (3 min.) Time for 2 min. 30 sec.

3. Review greatest common factor. (9 min.)

- 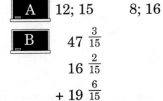 He lists factors, circle common factors, and identify greatest common factor.
- Child does **Ex. 1–2, p. 111.**

4. Review metric prefixes. (3 min.)

- *Concept Cards* **124–129:** Review briefly.
- Child does **Ex. 3.**

5. Review/Boardwork (12 min.) **Ex. 4–8**

6. Homework Ex. 9

Preparation

Lesson

61

wed 12/7

1. Chalkboard:

   A 12; 15   8; 16

   B $47 \frac{3}{15}$

        $16 \frac{2}{15}$

      $+ 19 \frac{6}{15}$

2. *Arithmetic 4:* pp. 113–114

3. *Lesson 61 Speed Drill*

4. Visuals:

   - *Process Flashcards*
   - *Concept Cards* 24–40, 43–44, 112–116, and 118–129
   - *Place Value (Arith Chart 2)*

Teaching Procedure

1. Oral review drills (9 min.)

Homework check

Processes (6 min.)
- Mult./Div. 8–9 Tables
- *Flashcards:* Expect quick, accurate responses.

Measures (2 min.)
- *Concept Cards* **24–40, 43–44, 112–116,** and **118–129:** Review with child. If he does well, play *Around the World.*

Place value (1 min.)
- *Arith Chart* **2**

2. Written speed drill (3 min.) Time for 2 min.

3. Review factoring. (9 min.)
- **A** Child lists factors, finds common factors, and identifies greatest common factor. If he is weak, call out several numbers for him to find factors and to list in numerical order. Have child work on paper and ckbd.
- Work **Ex. 1, p. 113** together. Child does **Ex. 2.** Be sure he understands chart in Ex. 1, since a similar chart is on Test 6.

4. Review fractions. (3 min.)
- **B** He works on paper as you work on ckbd.
- Child does **Ex. 3.**

5. Discuss story problems. (6 min.)
- Child does **Ex. 4.**

6. Review/Boardwork (6 min.) **Ex. 5–7**

7. Homework Ex. 8–9

Lesson
62

Preparation

Test 6, pp. 49–50 from *Student Tests and Speed Drills*

Teaching Procedure

1. Homework check

2. Administer test.

Notice that space has been allowed on this test for child to work story problems.

Preparation

1. Chalkboard:

    $\frac{2}{4}$ $\frac{3}{8}$ $\frac{4}{8}$ $\frac{2}{6}$ $\frac{5}{10}$ $\frac{6}{15}$

2. *Arithmetic 4:* pp. ~~115–116~~ 113-14

3. *Lesson 63 Speed Drill*

Anon 121.9

4. Visuals:
   - *Process Flashcards*
   - *Mixed Multiplication Facts (Arith 4, p. 319)*
   - *Concept Cards* 24–40, 43–44, 112–116, 118–129, and 80–84
   - Fractional Circles

Teaching Procedure

1. **Oral review drills** (9 min.)

   Processes (6 min.)
   - *Flashcards*
   - Mult./Div. 7–9 Tables
   - *Div. Cards:* Play *Fraction Fun.*
   - *Mixed Multiplication Facts*
   - Oral comb.

$12 \times 5 + 4 \div 8 \times 9 + 2 = 74$	$21 \div 3 + 5 \times 3 \div 9 - 4 = 0$
$132 \div 11 \times 12 - 44 + 5 = 105$	$78 + 2 \div 10 \times 3 - 4 \div 5 \times 5 = 20$
$2 \times 2 + 2 \div 2 \times 2 + 2 = 8$	$5 \times 6 + 2 \div 4 \times 3 + 1 \div 5 = 5$
$19 - 7 \times 5 \div 6 \times 9 = 90$	$22 - 6 \div 2 \times 9 - 2 \div 7 = 10$
$15 + 6 \div 3 \times 8 + 4 \div 6 = 10$	$35 \div 7 \times 6 \div 3 + 5 \div 5 + 4 = 7$

   Measures (3 min.)
   - *Concept Cards* **24–40, 43–44,** and **112–116:** Play a game.
   - *Concept Cards* **118–123:** Review metric linear measures.
   - *Concept Cards* **124–129:** Review metric prefixes.
   - Call out these measures and have child decide if he should mult. or div. to change from one to other.

hm to km *div.*	cm to mm *mult.*	km to m *mult.*
dkm to hm *div.*	dm to m *div.*	m to cm *mult.*

2. **Written speed drill** (3 min.) Time for 2 min.

3. **Introduce reducing fractions.** (15 min.)
   - **Fractional Circles:** Show $\frac{1}{2}$ and $\frac{2}{4}$. Use a story such as this to introduce reducing fractions. *John and Paul both had pizza for lunch. John ate $\frac{1}{2}$ of a small pizza that was cut into halves. Paul ate $\frac{2}{4}$ of a small pizza that was cut into fourths. Who ate more pizza?* Show with circles that boys ate same amount. Write $\frac{2}{4} = \frac{1}{2}$ on ckbd. Point to $\frac{1}{2}$ and say that this fraction is said to be reduced to lowest terms. Point out that numbers 1 and 2 are less than numbers 2 and 4, therefore making $\frac{1}{2}$ having smaller terms. Be sure that child under-

stands that even though terms are smaller, fraction size remains the same.

- Use **Fractional Circles** to show that $^2/_6$ is same as $^1/_3$.

- ▬ Point to $^2/_4$. Child finds greatest common factor for 2 and 4. Tell him that he has been finding g.c.f. for a reason. We can use g.c.f. to reduce fractions to lowest terms. **To reduce fractions to lowest terms, divide the numerator and denominator by the greatest common factor. The greatest common factor is the largest number that will evenly divide into the numerator and the denominator.** Div. both terms by 2 to get $^1/_2$. He should remember from demonstration that $^1/_2$ and $^2/_4$ name same amount and are equal fractions. You may want to point out that when we div. both terms by 2, we are div. by $^2/_2$ which is equal to 1. Child should understand that any number div. by 1 gives us same number.

  Continue to reduce fractions on ckbd by finding g.c.f.

- *Concept Cards* **80–84:** Show fronts of cards; child reduces by div. each term by 2. Emphasize again that fractions are equal.

- Read and discuss **box on p. 115.** Child does **Ex. 1–3.** As he does Ex. 2–3, he must check answers to be sure fractions are in lowest terms. Now that he has learned to reduce, he is responsible to make sure all fractional answers are reduced to lowest terms. You may want to work a few problems with him.

4. Review/Boardwork (9 min.) **Ex. 4–7**

Lesson
64

Preparation

1. Chalkboard:

    A   15; 20

    B $\frac{4}{10}$ $\frac{3}{15}$ $\frac{6}{8}$ $\frac{9}{12}$ $\frac{12}{15}$

    C $\frac{1}{3}$ of 15 $\frac{1}{3}$ of 22

2. *Arithmetic 4:* pp. 117–118

3. *Lesson 64 Speed Drill*

4. Visuals:

    - *Mixed Division Facts (Arith 4, p. 322)*
    - *Concept Cards 63, 80–84, and 85–89*
    - Fractional Circles

Teaching Procedure

1. Oral review drills (9 min.)

Processes (6 min.)
- Drill facts for all processes.
- *Mixed Division Facts*
- Mult./Div. Tables

Fractions (3 min.)
- *Concept Card* **63:** Review terms.
- **⬛ A** Child finds factors, common factors, and greatest common factor.
- *Concept Cards* **80–84:** He reduces by div. each term by 2. Remind him that g.c.f. is 2 for both numbers and that is why we reduce by div. by 2. Also emphasize that when we div. both terms by same number, we have not changed value of fraction.
- *Concept Cards* **85–89:** Show card **85.** He decides what g.c.f. is and then reduce fraction. Child reduces other cards by div. both terms by 3.

2. Written speed drill (3 min.) Time for 2 min. 30 sec.

3. Review reducing fractions. (9 min.)
- **Fractional Circles:** Show that $\frac{3}{6}$ and $\frac{2}{4}$ are both equal to $\frac{1}{2}$. Write $\frac{3}{6} = \frac{1}{2}$ on ckbd; child decides what both terms were div. by to get $\frac{1}{2}$.
- **⬛ B** Child decides what g.c.f. is for both terms and then reduces. Concept of reducing fractions may be difficult at first. With proper review and patience, he will master concept.
- Work **Ex. 1, p. 117** together. Child does **Ex. 2.**

4. Review fractional parts of whole numbers. (3 min.)
- **⬛ C** Work 2 problems together. He should give remainder in 2nd problem as a fraction.
- Child does **Ex. 3.**

5. Discuss story problems. (6 min.)
- Ask child to read **Ex. 4a.** Discuss it with him emphasizing clue word *average.* Have him work at ckbd. Have him read and work **b.** He should set up as a measurement equation.

6. Review/Boardwork (6 min.) **Ex. 5–7**

7. Homework **Ex. 8–9**

Preparation

Lesson
65

used 12/17

1. Chalkboard:
    $\frac{3}{6}$ $\frac{8}{10}$ $\frac{6}{15}$

2. *Arithmetic 4:* pp. 119–120

Lesson 65
(cont.)

3. *Lesson 65 Speed Drill*
4. Visuals:
   - *Process Flashcards*
   - *Concept Cards* 24–40, 43–44, 112–116, 118–129, 80–84, 85–89, and 90–94
   - *Rolling Ruler* (in.) *(Arith Chart 24)*

Teaching Procedure

1. **Oral review drills** (7 min.)

   Homework check

   Processes (4 min.)
   - *Flashcards:* Have child answer a few cards and then play *Giant Step*.
   - Mult./Div. Tables: Play *Just the Facts*.

   Measures (1 min.)
   - *Concept Cards* **24–40, 43–44, 112–116,** and **118–129**

   Fractions (2 min.)
   - *Concept Cards* **80–84:** Show front of 1 card; child gives g.c.f. and reduces to lowest terms. He reduces other cards by div. by 2. Remind him that reduced fraction is same size as original fraction. If fractions are not same size, it was not reduced correctly.
   - *Concept Cards* **85–89:** Show front of 1 card; child gives g.c.f. and reduces to lowest terms. He reduces other cards by div. by 3.
   - *Concept Cards* **90–94:** Show front of 1 card; child gives g.c.f. and reduces to lowest terms. He reduces other cards by div. by 4.

2. **Written speed drill** (6 min.) Time for 5 min.
   - Grade. Record as a speed drill/quiz grade. Count off 5 points for each incorrect answer.

3. **Review addition of fractions.** (6 min.)
   - Give him $3\frac{1}{2}$ min. to work **Ex. 1, p. 119.** Call out answers. Praise child who missed 2 or less.
   - ***Rolling Ruler:*** Discuss lines between inch lines. These lines represent a part of an inch. Show $\frac{1}{4}$, $\frac{2}{4}$, and $\frac{3}{4}$. He should understand that $\frac{2}{4}$ in. is same as $\frac{1}{2}$ in. Point out to him that any number between 0 and 1 must be a fraction of a number.
   - Work **Ex. 2** together.

4. **Discuss story problems.** (6 min.)
   - Work **Ex. 3** together.

5. **Review reducing fractions.** (6 min.)
   - ▪ Child explains as you reduce on ckbd. Have him repeat rule. **To reduce a fraction to lowest terms, div. both terms by the greatest common factor.**
   - Child does **Ex. 4.**

6. **Review/Boardwork** (6 min.) **Ex. 5–6**

7. **Homework Ex. 7–9** Child needs ruler with metric markings to complete Ex. 9.

Preparation

1. Chalkboard:

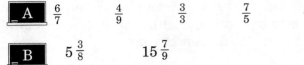

A $\frac{6}{7}$ $\frac{4}{9}$ $\frac{3}{3}$ $\frac{7}{5}$ $\frac{2}{2}$ $\frac{5}{6}$

B $5\frac{3}{8}$ $15\frac{7}{9}$

  $+7\frac{1}{8}$ $-4\frac{4}{9}$

2. *Arithmetic 4:* pp. 121–122

3. *Lesson 66 Speed Drill*

4. Visuals:
   - *Concept Cards* 24–40, 43–44, 112–116, 118–129, 80–84, 85–89, 90–94, 95–99, and 130–139
   - Fractional Circles

Teaching Procedure

1. **Oral review drills** (9 min.)

   Homework check

   Processes (4 min.)
   - Review facts for all processes.
   - Mult./Div. 11–12 Tables
   - Oral comb.

$8 \times 9 - 8 \div 8 \times 3 + 3 = 27$	$19 - 5 + 6 \div 10 \times 6 \times 12 = 144$
$56 \div 7 \times 5 \div 4 \times 3 - 3 = 27$	$200 + 50 - 150 \div 10 \times 5 = 50$
$16 + 4 \div 4 + 3 \div 2 \times 9 = 36$	$72 \div 9 \times 5 \div 10 + 3 \times 9 = 63$
$11 - 7 \times 9 + 8 \div 11 - 2 = 2$	$80 + 4 \div 7 + 3 - 7 + 2 \times 12 = 120$
$27 \div 3 \times 5 + 4 \div 7 \times 3 = 21$	$32 \times 2 \div 8 \times 10 + 20 + 500 = 600$

   Measures (2 min.)
   - *Concept Cards* **24–40, 43–44, 112–116,** and **118–129**

   Fractions (3 min.)
   - Review rule for reducing fractions to lowest terms.
   - *Concept Cards* **80–84:** Child reduces by div. by 2.
   - *Concept Cards* **85–89:** Child reduces by div. by 3.
   - *Concept Cards* **90–94:** Child reduces by div. by 4.
   - *Concept Cards* **95–99:** Show front of 1 card; child finds g.c.f. for both terms. He reduces by div. by 5.

2. **Written speed drill** (4 min.) Time for 3 min.

3. **Introduce proper and improper fractions.** (9 min.)
   - **Fractional Circles:** Show 1 whole and 1 half. Introduce improper fractions using a story similar to this one. *Mr. Taber ate a whole pizza and a half pizza. How many halves did he eat?* Write $^2/_2 + {}^1/_2 = {}^3/_2$ on ckbd. Point to $^1/_2$. $^1/_2$ is a proper fraction because numerator is less than denominator. **A**

Lesson 66
(cont.)

proper fraction is a fraction having a numerator that is less than the denominator. Point to ²/₂ and ³/₂. Ask students if ²/₂ and ³/₂ are proper fractions according to definition. ²/₂ and ³/₂ are improper fractions because numerator is equal to or greater than denominator. **An improper fraction is a fraction having a numerator that is equal to or greater than the denominator.**

- ☐ A ☐ Point to each fraction; child stands if improper.
- Send him to ckbd to write an improper fraction.
- *Concept Cards* **80–99** and **130–139:** Put cards in random order. Show backs of cards **80–99** and fronts of cards **130–139.** He responds with proper or improper.
- Read and discuss **box on p. 121.** Child does **Ex. 1–2.**

4. Review adding and subtracting fractions. (9 min.)

- ☐ B ☐ Child explains how to work 2 problems on ckbd. Be sure he includes reducing answers to lowest terms.
- Child does **Ex. 3.** Give help as needed.

5. Review/Boardwork (6 min.) **Ex. 4–6**

6. Homework **Ex. 7–8** Child needs to have a ruler in arithmetic tomorrow.

Lesson

67

Preparation

1. Chalkboard:

☐ A ☐ $12 \div 3 = 4$ $20 \div 2 = 10$

☐ B ☐ $\frac{3}{5}$ $\frac{6}{6}$ $\frac{7}{4}$ $\frac{2}{4}$ $\frac{8}{7}$

2. *Arithmetic 4:* pp. 123–124

3. *Lesson 67 Quiz*

4. Visuals:

- *Process Flashcards*
- *Concept Cards* 80–84, 85–89, 90–94, 95–99, 100–104, and 130–139
- coins
- play bills
- ruler

Teaching Procedure

1. Oral review drills (9 min.)

Homework check

Processes (4 min.)

- *Flashcards:* Play a game after child is warmed up.
- Mult./Div. Tables: Have him recite tables.

Fractions (3 min.)

- *Concept Cards* **80–84:** Child reduces by div. by 2.
- *Concept Cards* **85–89:** Child reduces by div. by 3.

- *Concept Cards* **90–94:** Child reduces by div. by 4.
- *Concept Cards* **95–99:** Child reduces by div. by 5.
- *Concept Cards* **100–104:** Show front of 1 card; child decides what to div. each term by to reduce to lowest terms. He reduces by div. by 6.

Money (2 min.)

- Coins/play bills: Have your child make change from $10. Tell price of item such as $2.26. He uses coins and play bills to count back change.

2. Quiz 7 (9 min.)

3. Introduce fraction bar. (6 min.)

- **_A_** Point to 1st problem. He gives another way to express this div. fact. ($3\overline{)12}$) Tell him that since he has learned about fractions, he can express division another way. Write $^{12}/_3$ on ckbd and explain this can also be read 12 div. by 3. Point to dividing bar and explain that bar can be called a fraction bar and that it means division.

  Point to 2nd problem. Child gives 2 other ways to express this div. problem.
- Read and discuss **box on p. 123.** Child does **Ex. 1–2.**

4. Review improper fractions. (3 min.)

- *Concept Cards* **80–104** and **130–139:** Put cards in random order. Show backs of cards **80–104** and fronts of cards **130–139.** Child stands if fraction is improper.

- **_B_** Point to each fraction. He claps if fraction is proper.

- Child does **Ex. 3.**

5. Discuss story problem. (3 min.)

- Child does **Ex. 4.**

6. Review/Boardwork (6 min.) **Ex. 5–9**

Preparation

Lesson 68

1. Chalkboard:

   _A_ $\frac{7}{3}$ $\frac{5}{2}$ $\frac{10}{5}$ $\frac{11}{5}$

   _B_ $57\frac{3}{8}$

         $16\frac{1}{8}$

      $+\ 73\frac{2}{8}$

   _C_ $41\overline{)163}$ $61\overline{)120}$

2. *Arithmetic 4:* pp. 125–126
3. *Lesson 68 Speed Drill*

4. Visuals:
   - *Process Flashcards*
   - *Mixed Addition Facts (Arith 4, p. 311)*
   - *Concept Cards 124–129, 80–104, and 130–139*

Teaching Procedure

1. **Oral review drills** (6 min.)

   Processes (3 min.)
   - Mult./Div. Tables
   - *Flashcards:* Have a brisk review.
   - *Mixed Addition Facts*: Point to problems in random order. Encourage your child to build speed and accuracy during these drills. The faster he is during drill time, the faster he will be when working worksheet.

   Measures (1 min.)
   - *Concept Cards* **124–129:** Review metric prefixes.

   Fractions (2 min.)
   - *Concept Cards* **80–104:** Mix up cards; child reduces to lowest terms.

2. **Written speed drill** (3 min.) Time for 2 min.

3. **Introduce changing improper fractions to whole or mixed numbers.** (9 min.)
   - Point to 1st problem. Child tells if proper or improper. Point to fraction bar in 1st problem. Have him explain what process fraction bar indicates. Tell him that just as we must reduce fractions to lowest terms, we must change improper fractions to whole numbers or mixed numbers. Show him that we do this by dividing numerator by denominator just as fraction bar tells us to do. Div. and show him how $7/3$ equals $2\frac{1}{3}$. Do next problem for him. Have him explain how to do last 2 problems.
   - *Concept Cards* **130–139:** Show fronts of cards; child changes to whole or mixed numbers.
   - Read and discuss **box on p. 125.** Child does **Ex. 1–3.** You may need to work a few in Ex. 3 on ckbd as he works in text.

4. **Review adding fractions.** (6 min.)
   - **B** Work as child explains.
   - Child does **Ex. 4.** Be sure he is reducing answer fractions.

5. **Review division.** (9 min.)
   - **C** Work 1st problem as child watches. We usually say *How many 4s in 16?* but this time 41 will not go 4 times. We then drop to next lower number. We find 41 will go 3 times into 163. Check answer.

   Work 2nd problem in same manner. Teach child to evaluate dividend and divisor before choosing a quotient. Sometimes a wrong number is chosen, but a wise student quickly finds mistake, erases wrong quotient, and chooses correct quotient. Emphasize step of comparing. He should catch mistakes when he has chosen a wrong quotient.

- Child does **Ex. 5.** You may want to work a few problems with him.

6. **Review/Boardwork** (3 min.) **Ex. 6–9** Notice that Ex. 8–9 are Extra Practice and are therefore optional.

wed

Lesson
69

Preparation

1. Chalkboard:

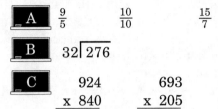

A $\frac{9}{5}$ $\frac{10}{10}$ $\frac{15}{7}$

B $32\overline{)276}$

C

$$924 \times 840 \qquad 693 \times 205$$

2. *Arithmetic 4:* pp. 127–128

3. *Lesson 69 Speed Drill*

4. Visuals:
   - *Process Flashcards*
   - *Mixed Facts chart* (refer to lesson 49)
   - *Concept Cards* 1–15 and 130–139

Teaching Procedure

1. **Oral review drills** (7 min.)

   Processes (5 min.)
   - *Flashcards:* Let child answer. After he gets warmed up, let him play a game.
   - Mult./Div. Tables
   - *Mixed Facts Chart*

   Place value (2 min.)
   - *Concept Cards* **1–15:** He reads cards and gives value of circled digits.

2. **Written speed drill** (6 min.) Time for 5 min.
   - Grade. Record as a speed drill/quiz grade. Count off 3 points for each incorrect answer.

3. **Review improper fractions.** (6 min.)
   - *Concept Cards* **130–139:** Review rule for changing improper fraction to whole or mixed numbers. Show fronts of cards; he changes to whole or mixed numbers.
   - A Send child to ckbd to change improper fractions.
   - Child does **Ex. 1, p. 127.**

Lesson 69
(cont.)

4. **Review division.** (6 min.)

-  **B** Work problem for him.

- Child does **Ex. 2.** You may want to do a couple problems with him.

5. **Introduce shortcuts in multiplication.** (6 min.)

-  **C** Work 1st problem and show how 0 can be dropped from 2nd factor into partial product. Then mult. by 4 as usual. This is a shortcut because it saves writing a partial product of just 0s. Child must be very careful when he mult. by 8 that he begins in hundreds' place.

  Work 2nd problem and show that we mult. by 5 as usual and then move over 2 places and mult. by 2. Again this saves writing a partial product of just 0s. Have him notice that every digit is in proper place. When we mult. by 2 in hundreds' place, we began in hundreds' place in partial product.

  Remind him that partial product always begins directly underneath number being used in 2nd factor.

- Child does **Ex. 3.** If necessary, work a couple problems with him.

6. **Review/Boardwork** (6 min.) **Ex. 4–6**

7. **Homework Ex. 7–9**

Thurs

Lesson 70

Preparation

1. Chalkboard:

    $32\overline{)184}$

2. *Arithmetic 4:* pp. 129–130

3. *Lesson 70 Speed Drill*

4. Visuals:

   - *Process Flashcards*
   - *Mixed Subtraction Facts (Arith 4, p. 316)*
   - *Concept Cards 24–40, 43–44, 112–116, 118–129, 80–104, and 130–139*
   - *Metric Units of Weight (Arith Chart 19)*

Teaching Procedure

1. **Oral review drills** (9 min.)

   Homework check

   Processes (5 min.)

   - *Div. Cards:* Challenge child to mult. quotients by 2.
   - *Flashcards:* Let him answer and then play *Four Corners.*
   - Mult./Div. Tables

- *Mixed Subtraction Facts*
- Oral comb.

   9 x 9 – 1 ÷ 8 + 90 = *100*   6 x 9 + 3 – 4 + 9 + 1 ÷ 7 x 8 = *72*

   6 x 5 + 6 ÷ 9 x 8 = *32*   8 x 8 – 1 ÷ 9 x 10 + 20 + 10 = *100*

   12 x 12 + 2 + 30 – 6 = *170*   10 – 6 + 80 – 4 ÷ 8 + 9 – 4 = *15*

   20 x 2 – 4 ÷ 9 + 60 ÷ 8 = *8*   50 + 50 ÷ 25 + 6 – 5 = *5*

   20 + 20 + 40 – 30 + 90 + 40 – 60 = *120*

   4 x 9 – 1 ÷ 7 + 10 + 10 ÷ 5 x 20 = *100*

Measures (2 min.)
- *Concept Cards* **24–40, 43–44, 112–116,** and **118–129**

Fractions (2 min.)
- *Concept Cards* **80–104:** Show in mixed-up order; he reduces to lowest terms.
- *Concept Cards* **130–139:** Review rule for changing improper fractions. Show fronts of cards; he changes to whole or mixed numbers.

2. **Written speed drill** (4 min.) Time for 3 min.

3. **Introduce metric units of weight.** (9 min.)
   - *Chart* 19: **A gram is the basic unit of weight (mass) in metric system. It is a very small unit. Many items in the grocery store are marked in both ounces and grams. The kilogram is frequently used. It is about 2 lb. 3 oz. The metric ton is used for weighing heavier objects, such as a car or truck. The same prefixes are used with gram as with meter.** Discuss chart and review units. If he knows metric prefixes, he should have little trouble.
   - Read and discuss **box on p. 129.** Child does **Ex. 1–3.**

4. **Review division.** (6 min.)
   - Work problem as child watches. Make sure he understands.
   - Child does **Ex. 4.**

5. **Review/Boardwork** (9 min.) **Ex. 5–7**

6. **Homework Ex. 8–9**

Fri

Preparation

1. Chalkboard:

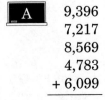

A	9,396	B	42⟌2,483	C	943
	7,217				x 806
	8,569				
	4,783				
	+ 6,099				

2. *Arithmetic 4:* pp. 131–132

3. *Lesson 71 Speed Drill*

4. *Visuals:*

- *Process Flashcards*
- *1–100 Chart (Arith Chart 23)*
- *Calculator (Arith Chart 20)*
- *Concept Cards* 24–40, 43–47, 112–116, 118–129, 80–104, and 130–139
- *Metric Units of Length (Arith Chart 17)*
- *Metric Units of Weight (Arith Chart 19)*

Teaching Procedure

1. Oral review drills (9 min.)

Homework check

Processes (6 min.)

- Mult./Div. Tables

> **Note:** Sometimes child says tables. You may want to have child have a certain amount of time to write a table. Child may write the table on ckbd. No matter what method you use for practicing tables, be sure child is getting the most from the drill.

- *Flashcards:* Have child answer and then play *Marching around Jericho.* Have your child go to one corner of the room. Show card. When he answers correctly, he gets to move to next corner. Each time he gets back to beginning corner, he has *marched around Jericho.*
- *1–100 Chart:* Point to numbers; child adds or subt. number that you say.
- *1–100 Chart:* He counts by 6 from 6 to 72 as you point to numbers on chart.
- See les. 14 for directions for fast oral addition.
- *Calculator:* Child presses keys to show answers. *What number must be added to 1,690 to make 1,890?* **200** *What number must be subtracted from 1,690 to make 1,670?* **20**

Measures (1 min.)

- *Concept Cards* **24–40, 43–47, 112–116,** and **118–129**

Fractions (2 min.)

- *Concept Cards* **80–104:** He reduces to lowest terms.
- *Concept Cards* **130–139:** He changes to whole or mixed numbers.

2. Written speed drill (3 min.) Time for 2 min.

3. Review metric system. (6 min.)

- ***Concept Cards* 124–129:** Review prefixes.
- ***Arith Charts* 17** and **19:** Review metric units of length and weight. Keep charts displayed so he can study during free times.

- Child does **Ex. 1–2, p. 131.**

4. Review division. (6 min.)

- **[B]** He works on paper as you work on ckbd.
- Child does **Ex. 3.**

5. Review multiplication with zeros. (3 min.)

- **[C]** Work problem on ckbd. Watch child closely when explaining at ckbd. He needs to be attentive, not working on worksheets. Watch his face to see if he appears to understand the concept and processes of problem you are teaching.
- Child does **Ex. 4.**

6. Review/Boardwork (9 min.) **Ex. 5–7**

7. Homework Ex. 8–10

Mon

Lesson
72

Preparation

Test 7, pp. 57–58 from *Student Tests and Speed Drills*

Teaching Procedure

1. Homework check

2. Administer test.

Notice that space has been allowed on this test for child to work story problems.

Tues

Lesson
73

Preparation

1. Chalkboard:

[A]
```
  9,783
  4,682
  7,886
  8,059
+ 9,328
_____
```

[B]

$$\begin{array}{r} \frac{5}{12} \\ \frac{7}{12} \\ + \frac{3}{12} \\ \hline \end{array} \qquad \begin{array}{r} 3\frac{2}{7} \\ 8\frac{5}{7} \\ + 7\frac{3}{7} \\ \hline \end{array}$$

[C] $43\overline{)2,817}$

2. *Arithmetic 4:* pp. 133–134
3. *Lesson 73 Speed Drill*
4. Visuals:
   - Mixed Facts Chart (see lesson 49)
   - *Concept Cards* 24–40, 43–47, 112–116, 118–129, 80–104, and 130–139

Teaching Procedure

1. **Oral review drills** (6 min.)

   Processes (3 min.)
   - Mult./Div. Tables
   - *Mixed Facts Chart*
   - ▨ A ▨ Use standard procedure.

   Measures (1 min.)
   - *Concept Cards* **24–40, 43–47, 112–116,** and **118–129**

   Fractions (2 min.)
   - *Concept Cards* **80–104:** Child reduces to lowest terms.
   - *Concept Cards* **130–139:** Child changes to whole or mixed numbers.

2. **Written speed drill** (4 min.) Time for 3 min.

3. **Introduce sums containing improper fractions.** (12 min.)

   - ▨ B ▨ Work 1st problem with child. He looks at sum of $^{15}/_{12}$ and decides if proper or improper. Since it is improper, numerator must be div. by denominator to change to the mixed number $1^3/_{12}$. He looks at $^3/_{12}$ and decides if reduced to lowest terms. Since it is not reduced, div. both terms by g.c.f. to reduce to $^1/_4$. Sum in correct terms is $1^1/_4$. Child is now responsible to make sure there are no improper fractions or fractions that are not reduced to lowest terms in sums.

     Use same procedure to work 2nd problem. This one is a little different since we are adding mixed numbers. When improper fraction is changed to a mixed number, whole number part must be added to whole number that is in sum already.

   - Read and discuss **box on p. 133.** Child does **Ex. 1–2.** You may want to work a few problems in Ex. 2 with him.

4. **Review division.** (9 min.)

   - ▨ C ▨ Inspect division problem before beginning. How many 4s are in 28? Since it goes exactly 7 times, check mentally to see if there is any carrying when we mult. 7 times 3. Since there is, it is impossible for 43 to go 7 times into 281. Try next lower number, which is 6. Continue to work problem. Encourage child to inspect his div. problems before working. Inspection can eliminate much erasing. He should mentally test quotient before putting anything on paper. Stress importance of being a good thinker while div.

   - Child does **Ex. 3.**

5. **Review/Boardwork** (6 min.) **Ex. 4–6**

Preparation

1. Chalkboard:

A
$$
\begin{array}{r}
54{,}895 \\
82{,}620 \\
67{,}718 \\
10{,}975 \\
+\ 35{,}885 \\
\end{array}
$$

B $\frac{7}{14}$ $\frac{6}{16}$ $\frac{8}{24}$

C $31\overline{)927}$

2. *Arithmetic 4:* pp. 135–136

3. *Lesson 74 Speed Drill*

4. Visuals:
   - *Concept Cards* 80–104, 130–139, 24–40, 43–47, 112–116, and 41–42
   - *English Measures of Capacity (Arith Charts* 9 and 11)

Teaching Procedure

1. **Oral review drills** (5 min.)

   Processes (1 min.)
   - **A** Use standard procedure.

   Fractions (2 min.)
   - *Concept Cards* **80–104:** Child reduces to lowest terms.
   - *Concept Cards* **130–139:** He changes to whole or mixed numbers.

   Measures (2 min.)
   - *Concept Cards* **24–40, 43–47,** and **112–116:** Let child answer to get warmed up and then play *Capture the Card.*

2. **Written speed drill** (6 min.) Time for 5 min.
   - Grade. Record as a speed drill/quiz grade. Count off 10 points for each incorrect answer.

3. **Introduce dry measures of capacity.** (6 min.)
   - *Arith Charts* **9** and **11:** Review liquid measures of capacity and introduce dry measures of capacity. Dry measures are not as common now as in the past, but they are still used in places such as farmers' markets. In dry measures, 2 pints still equals 1 quart, and 4 quarts equals 1 gallon. If possible have a container the size of a peck and another the size of a bushel to demonstrate size. A round laundry basket is good for bushel. A small bathroom trash basket is about the size of a peck.
   - *Concept Cards* **41–42:** Review measures.
   - Read and discuss **box on p. 135.** Child answers **Ex. 1.**

Lesson 74
(cont.)

4. **Review reducing fractions.** (3 min.)
   - *Concept Cards* **80–104:** Child reduces.
   - He goes to ckbd and reduces.
   - Child does **Ex. 2.**

5. **Review division.** (6 min.)
   - C Work problem on ckbd.
   - Child does **Ex. 3.**

6. **Discuss story problems.** (6 min.)
   - Child does **Ex. 4.**

7. **Review/Boardwork** (6 min.) **Ex. 5–7**

8. **Homework Ex. 8–9**

Thurs

Lesson
75

Preparation

1. Chalkboard:

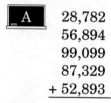

   A 28,782
      56,894
      99,099
      87,329
    + 52,893

   B $\frac{3}{4}$ $\frac{7}{8}$ $\frac{2}{5}$

   C $\frac{2}{3} = \frac{}{9}$ $\frac{5}{6} = \frac{}{12}$

2. *Arithmetic 4:* pp. 137–138

3. *Lesson 75 Speed Drill*

4. Visuals:
   - *Process Flashcards*
   - *1–100 Chart (Arith Chart 23)*
   - *Concept Cards 24–47, 112–116, 118–129, 80–104 and 130–139*
   - Fractional Circles

Teaching Procedure

1. **Oral review drills** (9 min.)

   Homework check

   Processes (6 min.)
   - *Flashcards:* Have child answer a few cards and then play *Four Corners.*
   - Mult./Div. Tables
   - *1–100 Chart:* He counts by 7s from 7 to 84 as you point to numbers.

- ▬ A ▬ Use standard procedure.
- Oral comb.

  9 x 7 + 3 ÷ 6 x 10 + 5 = *115*   72 ÷ 8 x 8 − 1 = *71*

  5 x 6 − 5 ÷ 5 x 2 x 10 = *100*   15 ÷ 5 x 9 − 3 + 1 x 4 = *100*

  100 ÷ 2 x 10 ÷ 2 = *250*   15 − 13 x 9 ÷ 6 x 30 = *90*

  6 x 9 + 6 = *60*   9 x 8 ÷ 9 x 8 + 6 ÷ 10 x 7 + 1 = *50*

Measures (1 min.)
- *Concept Cards* **24–47, 112–116,** and **118–129:** Especially review dry measures of capacity.

Fractions (2 min.)
- *Concept Cards* **80–104** and **130–139:** Show backs of cards **80–104** and fronts of cards **130–139.** He stands if proper and remains seated if improper.
- *Concept Cards* **130–139:** He changes to whole or mixed numbers.

2. **Written speed drill** (3 min.) Time for 2 min.

3. **Introduce equivalent fractions.** (12 min.)
- **Fractional Circles:** Show ½ and ²/₄. Write ½ and ²/₄ on ckbd. Ask child if they are equal fractions. Point to ²/₄. This fraction is in greater terms. Since we div. both terms by same number to get lower terms, what do you think we do to get greater terms? He should see that he mult. both terms by same number.
- *Concept Cards* **80–84:** Show backs of cards. He mult. both terms by 2 to make fraction with greater terms. Show front of cards to show him he is right.
- ▬ B ▬ He tells what he wants to mult. each term by to make fraction with greater terms.
- ▬ C ▬ Point to missing term in 1st problem. Tell your child that since 1 term in fraction with greater terms is already given, we cannot decide to mult. by just any number. We must decide what denominator in 1st fraction was mult. by to get denominator in 2nd fraction. We know that 3 times 3 is 9, so it was mult. by 3. We must mult. numerator of 1st fraction by 3 as well. Mult. 2 times 3 to get 6. Write 6 in place of missing term to make equal fractions. Use Fractional Circles to prove that ²/₃ equals ⁶/₉.

  Use same procedure to work 2nd problem. He should decide what 6 was mult. by to get 12. He then must mult. numerator of 1st fraction by same number.
- Read and discuss **box on p. 137.** Work **Ex. 1** together. If fractions are =, both terms in 1st fraction were mult. by same number. Fractions are if both terms in 1st fraction were not mult. by same number as in *b*. Show him how to write an unequal sign by making an equal sign and drawing a slanted line through it. You may want to have him practice making sign at ckbd to make sure he draws slanted line in right

Lesson 75
(cont.)

direction. Child does **Ex. 2–3.** You may want to work a few with him.

4. **Review/Boardwork** (12 min.) **Ex. 4–8**

5. **Homework Ex. 9–10**

Lesson
76

Fri

Preparation

1. Chalkboard:

 A
90,329
66,779
28,722
76,695
+ 14,339

B
2	5
3	6
4	10

C $\frac{5}{6} = \frac{}{12}$ $\frac{2}{5} = \frac{}{25}$

2. *Arithmetic 4:* pp. 139–140

3. *Lesson 76 Speed Drill*

4. Visuals:
   - Mixed Facts Chart (see lesson 49)
   - *Process Flashcards*
   - *1–100 Chart (Arith Chart 23)*
   - *Concept Cards 24–47, 112–116, 118–129, and 80–104*
   - *101–200 Chart (Arith Chart 25)*

Teaching Procedure

1. **Oral review drills** (7 min.)

   Homework check

   Processes (5 min.)
   - A Use standard procedure.
   - *Mixed Facts Chart*
   - *Flashcards:* Have child answer. Then play a favorite game.
   - *1–100 Chart:* He counts by 8s from 8 to 96 as you point to numbers on chart. If time permits count by other numbers. These counting exercises help him recognize multiples.

   Measures (1 min.)
   - *Concept Cards* **24–47, 112–116,** and **118–129:** Especially review dry measures of capacity.

   Fractions (1 min.)
   - *Concept Cards* **80–104:** He reduces to lowest terms.

2. **Written speed drill** (6 min.) Time for 5 min.

- Grade. Record as a speed drill/quiz grade. Count off 5 points for each incorrect answer.

3. **Introduce least common multiples.** (12 min.)
   - Have child say 9 Multiplication Table. He should stand as he says each product. Tell him that numbers he stood to say are called multiples of 9.
   - *1–100/101–200 Charts:* Have child count by 9s from 9 to 108 as you point to number on counting charts. Remind him that all numbers counted are multiples of 9. Show numbers on charts as he counts by 10s from 10 to 120. Tell child he just said multiples of 10. Have him come to counting chart and point to multiples of 5. Child should point to numbers that would be said if we counted by 5s.
   - **B** Point to 1st group of 3 numbers. Child lists a few multiples of each number in order. For 2, he lists 2, 4, 6, 8, 10, 12, etc. Put 3 dots after last listed multiple to show that they continue forever. For 3, list 3, 6, 9, 12, etc. For 4, list 4, 8, 12, 16, etc. Look at 3 lists of multiples. Child identifies least common multiple. 12 is least number that is common to all 3 lists of multiples.

   Repeat for 2nd list of 3 numbers. (30 is least common multiple.)
   - Read and discuss **box on p. 139.** Child does **Ex. 1–2.** You may want to work together.

4. **Review equal fractions.** (3 min.)
   - **C** Work 2 problems for child on ckbd. Remind him to find missing factor so he can multiply numerator by that number.
   - Child does **Ex. 3.** Give help as needed.

5. **Review/Boardwork** (9 min.) **Ex. 4–6**

6. **Homework   Ex. 7–8** Child needs to have a ruler in arithmetic tomorrow.

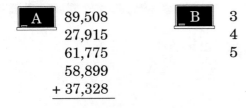

Lesson

77

Preparation

1. Chalkboard:

A 89,508	**B** 3
27,915	4
61,775	5
58,899	
+ 37,328	

2. *Arithmetic 4:* pp. 141–142

3. *Lesson 77 Quiz*

4. Visuals:
   - *Process Flashcards*
   - *1–100/101–200 Charts*   • coins
      (Arith Charts 23 and 25)   • play bills
   - *Concept Cards* 80–104 and   • ruler
      130–139

Teaching Procedure

1. Oral review drills (9 min.)

Homework check

Processes (4 min.)
   - *Flashcards:* Play a game after child is warmed up.
   - *1–100/101–200 Charts:* He counts by 7s from 7 to 84, by 8s from 8 to 96, and by 9s from 9 to 108. Either parent or child points to numbers on charts.
   - **A** Use standard procedure.
   - Mult./Div. Tables: Have him recite tables.

Fractions (3 min.)
   - *Concept Cards* **80–104:** Child reduces to lowest terms.
   - *Concept Cards* **130–139:** He changes to whole or mixed numbers.

Money (2 min.)
   - Coins/play bills: Have child make change from $20. Tell price of item such as $12.26. He uses coins and play bills to count back change.

2. Quiz 8 (9 min.)

3. Review least common multiple. (6 min.)
   - **B** Child lists several multiples in order. Then he finds least common multiple.
   - Child does **Ex. 1–2, p. 141.**

4. Review/Boardwork (12 min.) **Ex. 3–12** Child needs ruler to do Ex. 12.

Lesson 78

Preparation

1. Chalkboard:

   A   34,289
            99,616
            42,382
            68,559
          + 74,718

B $\frac{3}{4} = \frac{}{8}$ $\frac{2}{7} = \frac{}{14}$ $\frac{6}{9} = \frac{}{18}$ $\frac{4}{8} = \frac{}{24}$ $\frac{3}{5} = \frac{6}{}$

C 5   2
       8   6
              12

2. *Arithmetic 4:* pp. 143–144

3. *Lesson 78 Speed Drill*

4. Visuals:
   - *Process Flashcards*
   - *Mixed Division Facts (Arith 4, p. 322)*
   - story problem clue words flashcards (optional from les. 4)
   - *Concept Cards* 80–104, 130–139, 24–47, and 112–116

Teaching Procedure

1. Oral review drills (9 min.)

   Processes (4 min.)
   - Mult./Div. 4–9 Tables
   - *Flashcards:* Have a brisk review.
   - **A** Use standard procedure.
   - *Mixed Division Facts*

   Story problems (1 min.)
   - Story problem clue words flashcards

   Fractions (3 min.)
   - *Concept Cards* **80–104:** Child reduces to lowest terms.
   - *Concept Cards* **130–139:** Child changes to whole or mixed numbers.
   - **B** Child gives missing term. Tell him that last problem is no harder. He must decide what 1st numerator was mult. by to get 2nd numerator. He then mult. denominator by same number.

   Measures (1 min.)
   - *Concept Cards* **24–47** and **112–116**

2. Written speed drill (4 min.) Time for 3 min.

3. Review least common multiples. (9 min.)
   - Child counts by 11s from 11 to 132. He should know that numbers that he counted are multiples of 11.
   - **C** Child lists several multiples in order for 1st group of numbers. He then finds least common multiple (40). Repeat by having him find least common multiple (12) for 2nd group of numbers.
   - Child does **Ex. 1–2, p. 143.** Check child's work.

4. Discuss story problems. (6 min.)
   - Child does **Ex. 3.**

5. Review/Boardwork (9 min.) **Ex. 4–9**

Lesson
79

Preparation

1. Chalkboard:

A
89,371
29,804
78,278
14,668
+ 64,847

B
$\frac{1}{11}$ of 66 = $\frac{1}{9}$ of 72 = $\frac{1}{7}$ of 84 =

$\frac{1}{11}$ of 22 = $\frac{1}{7}$ of 50 = $\frac{1}{5}$ of 29 =

C
$\frac{1}{4}$ $\frac{1}{3}$

$\frac{1}{6}$ $\frac{1}{5}$

                         $\frac{1}{6}$

2. *Arithmetic 4:* pp. 145–146
3. *Lesson 79 Speed Drill*
4. Visuals:
   - *Process Flashcards*
   - *Concept Cards 80–104*

Teaching Procedure

1. Oral review drills (9 min.)

Processes (6 min.)
- *Flashcards:* Let child answer. After he gets warmed up, play *Conquer the Cards.* Show cards to child. When he answers correctly, he *conquered the card.* Give card to him.
- Mult./Div. Tables
- **A** Use standard procedure.
- Child stands if statement is sensible. He remains seated if statement does not make sense. Read statement and have him wait to respond until you indicate when to respond. Give him a few seconds to think about each statement before he responds.

Mark traveled for 8 hours. He traveled for $\frac{1}{3}$ of a day.

At 1:00 the temperature was 10°. The temperature rose 3° each hour for the next 4 hours. At 4:00 the temperature was 1°.

Janet saved $\frac{1}{2}$ of her allowance. Her allowance is $3.00. She saved $1.50.

William ran for 30 minutes. He ran a distance of 4,000 cm.

Mrs. Peters made a gallon of punch. She made 4 quarts of punch.

Fractions (3 min.)

- **B** Send child to ckbd to write answers. If there is a remainder, he should write as a fraction.
- *Concept Cards* **80–104:** Child reduces to lowest terms.
- Call out these fractions; he should reduce to lowest terms.

  $\frac{4}{8}$ $\frac{6}{8}$ $\frac{3}{6}$ $\frac{12}{26}$ $\frac{3}{9}$ $\frac{4}{12}$

2. **Written speed drill** (4 min.) Time for 3 min.

3. **Introduce finding the least common denominator.** (15 min.)
   - Child counts by 6s from 6 to 72. He should recognize that he gave multiples of 6.
   - **C** Child gives in order several multiples for denominators of 4 and 6. He then finds least common multiple. **The least common multiple for 2 or more denominators is called the least common denominator.** If he knows how to find least common multiple, finding least common denominator is the same.

     Find least common denominator for 2nd group of fractions. (30)
   - Read and discuss **box on p. 145.** Child does **Ex. 1–2.** You may want to do a few together.

4. **Review/Boardwork** (9 min.) **Ex. 3–5**

5. **Homework Ex. 6–8**

Fri

Preparation

Lesson 80

1. Chalkboard:

   A
   ```
     27,920
     86,559
     75,382
     28,177
   + 57,295
   ```

   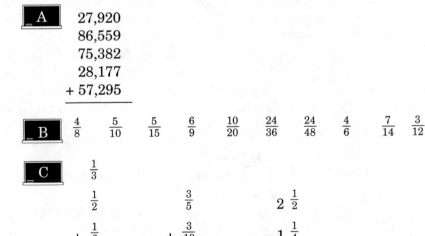

   B $\frac{4}{8}$ $\frac{5}{10}$ $\frac{5}{15}$ $\frac{6}{9}$ $\frac{10}{20}$ $\frac{24}{36}$ $\frac{24}{48}$ $\frac{4}{6}$ $\frac{7}{14}$ $\frac{3}{12}$

   C $\frac{1}{3}$

   $\frac{1}{2}$ $\frac{3}{5}$ $2\frac{1}{2}$

   $+\frac{1}{6}$ $+\frac{3}{10}$ $-1\frac{1}{4}$

2. *Arithmetic 4:* pp. 147–148

3. *Lesson 80 Speed Drill*

4. Visuals:
   - *Process Flashcards*
   - *Mixed Subtraction Facts (Arith 4, p. 316)*

- *Place Value (Arith Chart 2)*
- *Concept Cards* 24–47 and 112–116

Teaching Procedure

1. **Oral review drills** (9 min.)

   Homework check

   Processes (4 min.)
   - *Flashcards:* Let child answer and then play *Four Corners.*
   - Mult./Div. Tables
   - [A] Use standard procedure.
   - *Mixed Subtraction Facts*

   Place value (1 min.)
   - *Arith Chart* **2**

   Measures (2 min.)
   - *Concept Cards* **24–47** and **112–116**

   Fractions (2 min.)
   - [B] Child responds with reduced fraction as you point to each.

2. **Written speed drill** (4 min.) Time for 3 min.

3. **Introduce addition and subtraction of fractions with uncommon denominators.** (15 min.)

   - [C] Point to 1st problem. Have child read denominators and ask if we have ever added fractions that did not have same number for denominators. **We must have a common denominator before we can add or subtract fractions.** Show him how to use what he learned yesterday to find common denominator. He lists multiples of 3, 2, and 6 and find the least common multiple, which is the same as least common denominator.

     $$\frac{1}{3} = \frac{2}{6}$$
     $$\frac{1}{2} = \frac{3}{6}$$
     $$+\,\frac{1}{6} = +\,\frac{1}{6}$$
     $$\frac{6}{6} = 1$$

     Step 1: Write = to right of each addend. Draw a fraction bar and write the least common denominator for each new fraction.

     Step 2: Make equal fractions for each addend, using least common denominator. Since the last addend $\frac{1}{6}$ has the correct denominator, just rewrite as $\frac{1}{6}$.

     Step 3: Add as usual, since we have a common denominator.

     Step 4: Change the improper fraction to whole number.

     Work other 2 problems step by step for him.

   - Read and discuss **box on p. 147.** Child does **Ex. 1–4.** Work several problems with him. This is a complicated concept and may take him a few days to grasp.

4. **Review/Boardwork** (9 min.) **Ex. 5–8**

5. **Homework Ex. 9–10**

Preparation

1. Chalkboard:

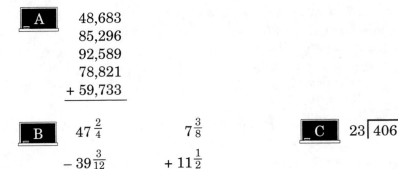

A
48,683
85,296
92,589
78,821
+ 59,733

B $47\frac{2}{4}$ $7\frac{3}{8}$ C $23\overline{)406}$

$- 39\frac{3}{12}$ $+ 11\frac{1}{2}$

2. *Arithmetic 4:* pp. 149–150

3. *Lesson 81 Speed Drill*

4. Visuals:
   - *Calculator (Arith Chart 20)*
   - *Concept Cards* 24–47, 112–116, 118–129, and 80–104

Teaching Procedure

1. Oral review drills (9 min.)

Homework check

Processes (4 min.)
   - Mult./Div. Tables
   - Review facts for all processes.
   - A Use standard procedure.
   - *Calculator:* Child presses keys to show answers. Ask him what number must be added to 2,306 to make 2,506. (200) Ask him what number must be subtracted from 3,409 to make 3,389. (20)

Measures (3 min.)
   - *Concept Cards* **24–47, 112–116,** and **118–129**
   - Call out these measures; he responds with mult. or div.

   bu. to pk. *mult.*   ft. to yd. *div.*   km to m *mult.*

   hr. to da. *div.*   qt. to gal. *div.*   cm to m *div.*

Fractions (2 min.)
   - Write ⁵/₅ on ckbd. Child decides if fraction is proper or improper. (improper) Have him explain why. (The numerator is equal to the denominator.)
   He gives value of a fraction when the numerator is the same number as the denominator. (1)
   Point to fraction bar and have him give name of line. (fraction bar or division bar)
   Ask him to tell what fraction bar tells us to do? (to divide the numerator by the denominator)

Lesson 81
(cont.)

Have him tell what 5 div. by 5 is. (1) Ask if 1 is the value of a fraction when the numerator and the denominator are the same number. (yes)

2. **Written speed drill** (4 min.) Time for 3 min.

3. **Review least common denominator.** (9 min.)
   - *Concept Cards* **80–104:** Show backs of 2 cards, such as cards **82** and **83**. Child gives l.c.d. Repeat for several cards. It is important that he learns to recognize l.c.d. quickly. After working with fractions for awhile, he should know l.c.d. immediately.
   -  **B** Work problems step by step for him. He can answer many questions as you work on ckbd.
   - Child does **Ex. 1–3, p. 149.**

4. **Review division.** (6 min.)
   - **C** He works on paper as you work on ckbd.
   - Child does **Ex. 4.**

5. **Review/Boardwork** (9 min.) **Ex. 5–7**

6. **Homework Ex. 8–10**

Lesson 82

Preparation

Test 8, pp. 65–66 from *Student Tests and Speed Drills*

Teaching Procedure

1. **Homework check**
2. **Administer test.**

   Notice that space has been allowed on this test for child to work story problems.

Lesson 83

Preparation

1. Chalkboard:

   A
   367,729
   279,517
   461,662
   355,892
   + 902,948

B   43 + __ = 81   __ − 15 = 50   __ x 5 = 250

C   I   II   III   IV   V   VI   VII   VIII   IX   X   XI   XII

D $3\frac{2}{3}$

$17\frac{4}{9}$

$+ 9\frac{1}{3}$
_____

2. *Arithmetic 4:* pp. 151–152
3. *Lesson 83 Speed Drill*
4. Visuals:
   - *Mixed Division Facts (Arith 4, p. 322)*
   - *Place Value (Arith Chart* 2)
   - Mixed Facts Chart (see lesson 49)
   - *Roman Numerals (Arith Chart 10)*
   - *Concept Cards* 1–15, 80–104, and 56–62

Teaching Procedure

1. Oral review drills (9 min.)

Processes (6 min.)
- *Mixed Division Facts*
- Mixed Facts Chart
- **A** Use standard procedure.
- Mult./Div. 11–12 Tables
- **B** Child gives missing terms. Help him to understand that he can find missing terms in addition problem by subtracting. He finds missing term in subtraction problem by adding. He finds missing term in multiplication problem by dividing.
- Oral comb.

  1 + 1 + 1 + 2 − 2 + 1 − 1 = *3*   9 ÷ 3 x 9 + 9 − 10 = *26*
  40 + 40 + 10 − 10 = *80*   6 x 9 − 4 + 4 − 8 = *46*
  16 + 2 + 2 + 1 + 2 + 3 = *26*   8 + 6 ÷ 2 + 1 ÷ 4 = *2*
  16 ÷ 2 x 3 + 1 x 2 = *50*   9 + 9 ÷ 2 = *9*
  9 + 2 − 4 ÷ 7 = *1*   2 x 8 + 4 ÷ 5 = *4*

Place value (1 min.)
- *Arith Chart* **2**
- *Concept Cards* **1–15:** Child adds 10,000 or subtracts 10,000 from several numbers.

Fractions (2 min.)
- *Concept Cards* **80–104:** He reduces to lowest terms.
- *Concept Cards* **80–104:** Show backs of 2 cards with different denominators; child finds common denominator. You may want to use 3 cards at once.

2. Written speed drill (4 min.) Time for 3 min.

3. Introduce Roman numerals. (9 min.)

- **C** Count from 1 to 12 as you point to Roman numerals. Tell child that these are Roman numerals. Ancient Romans invented them about 500 B.C. Tell him that B.C. means the time before Christ was born. Tell him that Roman numerals continued to be used in Europe until about A.D. 1500. A.D. means time after Christ was born.

- *Arith Chart* **10:** The numbers that we commonly use are Arabic numerals. They were probably invented around 200 B.C. Ask him if they were invented before or after Christ was born. (before) They were commonly used by the Arabs around 700 A.D. Ask him if they were commonly used by the Arabs before or after Christ was born. (after)

  Write 722 on ckbd to show that Arabic numerals use place value. Ask child if both 2s have same value? (no) 2 to right means 2 ones, and 2 in middle means 2 tens. Tell him that Roman numerals do not use place value. We know the values by using rules. We will study several rules today. Discuss chart with child.

- *Concept Cards* **56–62:** Review values.
- Read and discuss **box on p. 151.** Explain rules by writing values of these numbers, using Roman numerals.

  57 = *LVII*   19 = *XIX*   915 = *CMXV*

  2,000 = *MM*   83 = *LXXXIII*   429 = *CDXXIX*

  Child does **Ex. 1–2.** You may want to work together.

4. Review least common denominator. (6 min.)

- **D** Child works on paper as you work on ckbd. Discuss each step. Encourage him to be very neat as he works. It helps a great deal to have an organized problem.
- Child does **Ex. 3.**

5. Review/Boardwork (9 min.) **Ex. 4–7**

Lesson 84

Preparation

1. Chalkboard:

   A
   ```
     202,368
     589,771
     387,519
     271,994
   + 904,287
   ```

   B $3.99 $6.02   5 | $14.95   6 | $18.01
            x 2   x 4

C $21\frac{3}{5}$

$-9\frac{1}{3}$

2. *Arithmetic 4:* pp. 153–154

3. *Lesson 84 Speed Drill*

4. Visuals:
- *Process Flashcards*
- *Roman Numerals (Arith Chart* 10)
- *Concept Cards* 56–62, 24–47, and 112–116
- *1–100 Chart* (Arith Chart 23)
- *Calculator* (Arith Chart 20)

Teaching Procedure

1. **Oral review drills** (9 min.)

Processes (3 min.)
- *Flashcards: Beat the Clock*
- Mult./Div. Tables
- A Use standard procedure.
- Oral comb.

5 ÷ 1 x 10 + 20 = *70*	6 ÷ 3 x 20 + 20 = *60*
50 ÷ 10 + 10 = *15*	100 ÷ 10 + 90 x 2 = *200*
50 ÷ 10 + 90 − 20 + 10 = *85*	9 + 9 + 4 ÷ 2 = *11*
9 x 9 − 2 = *79*	10 ÷ 5 + 11 = *13*

Roman numerals (3 min.)
- *Arith Chart* **10:** Review with child.
- *Concept Cards* **56–62:** Review.
- *1–100 Chart:* Point to numbers; child gives Roman numerals. He can say aloud or write on ckbd.

Measures (3 min.)
- *Concept Cards* **24–47** and **112–116:** Let him answer and then play *Capture the Card.*
- *Calculator:* Point to 2. Have child name a measure that uses 2. (2 c. = 1 pt., 2 pt. = 1 qt.) Point to 3. Have him name a measure that uses 3. (3 tsp. = 1 tbsp., 3 ft. = 1 yd.) Point to 4. Have him name a measure that uses 4. (4 qt. = 1 gal., 4 pk. = 1 bu.) Point to 7. Have him name a measure that uses 7. (7 da. = 1 wk.) Point to 10. Have him name a measure that uses 10. (10 yr. = 1 decade, 10 mm = 1 dm)

2. **Written speed drill** (4 min.) Time for 3 min.

3. **Introduce estimation.** (9 min.)
- *1–100 Chart:* Point to 42 and tell child that 42 is an exact number. If we only needed to know an estimated amount, we could use the number 40. He should realize that numbers ending in 0 are easier to work with. Point to 78. He gives an estimated amount. (80) Point to several numbers, having child give estimated amounts.

Lesson 84
(cont.)

- **B** Point to 1st problem. Child gives an estimated amount for $3.99. ($4.00) He can then easily mult. by 2 to get $8.00.

  Point to 2nd problem. He gives estimated amount for $6.02. ($6.00) He can easily mult. by 4 to get $24.00.

  Point to 3rd problem, having child give $15.00 as estimated amount for $14.95. He can easily div. $15 by 5 to get $3. Repeat with last problem. Remind him that he is not finding exact answers, but estimated answers. Finding estimated answers lets us know if our exact answers make sense. Estimation is also very helpful when we are shopping. We can quickly estimate how much we have spent and how much money we have left.
- Read and discuss **box on p. 153.** Child answers **Ex. 1.**

4. Review Roman numerals. (3 min.)

- **1–100 Chart:** Review rules for writing Roman numerals. Point to numbers on chart for him to give as Roman numerals.
- Child does **Ex. 2–3.**

5. Review adding and subtracting fractions. (6 min.)

- **C** Child works on paper as you work on ckbd.
- Child does **Ex. 4.**

6. Review/Boardwork (6 min.) **Ex. 5–7**

7. Homework Ex. 8

Lesson
85

Preparation

1. Chalkboard:

A
892,774
482,399
801,615
325,250
+ 416,995

B $\frac{2}{3}$ $\frac{3}{4}$

C
$3.02 $4.99
x 6   x 3

D MCDXCV   CCCII   MMMXXI
CMXCIX   XLIV   XXXVII

2. *Arithmetic 4:* pp. 155–156
3. *Lesson 85 Speed Drill*

4. Visuals:
   - *Process Flashcards*
   - *Mixed Multiplication Facts (Arith 4, p. 319)*
   - *Concept Cards 124–129, 56–62, and 130–139*
   - *101–200 Chart (Arith Chart 25)*

Teaching Procedure

1. Oral review drills (7 min.)

Homework check

Processes (3 min.)
   - *Flashcards:* Have child answer cards.
   - Mult./Div. 6–9 Tables
   - **A** Use standard procedure.
   - *Mixed Multiplication Facts*

Measures (1 min.)
   - *Concept Cards* **124–129:** Review metric prefixes.

Roman numerals (1 min.)
   - *Concept Cards* **56–62**

Fractions (2 min.)
   - *Concept Cards* **130–139:** Child changes to whole or mixed numbers.
   - **B** Tell him that to compare fractions, he needs to have a common denominator. Have him change to equal fractions with a common denominator and then choose greater.

2. Written speed drill (6 min.) Time for 5 min.
   - Grade. Record as a speed drill/quiz grade. Count off 3 points for each incorrect answer.

3. Review estimation. (6 min.)
   - ***101–200 Chart:*** Point to several numbers; child gives estimated amount.
   - **C** Work for child, using estimation.
   - Child does **Ex. 1, p. 155.**

4. Review Roman numerals. (3 min.)
   - **D** Child gives Arabic value of each.
   - Child does **Ex. 2.**

5. Review adding and subtracting fractions. (6 min.)
   - Child does **Ex. 3.** Work **Ex. 4 *a–b*** together. He completes problems.

6. Review/Boardwork (9 min.) **Ex. 5–7**

7. Homework Ex. 8

Lesson
86

Mm

Preparation

1. Chalkboard:

A 118,450
  904,875
  776,229
  384,869
+ 519,495

B 78 ⟌ 3,021

C $8.98
  x 2

2. *Arithmetic 4:* pp. 157–158
3. *Lesson 86 Speed Drill*
4. Visuals:
   - *Process Flashcards*
   - *1–100 Chart (Arith Chart 23)*
   - *Concept Cards 24–47, 112–116, 118–129, and 56–62*

Teaching Procedure

1. Oral review drills (7 min.)

Homework check

Processes (4 min.)
- Mult./Div. 11–12 Tables
- **A** Use standard procedure.
- *Flashcards:* Have child answer. Then play a favorite game.
- *1–100 Chart:* Child counts by 7s from 7 to 84 as you point to numbers on chart.

Measures (2 min.)
- *Concept Cards* **24–47, 112–116,** and **118–129**
- Call out some measures, such as ft., in. He tells whether he mult. or div. to convert.

Roman numerals (1 min.)
- *Concept Cards* **56–62:** Expect quick, accurate responses.

2. Written speed drill (6 min.) Time for 5 min.
- Grade. Record as a speed drill/quiz grade. Count off 8 points for each incorrect answer.

3. Introduce estimating divisors. (9 min.)
- *1–100 Chart:* Point to several 2-digit numbers that have 0, 1, 2, 3, or 4 in ones' place. Have him tell you which number they div. by if these numbers are the divisors. (He div. by number in tens' place.)

  Point to 57. Have him notice that 57 has a 7 in ones' place. We cannot use the estimation rule for division that we have been using. Ask him if 57 is closer to 50 or 60. (60) Repeat with 56, 58, and 59. Because these numbers are closer to 60, it would be confusing to div. by 5. We have a new rule for estimating divisors. **If a two-digit divisor ends in 5, 6, 7, 8, or 9, we divide by one more than the first digit of the divisor.**

- Work problem step by step for him. Be sure that he understands that he mult. by actual divisor, not estimated divisor.
- Read and discuss **box on p. 157.** Child does **Ex. 1.** You may want to work together.

4. **Review estimation.** (3 min.)

- C Have child explain how to find estimated answer and exact answer. Compare 2 answers.
- Child does **Ex. 2.** Give help as needed.

5. **Review/Boardwork** (12 min.) **Ex. 3–6**

6. **Homework** **Ex. 7–8**

Tues

Lesson 87

Preparation

1. Chalkboard:

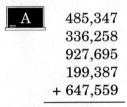

      485,347
      336,258
      927,695
      199,387
    + 647,559

B $15\frac{4}{9}$

   $- 7\frac{1}{6}$

2. *Arithmetic 4:* pp. 159–160

3. *Lesson 87 Quiz*

4. Visuals:
   - *Process Flashcards*
   - *1–100 / 101–200 Charts*
     (Arith Charts 23 / 25)
   - *Concept Card*s 80–104
     and 130–139
   - coins
   - play bills

Teaching Procedure

1. **Oral review drills** (9 min.)

   Homework check

Lesson 87
(cont.)

Processes (4 min.)
- *Flashcards:* Play a game after child is warmed up.
- *1–100/101–200 Charts:* Child counts by 9s from 9 to 108.
- Use standard procedure.
- Mult./Div. Tables

Fractions (3 min.)
- *Concept Cards* **80–104:** Child reduces to lowest terms.
- *Concept Cards* **130–139:** He changes to whole or mixed numbers.
- *Concept Cards* **80–104:** Show backs of 2 cards having different denominators. Child finds l.c.d.

Money (2 min.)
- Coins/play bills: Have child make change from $10. Tell price of item such as $5.13. Child uses coins and play bills to count back change.

2. Quiz 9 (9 min.)

3. Review fractions. (6 min.)
- He works on paper as you work at ckbd.
- Child does **Ex. 1–3, p. 159.**

4. Discuss story problems. (3 min.)
- Work **Ex. 4** together.

5. Review division. (6 min.)
- Work **Ex. 5** together. Review estimating rule.

6. Review/Boardwork (3 min.) **Ex. 6–9**

Wed

Lesson
88

Preparation

1. Chalkboard:

895,909	B 37⟌2,174
945,391	
728,629	
225,087	
+ 844,238	

2. *Arithmetic 4:* pp. 161–162

3. *Lesson 88 Speed Drill*

4. Visuals:
- *Process Flashcards*
- *Mixed Multiplication Facts (Arith 4, p. 319)*
- *Concept Cards 56–62, 80–104, 24–47, 112–116, 118–129, and 130–139*
- *101–200 Chart (Arith Chart 25)*

Teaching Procedure

1. **Oral review drills** (9 min.)

   Processes (4 min.)
   - Mult./Div. 7–9 Tables
   - *Flashcards:* Have a brisk review and play a favorite game.
   - *Mixed Multiplication Facts*
   - **A** Use standard procedure.

   Roman numerals (2 min.)
   - *Concept Cards* **56–62**
   - *101–200 Chart:* Point to numbers; child writes as Roman numerals.

   Fractions (1 min.)
   - *Concept Cards* **80–104:** Child reduces to lowest terms.

   Measures (1 min.)
   - *Concept Cards* **24–47, 112–116,** and **118–129**

2. **Written speed drill** (3 min.) Time for 2 min. 30 sec.

3. **Review fractions.** (9 min.)
   - *Concept Cards* **80–104:** Show backs of 2 cards with different denominators. Child gives l.c.d.
   - *Concept Cards* **130–139:** He changes to whole or mixed numbers.
   - Do **Ex. 1, p. 161** together.

4. **Review division.** (6 min.)
   - **B** Work together step by step. Write remainder as a fraction.
   - Child does **Ex. 2.**

5. **Review/Boardwork** (9 min.) **Ex. 3–7** Notice that 6–7 is Extra Practice and is therefore optional.

murs

Preparation

1. Chalkboard:

   A
   ```
     894,406
     501,339
     776,329
     893,792
   + 889,698
   ```

   B $1 = \overline{7}$ $1 = \overline{4}$ $3 = 2\,\overline{7}$ $5 = \underline{}\frac{6}{6}$

   C   MCCXXXIV   XCVII   CDLXXIX

2. *Arithmetic 4:* pp. 163–164

3. *Lesson 89 Speed Drill*

4. Visuals:
   - *Process Flashcards*
   - *Concept Cards* 24–47, 112–116, 80–104, 78, and 56–62
   - Fractional Circles

Teaching Procedure

1. **Oral review drills** (9 min.)

   Processes (6 min.)
   - *Flashcards:* Let child answer. After child gets warmed up, play a game.
   - Mult./Div. Tables
   - [A] Use standard procedure.
   - Oral comb.

8 x 5 ÷ 10 x 4 = *16*	35 ÷ 7 x 6 ÷ 3 = *10*
9 x 8 ÷ 6 x 12 = *144*	63 ÷ 9 x 6 ÷ 7 + 10 = *16*
10 x 4 ÷ 4 x 12 = *120*	16 + 10 + 2 ÷ 4 = *7*
11 x 6 ÷ 11 x 11 = *66*	9 x 6 ÷ 6 x 7 = *63*

   Measures (2 min.)
   - *Concept Cards* **24–47** and **112–116:** Show card 24; child responds with correct number. Then say *Change minutes to seconds by—*. He responds with mult. or div. Next say *Change seconds to minutes by—*. Ask similar questions with other cards to test child's ability to know when to mult. and div. to convert measures.

   Fractions (1 min.)
   - *Concept Cards* **80–104:** Child reduces to lowest terms.

2. **Written speed drill** (3 min.) Time for 2 min.

3. **Introduce writing whole numbers as improper fractions.** (12 min.)
   - *Concept Card* **78:** Have him notice that all of circle is colored. Since all of the parts of the circle are used, the numerator and denominator are the same number. **The value of a fraction when the numerator and denominator are both the same is one.**
   - **Fractional Circles:** Show 2 halves. Write ²⁄₂ on ckbd. Child gives value of fraction. Repeat with 3 thirds and 4 fourths.
   - [B] Point to 1st fraction. Child should notice that numerator is missing. It is easy to know what it should be since fraction is equal to 1. He should recognize that numerator must be same as denominator. Repeat with 2nd fraction.

     Point to 3rd fraction. Explain that fraction must equal 1 since $1 + 2 = 3$. As in 1st 2 examples, he needs to use same number for numerator that was used for denominator.

     Point to 4th problem. He gives value of ⁶⁄₆. (1) He should see that whole number must be 4, since $4 + 1 = 5$.

- Send child to ckbd to write 1 as improper fraction. No one answer is correct. The only necessity is that numerator and denominator must be same number.
- Read and discuss **box on p. 163.** Child does **Ex. 1–5.**

4. Review Roman numerals. (6 min.)
- *Concept Cards* **56–62**
- Child gives Arabic value.
- Child does **Ex. 6.**

5. Review/Boardwork (6 min.) **Ex. 7–8**

6. Homework Ex. 9

Lesson 90

Preparation

1. Chalkboard:

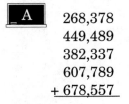

   268,378
   449,489
   382,337
   607,789
   + 678,557

 B

$\frac{8}{5}$ $\frac{11}{8}$ $\frac{15}{7}$ $\frac{18}{4}$ $\frac{20}{6}$ $\frac{36}{8}$

C

1 1 1 1

$-\frac{1}{4}$ $-\frac{3}{4}$ $-\frac{1}{2}$ $-\frac{6}{11}$

2. *Arithmetic 4:* pp. 165–166

3. *Lesson 90 Speed Drill*

4. Visuals:
   - *Process Flashcards*
   - *Concept Cards* 56–62, 130–139, and 80–104
   - Fractional Circles

Teaching Procedure

1. Oral review drills (9 min.)

Homework check

Processes (5 min.)
- *Flashcards:* Let child answer and then play *Giant Step.*
- Mult./Div. Tables
- Use standard procedure.

Roman numerals (1 min.)
- *Concept Cards* **56–62**

Fractions (3 min.)

- █ B █ Send child to ckbd to change to mixed numbers.
- *Concept Cards* **130–139:** Child changes to whole or mixed numbers.
- *Concept Cards* **80–104:** He reduces to lowest terms.

2. **Written speed drill** (3 min.) Time for 2 min. 30 sec.

3. **Introduce subtraction of fractions with borrowing.** (12 min.)

- **Fractional Circles:** Show 4 fourths and remind him that $^4/_4$ is same as 1.
- █ C █ Point to 1st problem. Write = $^4/_4$ to right of 1. Help him to see that 1 is equal to $^4/_4$. Now problem is easy to do. There is a common denominator, so we just subt. numerator 1 from numerator 4 to get $^3/_4$. Take 1 piece away from 4 pieces to show that $1 - ^1/_4$ is equal to $^3/_4$.

Use pieces and ckbd to do 2nd and 3rd problems.

Point to 4th problem. Work step by step for child.

$$0\left(\tfrac{11}{11}\right)$$
$$\cancel{1} = \frac{11}{11}$$
$$-\frac{6}{11} = -\frac{6}{11}$$
$$\overline{\frac{5}{11}}$$

Step 1: The minuend could be written as $1^0/_{11}$. $^6/_{11}$ cannot be subt. from $^0/_{11}$. Borrow from whole number 1 by rewriting as $^{11}/_{11}$. We write as $^{11}/_{11}$ since we want to keep a common denominator.

Step 2: Rewrite problem as $^{11}/_{11} - ^6/_{11}$.

Step 3: Subtract as usual to get $^5/_{11}$.

- Read and discuss **box on p. 165.** Child does **Ex. 1–3.** Work several problems with him.

4. **Review/Boardwork** (12 min.) **Ex. 4–8**

5. **Homework Ex. 9** You may want to begin giving the homework assignment orally.

mon

Lesson 91

Preparation

1. Chalkboard:

█ A █
```
  367,548
  783,783
  210,895
  895,388
+ 785,784
```

█ B █

$1.98	$4.01	$6.99	$.49
x 2	x 3	x 5	x 3

█ C █

CCCIII	MCMLXV	CLXVII
MMCMLX	CCXVII	XXIX

D $\frac{3}{5} = \frac{}{25}$ $\frac{4}{9} = \frac{}{81}$ $\frac{7}{12} = \frac{}{36}$

E 9 7
$-\frac{2}{3}$ $-\frac{1}{5}$

F $13\overline{)17{,}821}$

2. *Arithmetic 4:* pp. 167–168

3. *Lesson 91 Speed Drill*

4. Visuals:
   - *Subtraction Flashcards*
   - *Concept Cards 56–62*

Teaching Procedure

1. **Oral review drills** (9 min.)

   Homework check

   Processes (4 min.)
   - Mult./Div. Tables
   - *Subt. Flashcards:* Review with child.
   - A Use standard procedure.
   - B He gives estimated answers.

   Roman numerals (2 min.)
   - *Concept Cards* **56–62**
   - C He writes Arabic value on paper or ckbd.

   Fractions (3 min.)
   - Call out these fractions; he says *proper* or *improper*.
     $^6/_9$ $^5/_3$ $^4/_4$ $^6/_5$ $^1/_2$
   - Send child to ckbd to write 1 as improper fraction. He uses these numbers for denominators.
     5   7   3   2   8   11
   - D He writes missing numerators on paper or ckbd.

2. **Written speed drill** (4 min.) Time for 3 min.

3. **Introduce borrowing when minuend is not 1.** (9 min.)
   - Write 9 on ckbd. Have him tell you what whole number is left if you borrow 1 from 9. (8) Have him rewrite 1 that he borrowed as a fraction with a denominator of 5. ($^5/_5$) Ask them if 8 and $^5/_5$ is same as 9.
   - E Work 1st problem step by step for child.

$8\left(\frac{3}{3}\right)$

$\cancel{9} = 8\frac{3}{3}$

$-\frac{2}{3} = -\frac{2}{3}$

$\overline{\qquad\qquad 8\frac{1}{3}}$

Step 1: Tell him that we could say that we have $^0/_3$ in numerator. We cannot subt. $^2/_3$ from $^0/_3$. We must borrow. Mark out 9 and write 8 above it. The 1 that we borrowed is rewritten as $^3/_3$. We know that $^3/_3$ equals 1,

Lesson 91
(cont.)

and we want to keep a common denominator of 3.

Step 2: Write $8^3/_3 - {}^2/_3$ to right of problem.

Step 3: Subt. as usual.

Use same steps to work 2nd problem for him.

- Read and discuss **box on p. 167.** Child does **Ex. 1.** Work a few problems with him. Give help as needed.

4. Review division. (6 min.)

- [F] Work problem as he tells you what to do and what numbers to use in quotient. Emphasize choosing correct number 1st time.
- Child does **Ex. 2.**

5. Review Roman numerals. (3 min.)

- *Concept Cards* **56–62:** Drill briefly.
- Child does **Ex. 3.**

6. Review/Boardwork (6 min.) **Ex. 4–5**

7. Homework Ex. 6

Lesson 92

Preparation

Test 9, pp. 73–74 from *Student Tests and Speed Drills*

Teaching Procedure

1. Homework check

2. Administer test.

Lesson 93

Preparation

1. Chalkboard:

[A]
788,510
482,713
783,895
239,893
+ 894,444

[B]
19
$- 8\frac{3}{7}$

[C]
$13\overline{)493}$

2. *Arithmetic 4:* pp. 169–170

3. *Lesson 93 Speed Drill*

4. Visuals:
- *Place Value (Arith Chart 2)*
- *Concept Cards 1–15, 24–47, 112–116, 118–129, and 56–62*
- *1–100 Chart (Arith Chart 23)*

Teaching Procedure

1. Oral review drills (9 min.)

Processes (3 min.)

- Mult./Div. 10–12 Tables
- **A** Use standard procedure.

Place value (1 min.)

- *Arith Chart* 2
- *Concept Cards* **1–15:** Child adds 500 or subtracts 500 from several numbers.

Measures (2 min.)

- *Concept Cards* **24–47, 112–116,** and **118–129**

Roman numerals (1 min.)

- *Concept Cards* **56–62:** Let child answer.

Fractions (2 min.)

- *1–100 Chart:* Point to number, such as 5; he writes as mixed number with improper fraction, such as $4\frac{4}{4}$. Sometimes give denominator and sometimes let him choose.

2. Written speed drill (4 min.) Time for 3 min.

3. Review subtraction of fractions with borrowing. (9 min.)

- **B** Work problem step by step. Stress that 1 that is borrowed is rewritten as $\frac{7}{7}$ since 7 is denominator that is already used in subtrahend fraction.
- Child does **Ex. 1, p. 169.** You may want to work a few together. Let child who is doing well work at ckbd.

4. Review division with troublesome divisors. (9 min.)

- **C** Work problem with him. Make these suggestions to him.
  - (A) **When dividing by 13, 14, or 15, estimate the quotient by using the 12 multiplication table.**
  - (B) **When dividing by 16, 17, 18, or 19, round the divisor to 20 to find the correct quotient.**
- Child does **Ex. 2.**

5. Review/Boardwork (6 min.) **Ex. 3–7** Notice that Ex. 6–7 are Extra Practice and are therefore optional.

Thurs

Lesson 94

Preparation

1. Chalkboard:

A
$$
\begin{array}{r}
563{,}878 \\
895{,}632 \\
411{,}788 \\
894{,}951 \\
+\ 235{,}879 \\
\hline
\end{array}
$$

Lesson 94
(cont.)

B	$21.03	5 $\overline{)\$49.35}$
	$- 9.89$	

C 1
    $-\ \frac{2}{9}$

D 37
    $-14\frac{5}{6}$

E $15\overline{)5,067}$

2. *Arithmetic 4:* pp. 171–172
3. *Lesson 94 Speed Drill*
4. Visuals:
   - *Process Flashcards*
   - *Concept Cards* 80–104, 24–47, and 112–116
   - *1–100 / 101–200 Charts (Arith Charts 23 / 25)*

Teaching Procedure

1. **Oral review drills** (9 min.)

   Processes (4 min.)
   - *Flashcards:* Review. If child does well, play a game.
   - **A** Use standard procedure.
   - Mult./Div. 12 Table
   - **B** He gives estimated answers.

   Fractions (2 min.)
   - *Concept Cards* **80–104:** He reduces to lowest terms.

   Measures (3 min.)
   - *Concept Cards* **24–47** and **112–116:** Let child answer and then play *Capture the Card.*
   - Call out 2 measures in same table; he uses hands to show relative size and decides if he mult. or div. to convert.

2. **Written speed drill** (3 min.) Time for 2 min.

3. **Review subtraction.** (9 min.)
   - **C** Child explains how to borrow from 1 and what to rewrite the 1 as. (⁹⁄₉) If necessary, do another similar problem.
   - **D** Work problem for him, showing how to borrow 1 from 37 to have 36 left. Emphasize that borrowed 1 is rewritten as ⁶⁄₆ since that is common denominator.
   - Child answers **Ex. 1, p. 171.**

4. Review division with troublesome divisors. (6 min.)

- *1–100/101–200 Charts:* Since 15 is a troublesome divisor, it is helpful if child can count by 15s. Point to 15, 30, 45, 60, 75, 90, 105, 120, and 135 on charts. Point to numbers and have him say them with you.

- Child works on paper while you work and explain on ckbd.

- Child does **Ex. 2.**

5. Review/Boardwork (9 min.) **Ex. 3–5**

6. Homework Ex. 6–7

Fri

Lesson
95

Preparation

1. Chalkboard:

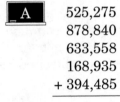

A	525,275
	878,840
	633,558
	168,935
	+ 394,485

B	$1\frac{3}{5}$		$7\frac{1}{3}$
	$-\ \frac{4}{5}$		$-4\frac{2}{3}$

C	$8\frac{3}{8}$
	$+17\frac{3}{4}$

2. *Arithmetic 4:* pp. 173–174

3. *Lesson 95 Speed Drill*

4. Visuals:
   - *Mixed Subtraction Facts (Arith 4, p. 316)*
   - *Mixed Multiplication Facts (Arith 4, p. 319)*
   - *Concept Cards 24–47, 112–116, and 118–129*

Teaching Procedure

1. Oral review drills (4 min.)

   Homework check

   Processes (3 min.)
   - *Tables/Facts Charts* **15–16**
   - Mult./Div. 10–12 Tables
   - A Use standard procedure.

- Oral comb.

  $4 \times 5 + 4 \div 6 \times 10 = 40$ $5 \times 4 \times 2 + 6 = 46$

  $2 \times 6 + 4 \div 4 \times 2 = 8$ $12 \div 2 \div 6 + 100 = 101$

Measures (1 min.)

- *Concept Cards* **24–47, 112–116,** and **118–129**

2. Written speed drill (6 min.) Time for 5 min.

- Grade. Record as a speed drill/quiz grade. Count off 10 points for each incorrect answer.

3. Introduce harder subtraction with borrowing. (12 min.)

- **B** Work 2 subt. problems on ckbd for child.

$$1\frac{3}{5} = \frac{8}{5}$$
$$-\frac{4}{5} = -\frac{4}{5}$$
$$\frac{4}{5}$$

Step 1: Notice that $^4/_5$ cannot be subt. from $^3/_5$. Borrow 1 by changing the 1 to $^5/_5$. Add $^5/_5$ and $^3/_5$ to get $^8/_5$.

Step 2: Subt. $^4/_5$ from $^8/_5$ to get $^4/_5$.

$$6\left(\frac{3}{3}\right)$$
$$7\frac{1}{3} = 6\frac{4}{3}$$
$$-4\frac{2}{3} = -4\frac{2}{3}$$
$$2\frac{2}{3}$$

Step 1: Notice that $^2/_3$ cannot be subt. from $^1/_3$. Borrow 1 from 7, leaving 6. The 1 that is borrowed is rewritten as $^3/_3$ to keep a common denominator. Add $^3/_3$ and $^1/_3$ to get $^4/_3$.

Step 2: Subt. $^2/_3$ from $^4/_3$ to get $^2/_3$. Subt. 4 from 6 to get 2. The final difference is $2^2/_3$.

- Read and discuss **box on p. 173.** Child does **Ex. 1–2, p. 173.** Work several problems in Ex. 2 together.

4. Review adding fractions. (6 min.)

- **C** Work problem together, emphasizing how to get common denominator.

- Child does **Ex. 3.**

5. Review/Boardwork (9 min.) **Ex. 4–7**

6. Homework Ex. 8

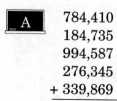

Lesson

96

Preparation

1. Chalkboard:

A   784,410
184,735
994,587
276,345
+ 339,869

B			

$12 \times \underline{} = 96$ $9 \times \underline{} = 45$ $\underline{} \times 6 = 42$

$11 \times \underline{} = 55$ $12 \times \underline{} = 60$ $5 \times \underline{} = 45$

C	

$$87\tfrac{5}{7}$$
$$-\ 29\tfrac{6}{7}$$

D	

$37\overline{\smash{\big)}\,6{,}209}$

2. *Arithmetic 4:* pp. 175–176
3. *Lesson 96 Speed Drill*
4. Visuals:
   - *1–100 / 101–200 Charts (Arith Charts 23 / 25)*
   - *Concept Cards 24–44, 112–116, 118–129, and 56–62*

Teaching Procedure

1. **Oral review drills** (9 min.)

   Homework check

   Processes (5 min.)
   - Mult./Div. 12 Table
   - **A** Use standard procedure.
   - *1–100 / 101–200 Charts:* Point to 15, 30, 45, 60, 75, 90, 105, 120, and 135; child says as you point.
   - **B** Child writes missing factors and gives multiples of 6, 7, and 9.

   Measures (2 min.)
   - *Concept Cards* **24–44, 112–116,** and **118–129**
   - Call out some measures, such as ft., in. Child tells whether he mult. or div.

   Roman numerals (2 min.)
   - *Concept Cards* **56–62**
   - Review rules for reading and writing Roman numerals.

2. **Written speed drill** (4 min.) Time for 3 min.

3. **Review subtraction of fractions.** (9 min.)
   - **C** Work problem step by step. Child should recognize that he must borrow because $^{6}/_{7}$ is greater than $^{5}/_{7}$. He borrows 1 as usual, making 87, 86. The 1 that is borrowed is rewritten as $^{7}/_{7}$ to keep a common denominator. The $^{7}/_{7}$ that was borrowed must be added to the $^{5}/_{7}$ that is already there. $^{6}/_{7}$ can be subt. from $^{12}/_{7}$, giving $^{6}/_{7}$. Subt. whole numbers as usual.
   - Child does **Ex. 1, p. 175.** You may want to work a few problems together.

4. **Review division.** (6 min.)

   - 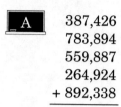 **D** Work problem on ckbd as he tells you what to do.

   - Child does **Ex. 2.** Give help as needed.

5. **Review/Boardwork** (9 min.) **Ex. 3–6**

6. **Homework** **Ex. 7–9** Child needs ruler for les. 97.

Tues

Lesson 97

Preparation

1. Chalkboard:

   A
   387,426
   783,894
   559,887
   264,924
   + 892,338

   B
   $15\frac{1}{6}$
   $-7\frac{5}{6}$

2. *Arithmetic 4:* pp. 177–178

3. *Lesson 97 Quiz*

4. Visuals:
   - *Process Flashcards*
   - *1–100/101–200 Charts (Arith Charts 23/25)*
   - *Concept Cards* 80–104, and 130–139
   - ruler

Teaching Procedure

1. **Oral review drills** (9 min.)

   Homework check

   Processes (6 min.)
   - *Flashcards:* Play *Beat the Clock.*
   - *1–100/101–200 Charts:* Child counts by 15s from 15 to 135.
   - **A** Use standard procedure.
   - Mult./Div. Tables

   Fractions (3 min.)
   - *Concept Cards* **80–104:** He reduces to lowest terms.
   - *Concept Cards* **130–139:** He changes to whole or mixed numbers.
   - *Concept Cards* **80–104:** Show backs of 2 cards, having different denominators. He finds l.c.d.

2. **Quiz 10** (9 min.)

3. **Review subtraction of fractions.** (6 min.)

   - **B** Child works on paper as you work at ckbd.

   - Child does **Ex. 1, p. 177.**

4. Review division. (3 min.)
  • Work **Ex. 2a** together.
5. Discuss story problems. (3 min.)
  • Work **Ex. 3** together.
6. Review/Boardwork (6 min.) **Ex. 4–13**

wed

Lesson

98

Preparation

1. Chalkboard:

A   457,782
       748,469
       829,284
       914,459
     + 458,662

B   27   15   34
       x 11   x 11   x 11

C $4\frac{1}{6}$ $8\frac{1}{4}$

       $-2\frac{2}{3}$ $-3\frac{1}{2}$

2. *Arithmetic 4:* pp. 179–180

3. *Lesson 98 Speed Drill*

4. Visuals:
  • *Process Flashcards*   • *101–200 Chart (Arith Chart 25)*
  • *Concept Cards* 56–62, 130–139,
     24–47, 112–116, and 118–129

Teaching Procedure

1. Oral review drills (9 min.)

  Processes (4 min.)
    • Mult./Div. 6–8 Tables
    • **A** Use standard procedure.
    • *Flashcards:* Play *Secret Code.*
    • **B** Child finds products on sheet of paper. He looks at products to see if he notices any pattern when he mult. by 11. **The product is the top factor separated by the sum of its digits in the tens' place.**

  Roman numerals (2 min.)
    • *Concept Cards* **56–62**
    • *101–200 Chart:* Point to numbers; he writes as Roman numerals.

Lesson 98
(cont.)

Fractions (2 min.)
- *Concept Cards* **130–139:** Child changes to whole or mixed numbers.
- Call out these fractions; he stands if fraction is reduced. He remains seated if not reduced.

$\frac{1}{2}$ $\quad$ $\frac{2}{4}$ $\quad$ $\frac{3}{5}$ $\quad$ $\frac{2}{7}$ $\quad$ $\frac{4}{6}$ $\quad$ $\frac{3}{6}$ $\quad$ $\frac{2}{8}$

Measures (1 min.)
- *Concept Cards* **24–47, 112–116,** and **118–129**

2. Written speed drill (4 min.) Time for 3 min.

3. Introduce borrowing with uncommon denominators. (12 min.)

C Work 2 problems step by step for child on ckbd.

$$3\left(\frac{6}{6}\right)$$

$$4\frac{1}{6} = \cancel{4}\frac{1}{6} = 3\frac{7}{6}$$
$$-2\frac{2}{3} = -2\frac{4}{6} = -2\frac{4}{6}$$
$$1\frac{3}{6} = 1\frac{1}{2}$$

Step 1: Get a l.c.d. for 6 and 3. Change $\frac{2}{3}$ to $\frac{4}{6}$.

Step 2: Because $\frac{4}{6}$ cannot be subt. from $\frac{1}{6}$, borrow 1 from 4 to get 3. Rewrite the borrowed 1 as $\frac{6}{6}$ to keep common denominator.

Step 3: Add borrowed $\frac{6}{6}$ to $\frac{1}{6}$ to get $\frac{7}{6}$.

Step 4: Subt. $\frac{4}{6}$ from $\frac{7}{6}$ to get $\frac{3}{6}$. Subt. 2 from 3 to get 1.

Step 5: Reduce $\frac{3}{6}$ to $\frac{1}{2}$. The final answer is $1\frac{1}{2}$.

$$7\left(\frac{4}{4}\right)$$

$$8\frac{1}{4} = \cancel{8}\frac{1}{4} = 7\frac{5}{4}$$
$$-3\frac{1}{2} = -3\frac{2}{4} = -3\frac{2}{4}$$
$$4\frac{3}{4}$$

Step 1: Get a common denominator of 4. Change $\frac{1}{2}$ to $\frac{2}{4}$.

Step 2: Because $\frac{2}{4}$ cannot be subt. from $\frac{1}{4}$, borrow 1 from 8 to get 7. Rewrite borrowed 1 as $\frac{4}{4}$ to keep common denominator.

Step 3: Add borrowed $\frac{4}{4}$ to $\frac{1}{4}$ to get $\frac{5}{4}$.

Step 4: Subt. to get $4\frac{3}{4}$.

- Read and discuss **box on p. 179.** Child does **Ex. 1.** You may need to work together.

4. Review division. (3 min.)
- Work 1st problem in **Ex. 2** together. Child works other 2 problems without aid.

5. Review/Boardwork (9 min.) **Ex. 3–8**

Thur

Lesson

99

Preparation

1. Chalkboard:

A
$$893,329$$
$$230,710$$
$$784,884$$
$$452,249$$
$$+\ 996,987$$

B $\quad \frac{2}{4} \quad \frac{3}{12} \quad \frac{7}{14} \quad \frac{6}{10} \quad \frac{5}{15} \quad \frac{4}{14}$

$6\frac{2}{9}$ $\qquad$ $14\frac{1}{5}$ $\qquad$ 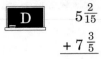 $5\frac{2}{15}$

$-3\frac{2}{3}$ $\qquad$ $-9\frac{1}{2}$ $\qquad$ $+7\frac{3}{5}$

2. *Arithmetic 4:* pp. 181–182

3. *Lesson 99 Speed Drill*

4. Visuals:
   - *Process Flashcards*
   - Mixed Fact Chart (see lesson 49)
   - *Concept Cards 24–47, 112–116, and 80–104*

Teaching Procedure

1. **Oral review drills** (15 min.)

   Processes (9 min.)
   - *Flashcards:* Let child answer. After he gets warmed up, play a game.
   - Mult./Div. Tables
   - **A** Use standard procedure.
   - Mixed Fact Chart
   - Oral comb.

$49 \div 7 \times 7 - 1 \div 6 = 8$	$9 \times 8 - 2 \div 10 = 7$
$3 \times 4 \div 6 \times 2 = 4$	$3 \times 9 + 1 \div 4 = 7$
$2 \times 2 + 2 + 1 \times 4 = 28$	$25 + 7 \div 4 \times 7 - 1 \div 5 = 11$

   Measures (3 min.)
   - *Concept Cards* **24–47** and **112–116:** Child gives answers. Then show card such as card 40. Give number of gal. such as 5 gal.; he gives numbers of qt. Help him to understand that because qt. is a smaller unit than gal. that it takes more qt. to make gal. Any time we find the number of qt. in gal., we must mult.

   Fractions (3 min.)
   - *Concept Cards* **80–104:** Child reduces to lowest terms.
   - **B** Point to each fraction; he reduces to lowest terms.

2. **Written speed drill** (5 min.) Time for 3 min.

3. **Review subtraction and addition of fractions.** (25 min.)
   - **C** Work 2 problems step by step on ckbd.
   - **D** Child explains as you work on ckbd.
   - Child does **Ex. 1, p. 181.** You may need to work a couple subtraction problems with him. Give help if needed. Most children understand and can work independently.

4. **Review/Boardwork** (15 min.) **Ex. 2–5**

5. **Homework Ex. 6–8**

Lesson
100

Preparation

1. Chalkboard:

A
$$554,825$$
$$892,690$$
$$637,768$$
$$190,935$$
$$+\ 345,895$$

B $1\frac{5}{9}$ $1\frac{2}{3}$ $1\frac{7}{8}$ $1\frac{6}{7}$ $1\frac{1}{4}$ $1\frac{2}{11}$

C $13\frac{3}{8}$
$$-\ 4\frac{7}{16}$$

2. *Arithmetic 4:* pp. 183–184
3. *Lesson 100 Speed Drill*
4. Visuals:
   - *Mixed Addition Facts (Arith 4, p. 311)*
   - *Mixed Subtraction Facts (Arith 4, p. 316)*
   - *Mixed Multiplication Facts (Arith 4, p. 319)*
   - *Mixed Division Facts (Arith 4, p. 322)*
   - Mixed Fact Chart (see lesson 49)
   - *Concept Cards* 56–62, 24–47, 112–116, 118–129, and 133–139
   - Fractional Circles

Teaching Procedure

1. **Oral review drills** (8 min.)

   Homework check

   Processes (4 min.)
   - *Mixed Addition Facts (Arith 4, p. 311)*
   - *Mixed Subtraction Facts (Arith 4, p. 316)*
   - *Mixed Multiplication Facts (Arith 4, p. 319)*
   - *Mixed Division Facts (Arith 4, p. 322)*
   - Mixed Fact Chart (see lesson 49)
   - Mult./Div. Tables
   - **A** Use standard procedure.

   Roman numerals (1 min.)
   - *Concept Cards* **56–62**

   Measures (3 min.)

   - *Concept Cards* **24–47, 112–116,** and **118–129:** If child does well, let him play a game.

2. **Written speed drill** (6 min.) Time for 5 min.
   - Grade. Record as a speed drill/quiz grade. Count off 8 points for each incorrect answer.

3. Introduce changing mixed numbers to improper fractions. (9 min.)

- **Fractional Circles:** Show 1 whole and $^1/_4$. Write $1^1/_4$ on ckbd. Child tells how many fourths in 1 whole. (4) He tells how many fourths in $1^1/_4$. ($^5/_4$) Write $1^1/_4 = {^5/_4}$ on ckbd. Have him notice that we could have gotten $^5/_4$ by mult. whole number by denominator and adding numerator.

  Repeat with $1^2/_3$. He gives number of thirds in $1^2/_3$. Write $1^2/_3 = {^5/_3}$ on ckbd. **To change a mixed number to an improper fraction, multiply the whole number by the denominator and add the numerator. Keep the same denominator.**
- ***Concept Cards* 133–139:** Show backs of cards; child changes to improper fraction by mult. whole number by denominator and adding numerator. They keep same denominator.
- **B** Work 1st problem for him.

  $$1\frac{5}{9} = \frac{1 \times 9 + 5}{9} = \frac{14}{9}$$

  Step 1: Multiply the whole number 1 by denominator 9 to get 9.
  Step 2: Add numerator 5 to product 9 to get 14.
  Step 3: Form improper fraction by making 14 numerator and by keeping same denominator of 9.

  Repeat steps for other fractions.

  $$1\frac{2}{3} = \frac{1 \times 3 + 2}{3} = \frac{5}{3}$$
  $$1\frac{7}{8} = \frac{1 \times 8 + 7}{8} = \frac{15}{8}$$
  $$1\frac{6}{7} = \frac{1 \times 7 + 6}{7} = \frac{13}{7}$$
  $$1\frac{1}{4} = \frac{1 \times 4 + 1}{4} = \frac{5}{4}$$
  $$1\frac{2}{11} = \frac{1 \times 11 + 2}{11} = \frac{13}{11}$$
- Read and discuss **box on p. 183.** Child does **Ex. 1.** Work several problems with him.

4. Review subtracting fractions. (6 min.)

- **C** Work problem for him.
- Child does **Ex. 2.**

5. Review/Boardwork (9 min.) **Ex. 3–6**

6. Homework Ex. 7–8

Lesson
101

Preparation

1. Chalkboard:

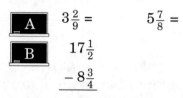

$3\frac{2}{9} =$ $5\frac{7}{8} =$

$17\frac{1}{2}$

$- 8\frac{3}{4}$

2. *Arithmetic 4:* pp. 185–186
3. *Lesson 101 Speed Drill*
4. Visuals:
   - *Process Flashcards*
   - *Mixed Division Facts (Arith 4, p. 322)*
   - *Concept Cards* 24–47, 112–116, 118–129, and 130–139

Teaching Procedure

1. **Oral review drills** (6 min.)

   Homework check

   Processes (3 min.)
   - Mult./Div. 11–12 Tables
   - *Flashcards:* Review with child.
   - *Mixed Division Facts*

   Measures (2 min.)
   - *Concept Cards* **24–47, 112–116,** and **118–129**

   Fractions (1 min.)
   - *Concept Cards* **130–139:** Show fronts; child changes to whole or mixed numbers.

2. **Written speed drill** (3 min.) Time for 2 min.

3. **Review changing mixed numbers to improper fractions.** (6 min.)
   - *Concept Cards* **133–139:** Show backs; he changes to improper fractions.
   - A Work 2 problems on ckbd for him. Remind him that he mult. whole number by denominator and adds numerator to get numerator. The denominator remains the same.
   - Child does **Ex. 1, p. 185.** If he needs help, work a couple problems with him.

4. **Review subtracting fractions.** (6 min.)
   - B Work problem as he tells you what to do.
   - Child does **Ex. 2.**

5. **Review division.** (6 min.)
   - Give him 5 min. to work and check division problems in **Ex. 3.** Check. Praise child who missed 0.

6. **Review/Boardwork** (9 min.) **Ex. 4–7**

7. **Homework** **Ex. 8–9**

Preparation

Test 10, pp. 81–82 from *Student Tests and Speed Drills*

Teaching Procedure

1. Homework check   **2. Administer test.**

Preparation

1. Chalkboard:

    $7\frac{4}{11}$ $25\overline{\smash{\big)}\,870}$

2. *Arithmetic 4:* pp. 187–188

3. *Lesson 103 Speed Drill*

4. Visuals:
   - *Mixed Facts Chart (see lesson 49)*
   - story problem clue words flash-cards (optional from les. 4)
   - *Concept Cards* 24–47, 112–116, 118–129, 56–62, and 130–139

Teaching Procedure

1. Oral review drills (10 min.)

   Processes (3 min.)
   - Mult./Div. 8–12 Tables
   - *Mixed Facts Chart*

   Story problems (1 min.)
   - Story problem clue words flashcards

   Measures (3 min.)
   - *Concept Cards* **24–47, 112–116,** and **118–129:** Play a game.

   Roman numerals (1 min.)
   - *Concept Cards* **56–62:** Let child answer.

   Fractions (2 min.)
   - *Concept Cards* **130–139:** Show fronts; he changes to whole or mixed numbers.

2. Written speed drill (3 min.) Time for 3 min.

3. Review changing mixed numbers to improper fractions. (6 min.)
   - *Concept Cards* **133–139:** Show backs; he changes to improper fractions.
   - ▢ **A** Child explains how to change to improper fraction as you work on ckbd.
   - Child does **Ex. 1, p. 187.**

4. **Review writing a remainder as a fraction.** (6 min.)
- **B** Work problem with child.

$$x \ 34\frac{20}{25} = 34\frac{4}{5}$$

He needs to remember to reduce fraction if necessary.

$$
\begin{array}{r}
25\overline{\smash)870} \\
\underline{-75\downarrow} \\
120 \\
\underline{-100} \\
20
\end{array}
$$

- Child does **Ex. 2.**

5. **Review subtracting fractions.** (3 min.)
- Work **Ex. 3** together. Have child give steps and answers.

6. **Review/Boardwork** (9 min.) **Ex. 4–9** Notice that Ex. 8–9 are Extra Practice and are therefore optional.

Lesson
104

Preparation

1. Chalkboard:

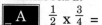 **A** $\frac{1}{2} \times \frac{3}{4} =$ $\frac{3}{8} \times \frac{2}{3} =$

 **B** $75\overline{\smash)8{,}950}$

2. *Arithmetic 4:* pp. 189–190
3. *Lesson 104 Speed Drill*
4. Visuals:
- *Process Flashcards*
- *Concept Cards* 24–47 and 112–116
- Fractional Circles

Teaching Procedure

1. **Oral review drills** (9 min.)

Processes (6 min.)
- *Flashcards:* Review. If he does well, play *Around the World.*
- Mult./Div. Tables: Play *Just the Facts.*
- Oral comb.

$6 \times 2 \div 3 \times 12 \div 6 \times 3 = 24$ $80 + 1 \div 9 \times 4 = 36$

$7 \times 3 + 3 \div 2 \times 12 = 144$ $30 + 6 \div 4 \times 1 = 9$

$12 \times 6 \div 8 \times 2 + 3 \div 3 = 7$ $108 \div 9 \times 4 + 4 = 52$

$12 - 7 \times 12 + 3 \div 7 = 9$ $3 \times 2 \times 2 \times 2 = 24$

Measures (3 min.)

- *Concept Cards* **24–47** and **112–116:** Let child answer and then play *Capture the Card.*
- Read these story problems to him.

  I have a recipe that calls for 2 cups of flour. How many pints should I use? **1**

  Jon picked 8¹/₂ bushels of apples. How many pecks did he pick? **34**

  Ned lived in Iowa for 6 years. How many months did he live in Iowa? **72**

  Cindy has a ribbon that is 96 inches long. She wants to cut it into 1-foot strips. How many strips will she have? **8**

2. **Written speed drill** (3 min.) Time for 3 min.

3. **Introduce multiplying fractions.** (9 min.)

   - **Fractional Circles:** Show ⁸/₈. Tell child that this is a pizza and that you want to put green peppers on ³/₄ of the pizza. How many pieces should have green peppers? (6) Write ⁶/₈ on ckbd and remind him that ³/₄ is same as ⁶/₈. We know that ⁶/₈ of pizza has green peppers. Suppose Zeddie ate ¹/₂ of pizza that has green peppers. How many pieces did he eat? (3) Write ¹/₂ of ³/₄ = ³/₈ on ckbd. Below write ¹/₂ x ³/₄ = ³/₈. Tell him that *of* means to mult. Point out that we could have gotten our answer by mult. numerators together to get product numerator and denominators together to get product denominator.

     Show ⁶/₆. Tell him that we want to put hamburger on ¹/₃ of pizza. How many pieces should have hamburger? (2) Write ²/₆ on ckbd. How many pieces did Zeddie eat if he ate ¹/₂ of the pizza with hamburger? (1) Write ¹/₂ x ¹/₃ = ¹/₆ on ckbd. **To multiply fractions, multiply the numerators together to get the product numerator and multiply the denominators together to get the product denominator.** The product must be reduced if it is not in lowest terms.

   - ▢ **A** Use rule to work both problems.

$$\frac{1}{2} \times \frac{3}{4} = \frac{1 \times 3}{2 \times 4} = \frac{3}{8}$$

   Step 1: Mult. numerators together to get 3.
   Step 2: Mult. denominators together to get 8.
   The fraction ³/₈ is in lowest terms.

$$\frac{3}{8} \times \frac{2}{3} = \frac{3 \times 2}{8 \times 3} = \frac{6}{24} = \frac{1}{4}$$

   Step 1: Mult. numerators together to get 6.
   Step 2: Mult. denominator together to get 24.
   ⁶/₂₄ reduces to ¹/₄.

   - Read and discuss **box on p. 189.** Child does **Ex. 1–3.** Work together. You will probably need to use Fractional Circles to demonstrate Ex. 2–3.

4. **Review division.** (6 min.)

   - ▢ **B** Child works on paper while you work and explain on ckbd. Write remainder as a fraction in lowest terms.
   - Child does **Ex. 4.**

5. **Review/Boardwork** (9 min.) **Ex. 5–7**

6. **Homework Ex. 8–9**

Lesson

105

Preparation

1. Chalkboard:

   A   CX   VII   M   IX   X   DCXVI   D

   B $\frac{1}{4} \times \frac{3}{5} =$ $\frac{2}{7} \times \frac{5}{9} =$ $\frac{1}{2} \times \frac{4}{5} =$

2. *Arithmetic 4:* pp. 191–192
3. *Lesson 105 Speed Drill*
4. Visuals:
   - *Process Flashcards*
   - *Mixed Multiplication Facts (Arith 4, p. 319)*
   - *Mixed Division Facts (Arith 4, p. 322)*
   - *Concept Cards 56–62*

Teaching Procedure

1. **Oral review drills** (4 min.)

   Homework check

   Processes (3 min.)
   - *Flashcards:* Have child answer.
   - Mult./Div. Tables: Child says tables that he most needs to practice. If he knows his tables, do not continue to practice them every day. Just practice them on occasion to keep them fresh in his mind.
   - Mixed Multiplication Tables
   - Mixed Division Tables

   Roman numerals (1 min.)
   - *Concept Cards* **56–62**
   - **A** Point to Roman numerals; he gives Arabic numerals.

2. **Written speed drill** (6 min.) Time for 5 min.
   - Grade. Record as a speed drill/quiz grade. Count off 3 points for each incorrect answer.

3. **Review multiplying fractions.** (9 min.)
   - **B** Work 1st problem for child reminding him to mult. numerators together to get product numerator and mult. denominators together to get product denominator. Let him explain how to work last 2 problems. He should remember to check product to see if it can be reduced.
   - Child does **Ex. 1, p. 191.** Work 1 or 2 problems together.

4. **Review division.** (4 min.)
   - Give child 4 min. to do **Ex. 2.** Check.

5. **Review subtracting fractions.** (6 min.)
   - Work **Ex. 3** together.

6. **Review/Boardwork** (9 min.) **Ex. 4–6**

7. **Homework** **Ex. 7–8**

Mon

Preparation

Lesson

106

1. Chalkboard:

    $\frac{4}{7} \times \frac{7}{9} =$ $\frac{2}{3} \times \frac{6}{7} =$

    $37\overline{)4,902}$

   C $16\frac{3}{5}$

        $- \ 9\frac{11}{15}$

2. *Arithmetic 4:* pp. 193–194

3. *Lesson 106 Speed Drill*

4. Visuals:
   - *1–100 / 101–200 Charts (Arith Charts 23 / 25)*
   - *Concept Cards 80–104, 130–139, and 56–62*

Teaching Procedure

1. **Oral review drills** (6 min.)

   Homework check

   Processes (3 min.)
   - Mult./Div. 3–7 Tables
   - *1–100 / 101–200 Charts:* Point to 15, 30, 45, 60, 75, 90, 105, 120, and 135; child says as you point.
   - Oral comb.

     $6 \times 9 - 1 + 1 \times 2 + 8 = 116$ $2 \times 9 + 8 - 10 = 16$

     $5 + 9 - 2 \times 12 + 12 - 6 = 150$ $50 \div 2 + 8 + 8 \times 2 = 82$

     $5 \times 8 + 8 \div 6 + 8 - 2 \div 7 = 2$ $60 \times 1 + 8 + 10 \div 2 = 39$

     $63 + 7 + 30 \times 9 \div 3 \times 2 = 600$ $40 \div 5 \times 8 + 6 - 2 \div 2 = 34$

   Fractions (2 min.)
   - *Concept Cards* **80–104:** Child reduces to lowest terms.
   - *Concept Cards* **130–139:** Show fronts; child changes to whole or mixed numbers.
   - *Concept Cards* **133–139:** Show backs; child changes to improper fractions.

   Roman numerals (1 min.)
   - *Concept Cards* **56–62:**
   - Review rules for reading and writing Roman numerals.

2. **Written speed drill** (3 min.) Time for 2 min. 30 sec.

3. **Review multiplying fractions.** (6 min.)
   - **A** Work 1st problem for him. Child explains as you work 2nd problem. Remind him to check to see if product can be reduced.
   - Child does **Ex. 1, p. 193.**

Arithmetic 4 • 143

4. **Review division.** (6 min.)

- **B** Work problem on ckbd as he tells you what to do.
- Child does **Ex. 2.** Give help if needed.

5. **Review subtraction of fractions.** (6 min.)

- **C** Work problem as he tells you what to do.
- Child does **Ex. 3.**

6. **Review/Boardwork** (9 min.) **Ex. 4–7**

7. **Homework Ex. 8–9**

Lesson 107

Preparation

1. Chalkboard:

   A
23 + 9 = __	17 − 9 = __	25 x 8 = __	34 − 8 = __
11 x 11 = __	81 − 9 = __	100 ÷ 4 = __	67 + 23 = __

   B CXXXIII   CLXVII   CXCV   CI

   C $21 \frac{1}{3}$
   $- 7 \frac{3}{5}$

   D $\frac{5}{7} \times \frac{4}{5} =$

2. *Arithmetic 4:* pp. 195–196

3. *Lesson 107 Quiz*

4. Visuals:
   - *Process Flashcards*
   - *Concept Cards* 56–62 and 133–139
   - *101–200 Chart (Arith Chart 25)*

Teaching Procedure

1. **Oral review drills** (6 min.)

   Homework check

   Processes (3 min.)
   - *Flashcards:* Play a favorite game.
   - **A** Child writes answers on ckbd. He says tables.

   Roman numerals (1 min.)
   - *Concept Cards* **56–62**
   - *101–200 Chart /* **B** : Child points to Arabic numeral on chart that is same as Roman numeral on ckbd.

Fractions (2 min.)

- *Concept Cards* **133–139:** Show backs; child changes to improper fractions. Have him give rule that he used to change to improper fraction.
- Send him to ckbd to give an example of each: whole number, proper fraction, improper fraction, and mixed number.

2. **Quiz 11** (9 min.)

3. **Review subtraction of fractions.** (3 min.)
- **C** Child works on paper as you work at ckbd.
- Child does **Ex. 1, p. 195.**

4. **Review multiplication of fractions.** (3 min.)
- **D** Child works on paper as you work on ckbd.
- Child does **Ex. 2.**

5. **Discuss story problems.** (6 min.)
- Work **Ex. 3** together. After he gets an answer, he should read problem again to make sure answer makes sense.

6. **Review/Boardwork** (9 min.) **Ex. 4–9**

wed

Lesson

108

Preparation

1. Chalkboard:

A	4	9	10	13	21
B	24	81	19	33	14
C	500	419	716	102	332
D	303	420	105	717	900
E	117	203	540	183	702
F	50	21	700	810	505

2. *Arithmetic 4:* pp. 197–198

3. *Lesson 108 Speed Drill*

4. Visuals:
- *Division Flashcards*
- *Mixed Addition Facts (Arith 4, p. 311)*
- *Place Value (Arith Chart 2)*
- *Divisibility Rules (Arith Chart 12)*
- *Concept Cards 1–15, 24–47, 112–116, and 118–129*
- story problem clue words flashcards (optional from les. 4)
- 10 objects, such as wrapped candies, pencils, or erasers

Teaching Procedure

1. Oral review drills (9 min.)

Processes (4 min.)
- *Div. Cards:* Let child answer. If he does well, play *Four Corners.*
- *Mixed Addition Facts*

Place value (1 min.)
- *Arith Chart* **2**
- *Concept Cards* **1–15:** Child reads numbers and gives value of circled digits.

Story problems (1 min.)
- Story problem clue words flashcards

Measures (3 min.)
- *Concept Cards* **24–47, 112–116,** and **118–129:** Let him answer.
- Review rules for converting measures.

2. Written speed drill (4 min.) Time for 3 min.

3. Introduce divisibility rules. (15 min.)
- **10 objects:** Use this story problem or similar one to introduce divisibility rule for 2. *I have 10 candies that I want to share with 2 friends. Will each friend get an equal number of candies?* Demonstrate that each one gets 5 pieces. Tell him that when a number can be divided evenly, it is said to be divisible by that number. We can say that 10 is divisible by 2 because there is no remainder.
- *Arith Chart* **12:** Teach divisibility rule for 2.
- **A** Point to each number; child stands if divisible by 2.
- *Arith Chart* **12/ B–F :** Use chart to teach 1 rule at a time and then practice each rule, using ckbd. Ckbd B is for div. by 3, Ckbd C is for div. by 4, Ckbd D is for div. by 5, Ckbd E is for div. by 9, and Ckbd F is for div. by 10.
- Read and discuss **box on p. 197.** Child does **Ex. 1–7.** Keep chart displayed so he can refer to it. Child should study it during free time. You may want to work 1 or 2 problems in each ex. together.

4. Review/Boardwork (9 min.) **Ex. 8–11**

Thurs

Lesson 109

Preparation

1. Chalkboard:

A $\frac{24}{48}$ $\frac{310}{320}$ $\frac{45}{60}$ **B** $\frac{3}{8} \times \frac{4}{5} =$

2. *Arithmetic 4:* pp. 199–200

3. *Lesson 109 Speed Drill*

4. Visuals:
   - *Process Flashcards*
   - *Concept Cards* 56–62 and 133–139
   - *Divisibility Rules (Arith Chart 12)*
   - *1–100 Chart (Arith Chart 23)*

Teaching Procedure

1. Oral review drills (7 min.)

   Processes (4 min.)
   - *Flashcards:* Let child answer. After he gets warmed up, play a game.
   - Oral comb.

$7 + 8 - 6 + 4 = 13$	$5 + 8 + 1 \div 2 = 7$
$8 - 6 + 1 \div 1 = 3$	$5 + 10 \div 3 \times 4 = 20$
$7 + 4 - 4 + 10 = 17$	$8 + 8 \div 4 + 7 = 11$
$4 + 9 - 1 \div 2 = 6$	$10 + 10 + 11 + 2 = 33$

   Roman numerals (1 min.)
   - *Concept Cards* **56–62**

   Fractions (2 min.)
   - *Concept Cards* **133–139:** Show backs; child changes to improper fractions.
   - Call out these fractions; he reduces to lowest terms.
     $\frac{2}{4}$ $\frac{3}{6}$ $\frac{5}{15}$ $\frac{4}{8}$ $\frac{6}{9}$ $\frac{5}{10}$

2. Written speed drill (6 min.) Time for 5 min.
   - Grade. Record as a speed drill/quiz grade. Count off 5 points for each incorrect answer.

3. Introduce using divisibility rules. (9 min.)
   - *Arith Chart* **12:** Review rules.
   - *1–100 Chart:* Point to several numbers; child tells you if divisible by 2, 3, 4, 5, 9, or 10.

   - **A** Work problems step by step.

$\frac{24}{48} = \frac{6}{12} = \frac{2}{4} = \frac{1}{2}$
   Step 1: Both 24 and 48 are divisible by 4.
   Step 2: Both 6 and 12 are divisible by 3.
   Step 3: Both 2 and 4 are divisible by 2. (Child may notice that $\frac{6}{12}$ reduces to $\frac{1}{2}$ and skip dividing by 3 and 2.)

$\frac{310}{320} = \frac{31}{32}$
   Step 1: Both 310 and 320 are divisible by 10. $\frac{31}{32}$ is in lowest terms.

$\frac{45}{60} = \frac{9}{12} = \frac{3}{4}$
   Step 1: Both 45 and 60 are divisible by 5.
   Step 2: Both 9 and 12 are divisible by 3.
   - Read and discuss **box on p. 199.** Child does **Ex. 1.** You may need to work a couple problems with him. Give any needed help. Most students understand and can work independently.

4. **Review multiplying fractions.** (3 min.)
   - **B** Child explains as you work on ckbd.
   - Child does **Ex. 2.**
5. **Discuss story problems.** (6 min.)
   - Do **Ex. 3** together.
6. **Review/Boardwork** (6 min.) **Ex. 4–6**
7. **Homework Ex. 7**

Fri

Lesson 110

Preparation

1. Chalkboard:

   A $1\frac{4}{7}$ $\quad 1\frac{3}{19}$ $\quad 1\frac{4}{9}$ $\quad 1\frac{3}{5}$ $\quad 1\frac{7}{8}$

   B $\frac{2}{3} \times \frac{3}{4} =$ $\quad \frac{5}{6} \times \frac{4}{15} =$ $\quad \frac{2}{9} \times \frac{3}{4} =$

2. *Arithmetic 4:* pp. 201–202

3. *Lesson 110 Speed Drill*

4. Visuals:
   - *Process Flashcards*
   - *Divisibility Rules (Arith Chart* 12)
   - *Concept Cards* 80–104, 24–47, 112–116, and 118–129

Teaching Procedure

1. **Oral review drills** (9 min.)

   Homework check

   Processes (4 min.)
   - *Flashcards:* Review. If child does well, play a favorite game.
   - Mult./Div. Tables
   - *Arith Chart* **12:** Review divisibility rules.

   Fractions (3 min.)
   - **A** Point to each mixed number; he changes to improper fractions.
   - *Concept Cards* **80–104:** Child reduces to lowest terms.
   - *Concept Cards* **80–104:** Show backs of 2 cards; he gives l.c.d.

   Measures (2 min.)
   - *Concept Cards* **24–47, 112–116,** and **118–129**

2. **Written speed drill** (4 min.) Time for 3 min.

3. **Introduce cancellation.** (9 min.)
   - **B** Work 1st problem for him as usual. Reduce answer to lowest terms. Tell him that we can save some work of reducing large fractions in the product by using a process called cancellation. Work 1st problem again, using cancellation.
     Step 1: Check numerator 2 of 1st fraction and denomi-

$$\overset{1}{\underset{1}{\cancel{2}}} \times \overset{1}{\underset{2}{\cancel{3}}} = \frac{1 \times 1}{1 \times 2} = \frac{1}{2}$$

nator 4 of 2nd fraction to see if they have a common factor. Since they both have 2 as a common factor, they are both divisible by 2. Divide both terms by 2.

Step 2: Check the denominator 3 of 1st fraction and numerator 3 of 2nd fraction to see if they have a common factor. Divide both terms by 3.

Step 3: Multiply the new numerator by the new numerator. Multiply the new denominator by the new denominator. If cancellation was done completely, there is no need to reduce the product.

Multiply other 2 problems, using cancellation.

- Read and discuss **box on p. 201.** Work **Ex. 1** together. Child works **Ex. 2.** It may be necessary to work a few problems together.

4. Review fraction problems. (6 min.)

- Give child 2½ min. to answer **Ex. 3.** Check. Child does **Ex. 4.**

5. Review/Boardwork (9 min.) **Ex. 5–8**

6. Homework Ex. 9

Lesson
111

Preparation

1. Chalkboard:

| A | $\frac{3}{4}$ x $\frac{4}{5}$ = | $\frac{4}{9}$ x $\frac{3}{4}$ = | $\frac{6}{11}$ x $\frac{11}{12}$ = |

| B | $\frac{18}{108}$ | $\frac{56}{100}$ | $\frac{35}{55}$ |

2. *Arithmetic 4:* pp. 203–204

3. *Lesson 111 Speed Drill*

4. Visuals:
   - *Process Flashcards*
   - *Divisibility Rules (Arith Chart* 12)
   - Story problem clue words flashcards (optional from les. 4)
   - *Concept Cards* 80–104 and 63
   - *1–100 Chart (Arith Chart* 23)

Teaching Procedure

1. Oral review drills (6 min.)

Homework check

Processes (4 min.)
   - Mult./Div. 9–12 Tables
   - *Flashcards:* Review with child.
   - *Arith Chart* **12:** Review divisibility rules.

Story problems (1 min.)
- Story problem clue words flashcards

Fractions (1 min.)
- *Concept Cards* **80–104:** Show fronts of some cards and backs of others; child stands if fraction is reduced to lowest terms.
- *Concept Card* **63:** Review fraction terminology and job of each term.

2. **Written speed drill** (3 min.) Time for 2 min.

3. **Review cancellation.** (6 min.)
- [A] Work 3 problems on ckbd for him. Use cancellation when working problems.
- Child does **Ex. 1, p. 203.** If he needs help, work a couple problems with him.

4. **Review divisibility rules.** (9 min.)
- *Arith Chart* **12:** Review rules.
- *1–100 Counting Chart:* Point to numbers; he tells if they are divisible by number that you say.
- [B] Reduce fractions by using divisibility rules.
- Child does **Ex. 2–3.**

5. **Review/Boardwork** (12 min.) **Ex. 4–8**

6. **Homework Ex. 9**

Lesson 112

Preparation

Test 11, pp. 89–90 from *Student Tests and Speed Drills*

Teaching Procedure

1. **Homework check**

2. **Administer test.**
This test allows space to work story problems on test sheet.

Lesson 113

Preparation

1. Chalkboard:

[A]	24	71	29	38	50
[B]	121	821	306	711	345

2. *Arithmetic 4:* pp. 205–206

3. *Lesson 113 Speed Drill*

4. Visuals:
   - *Mixed Addition Facts (Arith 4, p. 311)*
   - *Mixed Subtraction Facts (Arith 4, p. 316)*
   - *Mixed Multiplication Facts (Arith 4, p. 319)*
   - *Mixed Division Facts (Arith 4, p. 322)*
   - *Concept Cards 24–47, 112–116, 118–129, and 56–62*
   - *101–200 Chart (Arith Chart 25)*
   - *Divisibility Rules (Arith Chart 12)*

Teaching Procedure

1. Oral review drills (9 min.)

Processes (4 min.)
   - Mult./Div. 4–6 Tables
   - **A** Point to each number; child stands if divisible by 2.
   - **B** Point to each number; he stands if divisible by 3.
   - Mixed Facts for Addition, Subtraction, Multiplication, and Division

Measures (3 min.)
   - *Concept Cards* **24–47, 112–116,** and **118–129:** After child answers, play a game.

Roman numerals (2 min.)
   - *Concept Cards* **56–62:** Let him answer.
   - *101–200 Chart:* Point to numbers; he writes Roman numeral equivalent on ckbd.

2. Written speed drill (4 min.) Time for 3 min.

3. Review factoring and least common multiple. (6 min.)
   - Work **Ex. 1a, p. 205** together. He completes ex.
   - Work **Ex 2a–c** together. Child completes ex.

4. Review divisibility rules. (3 min.)
   - *Arith Chart* **12:** Review rules.
   - Child does **Ex. 3.** Have him read statements and give answers.

5. Review cancellation. (6 min.)
   - Work **Ex. 4** together. Be sure he understands concept of cancellation.

6. Review/Boardwork (9 min.) **Ex. 5–9** Notice that Ex. 8–9 are Extra Practice and are therefore optional.

Preparation

Lesson
114

1. Chalkboard:
   $$\frac{3}{5} \times \frac{14}{15} = \qquad \frac{7}{9} \times \frac{3}{8} =$$

2. *Arithmetic 4:* pp. 207–208

3. *Lesson 114 Speed Drill*

4. Visuals:
- *Process Flashcards*
- *Divisibility Rules (Arith Chart* 12)
- *Concept Cards* 24–47 and 112–116

Teaching Procedure

1. **Oral review drills** (9 min.)

    Processes (6 min.)
    - *Flashcards:* Review. If he does well, play a favorite game.
    - *Arith Chart* **12:** Review rules.
    - Mult. Tables: Play *Just the Facts.*
    - Oral comb.

$5 \times 10 - 20 + 45 = 75$	$4 \times 5 + 20 \times 4 + 2 = 162$
$14 + 2 \div 4 + 4 \times 9 = 72$	$1 + 1 + 1 + 1 \times 9 \div 9 = 4$
$2 \times 8 + 16 \div 8 + 10 = 14$	$4 + 7 + 7 - 18 + 2 = 2$
$8 \times 5 - 5 \div 5 + 2 = 9$	$14 - 14 + 5 + 8 = 13$
$12 \times 2 \times 1 - 2 = 22$	$13 + 8 \div 7 \times 4 = 12$

    Measures (3 min.)
    - *Concept Cards* **24–47** and **112–116:** Let him answer and then play *Capture the Card.*

2. **Written speed drill** (3 min.) Time for 2 min.

3. **Discuss story problems.** (6 min.)
    - Have child listen to these story problems and tell you what facts are needed to be able to solve.
        - 1: *I want to buy 3 pounds of oranges. How much will all three pounds cost?* **what is cost per pound**
        - 2: *Quentin ran the mile in 9 minutes. Adam was faster. How long did it take Adam to run the mile?* **how much faster was Adam than Quentin**
        - 3: *Millie missed 3 words on her spelling test. How many words did she spell correctly?* **how many words were on test**
        - 4: *Greg went to bed $\frac{1}{2}$ hour after his sister. What time did Greg go to bed?* **what time did sister go to bed**
        - 5: *William ate $\frac{1}{3}$ of the chocolate chip cookies. How many cookies did he eat?* **how many chocolate chip cookies were there**
    - Work **Ex. 1, p. 207** together.

4. **Review multiplication of fractions.** (6 min.)
    - ▇▇▇ He explains cancellation and how to mult. as you work on ckbd.
    - Child does **Ex. 2.**

5. **Review/Boardwork** (12 min.) **Ex. 3–5**

6. **Homework Ex. 6**

Preparation

1. Chalkboard:

   A $\frac{2}{4}$ $\frac{4}{10}$ $\frac{7}{14}$ $\frac{6}{9}$ $\frac{5}{25}$

   B $5 \times \frac{3}{5} =$ $\frac{4}{9} \times 12 =$ $\frac{2}{3} \times 6 =$

   C $27\overline{)2{,}654}$

2. *Arithmetic 4:* pp. 209–210

3. *Lesson 115 Speed Drill*

4. Visuals:
   - *Process Flashcards*
   - *Averaging Numbers (Arith Chart* 6)
   - *Concept Cards* 130–139, 80–104, 24–47, 112–116 and 118–129

Teaching Procedure

1. **Oral review drills** (8 min.)

   Homework check

   Processes (4 min.)
   - *Flashcards:* Have child answer. Play a game if he does well.
   - Mult./Div. 10–12 Tables
   - *Arith Chart* 6: Review steps to average numbers.

   Fractions (2 min.)

   - A   Point to each fraction; he reduces to lowest terms.
   - *Concept Cards* **130–139:** Show fronts; child changes to whole or mixed numbers.
   - *Concept Cards* **133–139:** Show backs; he changes to improper fractions.
   - *Concept Cards* **80–104:** He reduces to lowest terms.

   Measures (2 min.)
   - *Concept Cards* **24–47, 112–116,** and **118–129**
   - Review measurement rules.

2. **Written speed drill** (6 min.) Time for 5 min.
   - Grade. Record as a speed drill/quiz grade. Count off 3 points for each incorrect answer.

3. **Introduce multiplying a fraction and a whole number.** (9 min.)
   - Write $^5/_1$ on ckbd. Point to fraction bar and remind him that it is another way to show division. Have child tell you what 5 div. by 1 is. (5) Point out that when we take a whole number and put it over denominator 1 that it does not change value of whole number.
   - B   Work 1st problem for him.

   $5 \times \frac{3}{5} = 3$

   $\frac{\cancel{5}^1}{1} \times \frac{3}{\cancel{5}_1}$

   $\frac{3}{1} = 3$

   Step 1: Make 5 an improper fraction by placing it over 1. Remind students that this does not change value of number.

Lesson 115
(cont.)

Step 2: Use cancellation.
Step 3: Multiply as usual.
Use same steps to work other problems.

- Read and discuss **box on p. 209.** Child does **Ex. 1.** Work a few problems in **Ex. 2** together. Let him finish ex.

4. Review division. (6 min.)

- Work problem as child tells you what to do.
- Child does **Ex. 3.**

5. Review/Boardwork (9 min.) **Ex. 4–6**

6. Homework Ex. 7–8

mon

Lesson 116

Preparation

1. Chalkboard:

A $\frac{4}{7}$ x $\frac{21}{22}$ =   12 x $\frac{3}{4}$ =

B $13\frac{2}{5}$

2. *Arithmetic 4:* pp. 211–212

3. *Lesson 116 Speed Drill*

4. Visuals:

- Mixed Facts Chart (see lesson 49)
- *Calculator (Arith Chart 20)*
- Story problem clue words flash-cards (optional from les. 4)

- *Concept Cards 56–62*

Teaching Procedure

1. Oral review drills (7 min.)

Homework check

Processes (4 min.)

- Mult./Div. 7–9 Tables
- Mixed Facts Chart
- Call out these numbers; child gives 2 factors of each.
  32   72   14   25   63   36
- *Calculator:* Point to numbers; he mult. by 9 and add 7.
- Oral comb.

  5 x 5 + 5 − 10 ÷ 5 = *4*   5 x 6 − 5 + 9 + 1 ÷ 5 = *7*

  10 x 2 + 12 − 9 + 1 ÷ 6 = *4*   5 + 5 + 6 − 3 + 2 = *15*

  3 + 5 + 2 − 3 + 4 = *11*   4 x 6 + 4 ÷ 4 = *7*

Story problems (1 min.)

- Story problem clue words flashcards

Roman numerals (2 min.)

- *Concept Cards* **56–62**
- Review rules for reading and writing Roman numerals.

2. Written speed drill (6 min.) Time for 5 min.
- Grade. Record as a speed drill/quiz grade. Count off 5 points for each incorrect answer.

3. Review multiplying fractions. (9 min.)
- **A** Work problems for him. Remind him that in 2nd problem we can make whole number an improper fraction by placing over 1. The value is not changed.
- Child does **Ex. 1, p. 211.**

4. Review changing mixed numbers. (3 min.)
- **B** He gives steps to change mixed number to improper fraction.
- Child does **Ex. 2.**

5. Review/Boardwork (12 min.) **Ex. 3–6**

6. Homework Ex. 7–10

Lesson 117

Preparation

1. Chalkboard:

   A

$27 - 19 =$ __	$47 + 9 =$ __	$15 \times 8 =$ __	$40 - 8 =$ __
$12 \times 10 =$ __	$34 - 19 =$ __	$400 \div 4 =$ __	$63 - 25 =$ __

   B   XCIX   LXXIV   XXXIX   XLVI

   C $\frac{1}{2} \times \frac{1}{4} =$ $\frac{3}{7} \times \frac{14}{15} =$

   D $16\frac{2}{5}$
   $-\ 7\frac{1}{2}$

2. *Arithmetic 4:* pp. 213–214

3. *Lesson 117 Quiz*

4. Visuals:
   - *Process Flashcards*
   - *1–100 Chart*
   - *Concept Card*s 56–62, 133–139, and 80–104

Teaching Procedure

1. Oral review drills (9 min.)

Homework check

Processes (3 min.)
- *Flashcards:* Play a favorite game.
- **A** Child writes answers on ckbd. Child says tables.

Lesson 117
(cont.)

Roman numerals (1 min.)
- *Concept Cards* **56–62**
- *1–100 Chart /* He points to Arabic numeral on chart that is same as Roman numeral on ckbd.

Fractions (5 min.)
- *Concept Cards* **133–139:** Show backs; he changes to improper fractions. Have him give rule that they used to change to improper fraction.
- C/D Child works on paper as you work at ckbd.
- *Concept Cards* **80–104:** Show fronts of some cards and backs of others; he stands if in lowest terms.

2. **Quiz 12** (9 min.)

3. **Review division.** (9 min.)
- Give child 30 sec. to do **Ex. 1, p. 213.** Call out answers and praise child who missed 0.
- Child does **Ex. 2–4.**

4. **Review/Boardwork** (9 min.) **Ex. 5–9**

wed

Lesson
118

Preparation

1. Chalkboard:

   $\frac{1}{2}$ x $1\frac{3}{4}$ = $\frac{3}{4}$ x $1\frac{1}{3}$ = $\frac{2}{5}$ x $2\frac{1}{6}$ =

2. *Arithmetic 4:* pp. 215–216

3. *Lesson 118 Speed Drill*

4. Visuals:
   - *Process Flashcards*
   - *Averaging Numbers (Arith Chart 6)*
   - *Divisibility Rules (Arith Chart 12)*
   - *Concept Cards 133–139*
   - *Fractional Circles*

Teaching Procedure

1. **Oral review drills** (9 min.)

   Processes (6 min.)
   - *Flashcards:* Let child answer. If he does well, play *Four Corners.*
   - *Arith Chart* **6:** Review steps for averaging numbers.
   - *Arith Chart* **12:** Review divisibility rules.
   - Mult./Div. Tables

   Fractions (3 min.)
   - *Concept Cards* **133–139:** He changes to improper fractions.
   - Child explains how to mult. a fraction by a fraction.

  • Send him to ckbd to write several whole numbers as improper fractions. Be sure he understands that value has not changed.

2. Written speed drill (4 min.) Time for 3 min.

3. Introduce multiplying fractions and mixed numbers. (9 min.)
  • **Fractional Circles:** Have 2 halves and 6 eighths displayed. Write $\frac{1}{2}$ x $1\frac{3}{4}$ on ckbd. Child tells what $\frac{1}{2}$ of 1 whole is. ($\frac{1}{2}$) He tells what $\frac{1}{2}$ of $\frac{3}{4}$ is. Show $\frac{6}{8}$ which is equal to $\frac{3}{4}$. He can easily see that $\frac{1}{2}$ of $\frac{6}{8}$ is $\frac{3}{8}$. That means that $\frac{1}{2}$ of $\frac{3}{4}$ is also $\frac{3}{8}$. Write $\frac{1}{2}$ + $\frac{3}{8}$ on ckbd. Find sum after you get a common denominator. ($\frac{7}{8}$)

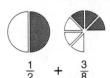

$$\frac{1}{2} \quad + \quad \frac{3}{8}$$

  • 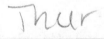 Tell him there is an easier way to mult. a fraction and a mixed number. Work 1st problem step by step for him.

$$\frac{1}{2} \times 1\frac{3}{4} = \frac{7}{8}$$
$$\frac{1}{2} \times \frac{7}{4} =$$
$$\frac{7}{8}$$

  Step 1: Change mixed number to improper fraction.
  Step 2: Use cancellation.
  Step 3: Mult. as usual. Have him notice that $\frac{7}{8}$ is same answer that we got when we used our Fractional Circles.

  Use same steps to work last 2 problems. Remind him that he must change any whole number or mixed number to improper fraction before mult.

  • Read and discuss **box on p. 215.** Child does **Ex. 1.** Work a few problems together.

4. Discuss story problems. (6 min.)
  • Read, discuss, and work **Ex. 2** together.

5. Review/Boardwork (9 min.) **Ex. 3–5**

Thur

Preparation

1. Chalkboard:

   $7 \times \frac{3}{14} =$ $1\frac{1}{6} \times \frac{3}{7} =$ $\frac{3}{8} \times \frac{4}{11} =$

2. *Arithmetic 4:* pp. 217–218

3. *Lesson 119 Speed Drill*

4. Visuals:
   • *Process Flashcards*
   • *Mixed Subtraction Facts (Arith 4, p. 316)*
   • *Concept Cards* 133–139, 24–47, 112–116, and 118–129

Teaching Procedure

1. Oral review drills (9 min.)

  Processes (6 min.)
  • *Flashcards:* Play *Stepping over the Park.* Tell child that the smallest official park is in Oregon and that it is only 24 inches across. He uses hands to show about how wide park is. Child

is a camper. Show cards to him; when he answers correctly he goes to back of room. The camper gets to move forward by stepping about 24 inches every time he answers correctly. When camper reaches front of room he is a winner.

- Mult./Div. Tables
- *Mixed Subtraction Facts*

Fractions (1 min.)

- *Concept Cards* **133–139:** Show backs; child changes to improper fractions.

Measures (2 min.)

- *Concept Cards* **24–47, 112–116,** and **118–129**

2. Written speed drill (3 min.) Time for 2 min.

3. Review multiplication of fractions. (9 min.)

- ▮ Work problems step by step.
- Child does **Ex. 1, p. 217.** You may need to work a couple problems with him. Give help if needed. Most children understand and can work independently.

4. Discuss story problems. (6 min.)

- Do **Ex. 2** together.

5. Review/Boardwork (9 min.) **Ex. 3–5**

6. Homework Ex. 6–7

Lesson 120

Preparation

1. Chalkboard:

   A | VIII   XII   DCVI   MCD   IV   LXXX

   B | $14 \times \frac{3}{7} =$ $\frac{5}{8} \times 1\frac{1}{5} =$ $\frac{3}{5} \times \frac{4}{7} =$

2. *Arithmetic 4:* pp. 219–220

3. *Lesson 120 Speed Drill*

4. Visuals:

   - *Process Flashcards*
   - *Mixed Multiplication Facts (Arith 4, p.319)*
   - *Concept Cards 56–62, 24–47, 112–116,* and *118–129*

Teaching Procedure

1. Oral review drills (9 min.)

Homework check

Processes (6 min.)

- *Flashcards:* Play a favorite game.
- Mult./Div. Tables
- *Mixed Multiplication Facts*

- Oral comb.

  $15 + 5 - 2 \div 2 + 1 - 4 \div 2 = 3$ $4 + 4 \div 4 + 2 \div 2 + 9 \div 11 = 1$

  $8 - 3 + 30 \div 5 = 7$ $1 + 9 \times 10 - 10 \div 10 = 9$

  $6 \times 9 + 9 \div 7 = 9$ $2 + 2 \div 4 + 5 \div 2 = 3$

  $5 + 5 \div 10 = 1$ $2 - 1 \times 10 + 10 \div 10 = 2$

  $5 - 4 + 3 \div 2 = 2$ $9 \times 7 + 1 \div 8 \times 2 = 16$

Roman numerals (1 min.)

- *Concept Cards* **56–62**

- **A** Point to Roman numeral on ckbd; he responds with correct Arabic numeral.

Measures (2 min.)

- *Concept Cards* **24–47, 112–116,** and **118–129**

2. **Written speed drill** (3 min.) Time for 2 min.

3. **Review multiplication.** (6 min.)

- **B** Work problems for child as he explains how to work.

- Child works **Ex. 1, p. 219.**

4. **Review division.** (6 min.)

- Have a ckbd contest, using **Ex. 2.**

5. **Discuss story problems.** (3 min.)

- Work **Ex. 3** together.

6. **Review/Boardwork** (9 min.) **Ex. 4–7**

7. **Homework Ex. 8–9**

Lesson

121

Preparation

1. Chalkboard:

A

$7\frac{3}{5}$ $6\frac{3}{4}$

$-4\frac{2}{15}$ $+5\frac{1}{2}$

B $7\frac{1}{2}$ x $\frac{4}{5}$ =

2. *Arithmetic 4:* pp. 221–222

3. *Lesson 121 Speed Drill*

4. Visuals:
   - *Process Flashcards*
   - *Divisibility Rules (Arith Chart 12)*
   - *Concept Cards* 80–104, 130–139, 24–47, 112–116, and 118–129

Teaching Procedure

1. **Oral review drills** (9 min.)

   Homework check

   Processes (3 min.)
   - Mult./Div. Tables
   - *Flashcards:* Review with child.
   - *Arith Chart* **12:** Review divisibility rules.
   - Call out these numbers; students give factors.

     32   16   80   72   24   12   96   48   35   15

   Fractions (3 min.)
   - *Concept Cards* **80–104:** Show fronts of some cards and backs of others; he stands if fraction is reduced to lowest terms.
   - *Concept Cards* **130–139:** He changes to whole or mixed numbers.
   - Send child to ckbd to write an example of an improper fraction. Then have him write an example of a proper fraction.

   Measures (3 min.)
   - *Concept Cards* **24–47, 112–116,** and **118–129:** Review with child and then play a game.

2. **Written speed drill** (4 min.) Time for 3 min.

3. **Review fractions.** (9 min.)
   - **A/B** Work 3 problems on ckbd for him. He should explain each step and answer.
   - Child does **Ex. 1, p. 221.** If he needs help, work a couple problems with him.

4. **Discuss story problems.** (6 min.)
   - Read, discuss, and work **Ex. 2** together.

5. **Review/Boardwork** (9 min.) **Ex. 3–7**

6. **Homework Ex. 8–9**

───────────────────────────────

Preparation

Test 12, pp. 97–98 from *Student Tests and Speed Drills*

Teaching Procedure

1. Homework check **2. Administer test.**

wed

───────────────────────────────

Preparation

1. Chalkboard:
    $4 \times 1\frac{1}{3} =$ $\frac{7}{8} \times \frac{2}{5} =$ $2\frac{1}{2} \times 1\frac{1}{3} =$

2. *Arithmetic 4:* pp. 223–224

3. *Lesson 123 Speed Drill*

4. Visuals:
   - *Divisibility Rules (Arith Chart* 12)
   - *1–100 Chart (Arith Chart* 23)
   - *Mixed Division Facts (Arith 4, p.322)*
   - *Concept Cards* 24–47, 112–116, and 118–129
   - story problem clue words flashcards (optional from les. 4)
   - samples of pictographs from newspapers, magazines, or other sources (optional)
   - books of several types: mysteries, animal stories, information Have a few of each type on table.

Teaching Procedure

1. Oral review drills (9 min.)

Processes (6 min.)
- Mult./Div. Tables
- *Arith Chart* **12:** Review divisibility rules.
- *1–100 Chart:* Point to numbers; child tells if divisible by number that you say.
- *Mixed Division Facts*
- Oral comb.

   $108 \div 12 \times 6 - 4 \div 10 \times 3 = 15$ $33 \div 11 \times 9 + 6 - 5 \div 7 + 2 = 6$

   $50 \div 2 + 5 \div 6 \times 9 + 3 \div 6 = 8$ $19 - 9 \times 12 \div 12 \times 4 \div 8 = 5$

   $6 \times 9 - 1 \times 2 + 8 = 114$ $6 + 5 + 4 \div 3 - 5 \times 6 + 3 = 3$

Measures (2 min.)
- *Concept Cards* **24–47, 112–116,** and **118–129:** After he answers several, play a favorite game.

Story problems (1 min.)
- Story problem clue words flashcards

Lesson 123
(cont.)

2. **Written speed drill** (4 min.) Time for 3 min.

3. **Introduce pictographs.** (9 min.)
   - **Pictograph samples: A graph is a picture of information. A pictograph uses pictures to show the information.** Discuss that we are not always interested in a column of numbers, but we like to look at a picture that explains the numbers. A pictograph also lets us easily make comparisons.
   - Develop a simple pictograph on ckbd with child. Write title of *Books We Read*. To the left write labels of *mysteries, animal stories,* and *information books*. Below draw a little book and make it equal to 2 books. Separate books on the table into 3 types. Count the number of mystery books. Draw 1 book for every 2 mystery books. If odd number of books, represent last book with half book. Continue with other 2 labels. Point out that symbols for each label should be aligned right under each other. Have child look at graph to see how easy it is to compare preferences.

Books We Read

mysteries

animal stories

information books

(Books are samples. Develop graph according to your sample.)

= 2 books

   - Read and discuss **box on p. 223.** Work **Ex. 1** together.

4. **Review multiplying fractions.** (6 min.)
   - Child works on paper while you work and explain on ckbd.
   - Child does **Ex. 2.**

5. **Review/Boardwork** (9 min.) **Ex. 3–7** Notice that Ex. 6–7 are Extra Practice and are therefore optional.

Thur

Lesson
124

Preparation

1. Chalkboard:

   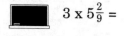 $3 \times 5\frac{2}{9} =$ 532
                                          x 629

2. *Arithmetic 4:* pp. 225–226

3. *Lesson 124 Speed Drill*

4. Visuals:

- *Process Flashcards*
- *Divisibility Rules (Arith Chart* 12)
- *Concept Cards* 56–62, 24–47, and 112–116

Teaching Procedure

1. **Oral review drills** (10 min.)

   Processes (6 min.)
   - *Flashcards:* Review. Encourage child to be fast with answers. If he does well, play a game.
   - *Arith Chart* **12:** Review rules.
   - Mult. Tables: Play *Just the Facts.*

   Roman numerals (1 min.)
   - *Concept Cards* **56–62**

   Measures (3 min.)
   - *Concept Cards* **24–47** and **112–116:** Review briefly.
   - Review 2 rules for converting measures. Call out 2 units, such as ounces to pounds; he responds with mult. or div.

2. **Written speed drill** (2 min.) Time for 1 min. 30 sec.

3. **Review pictographs.** (6 min.)
   - Work **Ex. 1–3, p. 225** together.

4. **Review multiplication.** (12 min.)
   - Child works on paper as you work on ckbd.
   - Child does **Ex. 4.** Check child's work.

5. **Review/Boardwork** (6 min.) **Ex. 5–6**

6. **Homework Ex. 7** Child needs ruler for les. 125.

Preparation

1. Chalkboard:

   A Rebecca: 15 votes   Jim: 10 votes   Blake: 5 votes

   B $\frac{1}{5} \times 4\frac{2}{7} =$

2. *Arithmetic 4:* pp. 227–228

3. *Lesson 125 Speed Drill*

4. Visuals:
   - *Process Flashcards*
   - *Concept Cards* 130–139 and 80–104

• samples of bar graphs from newspapers, magazines, and other sources (optional)
• yardstick
• ruler

Teaching Procedure

1. **Oral review drills** (4 min.)

   Homework check

   Processes (2 min.)
   • *Flashcards:* Have child answer a few cards.
   • Mult./Div. Tables

   Fractions (2 min.)
   • *Concept Cards* **130–139:** Show fronts; child changes to whole or mixed numbers.
   • *Concept Cards* **133–139:** Show backs; child changes to improper fractions.
   • *Concept Cards* **80–104:** Child reduces to lowest terms.

2. **Written speed drill** (6 min.) Time for 5 min.
   • Exchange and grade. Record as a speed drill/quiz grade. Count off 10 points for each incorrect answer.

3. **Introduce bar graphs.** (12 min.)
   • **Bar graph samples:** Tell child that a pictograph is only 1 type of graph. Another common graph is a bar graph. **A bar graph uses vertical or horizontal bars to picture information.** Demonstrate vertical and horizontal directions.
   • **A** yardstick. Use information on ckbd to develop bar graph. Write title of *Votes for Class President*. To left, write labels of *Rebecca, Jim,* and *Blake*. Draw a rectangular box to hold horizontal bars. Write *0* under left vertex. Write *5, 10,* and *15* to complete scale. *15* should be under right vertex with *5* and *10* evenly spaced. Draw vertical lines from top of rectangle to number scales. Use yardstick to draw 3 bars corresponding to information on ckbd. You may want to use different colors of chalk for each bar to make graph more attractive. Discuss graph with child.

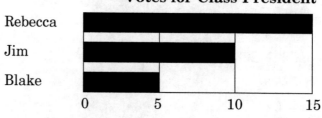

Votes for Class President

   • Read and discuss **box on p. 227.** Do **Ex. 1–3** together. He should use ruler to make bars straight in Ex. 3. You may want to suggest that he uses colored pencils to make bar graph more attractive.

4. Review multiplying fractions. (6 min.)

- ▎B▎ Work problem as he tells you what to do.
- Child does **Ex. 4.**

5. Review/Boardwork (9 min.) **Ex. 5–6**

6. Homework Ex. 7 Child needs ruler for les. 126.

Lesson
126

Preparation

1. Chalkboard:

▎A▎
$$\begin{array}{r} 73{,}246 \\ 59{,}732 \\ 74{,}957 \\ 54{,}029 \\ +\,83{,}575 \\ \hline \end{array}$$

▎B▎ $36\overline{)3{,}264}$

2. *Arithmetic 4:* pp. 229–230

3. *Lesson 126 Speed Drill*

4. Visuals:
   - *Process Flashcards*
   - *Divisibility Rules (Arith Chart* 12)
   - *Calculator (Arith Chart 20)*
   - story problem clue words flash-
     cards (optional from les. 4)
   - *Concept Cards* 80–104
     and 133–139
   - ruler

Teaching Procedure

1. Oral review drills (9 min.)

Homework check

Processes (6 min.)
- *Flashcards:* Review. Play *Around the World.*
- Mult./Div. Tables
- *Arith Chart* **12:** Review divisibility rules.
- ▎A▎ Use standard procedure.
- *Calculator:* Child pushes numbers to make 2,000 more than
  56,400. Then he pushes 2,000 less than 27,800.

Story problems (1 min.)
- Story problem clue words flashcards

Fractions (2 min.)
- *Concept Cards* **80–104:** Child reduces to lowest terms.
- *Concept Cards* **133–139:** Show backs; he changes to improper
  fractions.

2. **Written speed drill** (4 min.) Time for 3 min.

3. **Review graphs.** (9 min.)
- Child does **Ex. 1–3, p. 229.** He should use ruler to make neat bars in Ex. 1–2. Remind him to align faces for each label in Ex. 3. If the symbols are not aligned, it is not easy to compare.

4. **Review division.** (6 min.)
- **B** Work problem on ckbd. Write remainder as a fraction. Let him decide what reduced fraction will be.
- Child does **Ex. 4.**

5. **Review/Boardwork** (9 min.) **Ex. 5–6**

6. **Homework Ex. 7** Child needs ruler in les. 127.

Lesson 127

Preparation

1. Chalkboard:

A
237,893
896,783
783,904
893,429
+ 206,774

B (5, 10) (10, 15)
C (6, 7) (11, 13)

2. *Arithmetic 4:* pp. 231–232

3. *Lesson 127 Quiz*

4. Visuals:
- *Process Flashcards*
- *Concept Cards* 133–139 and 80–104
- *"Lion" Graph (Arith Chart* 22)—(Cut out small circles from sticky notes. Half of circle should be sticky and half should not be sticky. If all is sticky, it is hard to remove from graph. If only part is sticky, it will stick easily and remove easily.)
- ruler

Teaching Procedure

1. **Oral review drills** (6 min.)

   Homework check

   Processes (3 min.)
   - *Flashcards:* Play a favorite game.
   - **A** Use standard procedure.
   - Mult./Div. Tables

Fractions (3 min.)

- *Concept Cards* **133–139:** Show backs; child changes to improper fractions. Have him give rule that he used to change to improper fraction.
- *Concept Cards* **80–104:** Show fronts of some cards and backs of others; child stands if in lowest terms.

2. Quiz 13 (9 min.)

3. Introduce line graphs. (12 min.)

- *"Lion" Graph*/sticky circles: Tell him that we are going to learn about line graphs. Show graph and tell them a line graph is made on a grid similar to this. Show horizontal scale and vertical scale. To make a line graph, we use our information to plot points.

- **B** Point to 1st pair of numbers. Tell him that we can easily plot this information on line graph. Point to 5 and tell child that 1st number tells us how far to go across on horizontal scale. Point to 10 and tell child 2nd number tells us how far to go up on vertical scale. Put sticky circle at (5, 10). He should notice that we just put 1 point.

  Show child how to plot (10, 15) on graph. Let him plot (10, 5) on graph.

- **C** Point to 6 in 1st pair of numbers. Show about where 6 is on horizontal scale. Point to 7 and show him about where 7 is on vertical scale. Put point. Demonstrate how to estimate about where (11, 13) is on graph.

  Tell child that a line graph is a picture of information, using the grid. **A line graph often is used to picture change over a period of time.**

- Read and discuss **box on p. 231.** Point out that points are connected after they are all plotted. The connected points make the line. (Lines are neater if connected with ruler.) Do **Ex. 1–4** together. As child does Ex. 4, point out that test number is horizontal scale and test score is vertical scale. He goes across to test number and up to score and then plots point. He should have 5 points to represent each of 5 tests. Tell him that graph shows how he goes up and down on tests.

4. Review place value. (3 min.)

- Call these numbers for **Ex. 5.**
  - **a.** 103,260,000
  - **b.** 14,000,180
  - **c.** 500,006,006
  - **d.** 3,002,500

5. Review/Boardwork (6 min.) **Ex. 6–11**

Lesson
128

Tues

Preparation

1. Chalkboard:

   A 554,823
   892,644
   637,768
   190,942
   + 385,855

   B .6 .3 .21 .03 .37 .721 .632 .032 .001 .7

2. *Arithmetic 4:* pp. 233–234
3. *Lesson 128 Speed Drill*
4. Visuals:
   - *Process Flashcards*
   - Concept Cards 130–139, 140–174
   - Coins
   - *Decimals (Arith Chart* 14)

Teaching Procedure

1. **Oral review drills** (9 min.)

   Processes (7 min.)
   - *Flashcards:* Let child answer. If time permits, play a favorite game.
   - **A** Use standard procedure.
   - Mult./Div. Tables

   Fractions (2 min.)
   - *Concept Cards* **130–139:** Child changes to whole or mixed numbers.

2. **Written speed drill** (3 min.) Time for 2 min.

3. **Introduce decimals.** (15 min.)
   - **Dime:** Have child tell you what fraction of a dollar a dime is. ($1/10$) 10 is denominator because it takes 10 dimes to make dollar. 1 is numerator because we have 1 dime. Write $1/10$ on ckbd. Tell him we can also write value of dime by using a decimal point. Write $1/10 = \$.10$ on ckbd. The amounts are equal because both equal 1 dime. Erase dollar sign and 0 at end of decimal. Point to .1. Tell him that this number is a decimal. **A decimal is another way to write a fraction. Both are parts of a whole.** Both numbers are read *1 tenth.* Tell him that it was fine to take 0 away at end of decimal. We can take away or add a 0 to end of a decimal without changing its value.
   - *Arith Chart* **14:** Discuss decimals with child. Teach place values of tenths, hundredths, and thousandths. Look at diagram illustrating each place. Discuss mixed decimals and how they compare to mixed numbers.

- **B** Read decimals for child. Be sure he understands if there is only 1 place to right of decimal point, the name of decimal is tenths. If there are 2 places, its name is hundredths. If there are 3 places, its name is thousandths. After you read decimals, allow him to read decimals with you.
- *Concept Cards* **140–174:** Choose a few cards. Show fraction side; child reads. After he reads, show decimal side. After a few cards, show decimal side and allow child to read. Show corresponding fraction side.
- Read and discuss **box on p. 233.** Work **Ex. 1–3** together.

4. **Review/Boardwork** (9 min.) **Ex. 4–7** Child needs rulers for les. 129.

wed

Lesson 129

Preparation

1. Chalkboard:

 A
$$
\begin{array}{r}
783,399 \\
590,478 \\
893,939 \\
902,445 \\
+\ 442,777 \\
\hline
\end{array}
$$

B .47 .5 .618 .9 1.32 .815 .93 .05 4.632

2. *Arithmetic 4:* pp. 235–236

3. *Lesson 129 Speed Drill*

4. Visuals:
   - *Process Flashcards*
   - *Place Values (Arith Chart 2)*
   - *Decimals (Arith Chart 14)*
   - *Concept Cards* 1–15, 56–62, 24–47, 112–116, 118–129, 140–148, 150–161, and 162–170
   - ruler

Teaching Procedure

1. **Oral review drills** (9 min.)

   Processes (3 min.)
   - *Flashcards:* Have a ckbd contest.
   - **A** Use standard procedure.
   - Mult./Div. Tables

   Place value (3 min.)
   - *Arith Chart* **2:** Review places of whole numbers.
   - *Concept Cards* **1–15:** Child reads numbers. Give him 5 cards.

Lesson 129
(cont.)

Child puts them in order from least to greatest. Repeat with other cards.
- *Arith Chart* **14:** Review places of decimals.

Roman numerals (1 min.)
- *Concept Cards* **56–62**

Measures (2 min.)
- *Concept Cards* **24–47, 112–116,** and **118–129**

2. **Written speed drill** (4 min.) Time for 3 min.

3. **Introduce writing decimals as fractions.** (15 min.)
- *Arith Chart* **14:** Review information on decimals.
- *Concept Cards* **140–148:** Show fraction side of several cards and have child tell you what denominator is of each. (10) Show decimal side of cards and read decimal to him. Tell him that a decimal with only 1 place is tenths. If it is written as a fraction, the denominator is 10. Show decimal side of several cards and have child write fraction equivalent on ckbd.
- *Concept Cards* **150–161:** Show fraction side of several cards and have him tell you what denominator is of each. (100) Show decimal side and read to him. Tell child that a decimal with only 2 places is hundredths. If it is written as a fraction, the denominator is 100. Show decimal side of several cards; child writes fractions on ckbd.
- *Concept Cards* **162–170:** Show fraction side of several cards and have child tell you what denominator is of each. (1,000) Show decimal side and read to him. Tell child that a decimal with only 3 places is thousandths. If it is written as a fraction, the denominator is 1,000. Show decimal side of several cards; he writes fractions on ckbd.
- **B** Have child read. Let him write some of them as fractions.
- Read and discuss **box on p. 235.** Child does **Ex. 1–4.** You may need to work a couple problems with him. Give necessary help. Most students understand and can work independently.

4. **Review bar graphs.** (3 min.)
- Work **Ex. 5** together.

5. **Discuss story problems.** (6 min.)
- Do **Ex. 6** together.

6. **Homework Ex. 7**

Thurs

Lesson

130

Preparation

1. Chalkboard:

A
$$\begin{array}{r} 294{,}903 \\ 562{,}669 \\ 847{,}368 \\ 770{,}484 \\ +\ 455{,}947 \end{array}$$

B $\frac{7}{10}$ $\frac{13}{100}$ $\frac{239}{1,000}$ $\frac{61}{1,000}$ $\frac{9}{100}$

C   .79   .003   .137   .1

2. *Arithmetic 4:* pp. 237–238

3. *Lesson 130 Speed Drill*

4. Visuals:
   - *Division Flashcards*
   - *Divisibility Rules (Arith Chart* 12)
   - *Decimals (Arith Chart* 14)
   - *Concept Cards* 80–104, 130–139, 124–129, and 140–170

Teaching Procedure

1. Oral review drills (7 min.)

Homework check

Processes (4 min.)
   - *Div. Flashcards:* Play *Four Corners* or other favorite game.
   - **A** Use standard procedure.
   - *Arith Chart* **12:** Review divisibility rules.
   - Call out these numbers; child adds 9.
     16   32   4   82   74   57   23   11

Decimals (1 min.)
   - *Arith Chart* **14:** Review place value. Have him tell how many 0s are in denominator if decimal is changed to fraction for tenths, hundredths, and thousandths.

Fractions (2 min.)
   - *Concept Cards* **80–104:** Child reduces to lowest terms.
   - *Concept Cards* **130–139:** Show fronts; he changes to whole or mixed numbers. Have him give rule.
   - *Concept Cards* **133–139:** Show backs; he changes to improper fractions. Have him give rule.

2. Written speed drill (6 min.) Time for 5 min.
   - Grade. Record as a speed drill/quiz grade. Count off 10 points for each incorrect answer.

3. Review decimals. (12 min.)
   - ***Concept Cards* 124–129:** Review metric prefixes. Child should look at decimal and fraction values.
   - ***Concept Cards* 140–170:** Show decimal side of several cards; he writes fractions on ckbd.
   - **B** Child writes decimal equivalents on ckbd. Tell him that number of 0s in denominator tells him how many places in decimal. Since there are 3 zeros in 1,000, there must be 3 decimal places. Child must put a 0 in front of 61 to make it 61 thousandths. If he puts 0 at end of 61 it would make it 610 thousandths.

Lesson 130
(cont.)

- He writes fraction equivalents on paper.
- Child works **Ex. 1–4, p. 237.**

4. Review multiplication. (6 min.)

- Child does **Ex. 5.** Encourage him to work neatly, quickly, and correctly.

5. Review/Boardwork (6 min.) **Ex. 6–7**

6. Homework Ex. 8–9

Lesson 131

Mon

Preparation

1. Chalkboard:

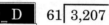
```
        894,672
        348,934
        209,835
        458,210
      + 227,784
```

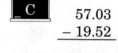
```
B        9.78              C       57.03
         5.62                    – 19.52
       + 17.19
```

```
D    61⟌3,207
```

2. *Arithmetic 4:* pp. 239–240

3. *Lesson 131 Speed Drill*

4. Visuals:
   - *Process Flashcards*
   - *Concept Cards* 24–47, 112–116, and 118–129

Teaching Procedure

1. Oral review drills (6 min.)

   Homework check

   Processes (3 min.)

   - *Flashcards:* Review with child.
   - A Use standard procedure.

   Measures (3 min.)

   - *Concept Cards* **24–47, 112–116,** and **118–129:** Review with him and then play a game.

2. Written speed drill (2 min.) Time for 1 min.

3. Introduce addition and subtraction of decimals. (12 min.)

- **B** Have child read addends aloud. Tell him since he is adding hundredths, he needs to have hundredths in sum. He adds columns as usual, but he must remember to include decimal point. **When adding and subtracting decimals in a column, keep the decimal point in the sum or difference aligned with decimal points in problem.** Work 1st problem with him. Have him read sum.

- **C** Have child read terms in subt. problem. Again, since we have hundredths in problem, we need hundredths in difference. Work problem for him. Remember to stress that decimal point in difference must align with decimal points in problem. He reads difference.

- Read and discuss **box on p. 239.** Child does **Ex. 1–4.** Let him work Ex. 1–2 on ckbd. Be sure to let him read answers aloud to get practice reading decimals. Tell him that if decimal point is not there or is in wrong place, entire answer is wrong. He must train himself to be very careful with decimal point.

4. **Review division.** (6 min.)

- **D** Child works on paper while you work and explain on ckbd.
- Child does **Ex. 5.**

5. **Review/Boardwork** (9 min.) **Ex. 6–7**

6. **Homework Ex. 8**

Mon.

Preparation

Test 13, pp. 105–106 from *Student Tests and Speed Drills*

Teaching Procedure

1. **Homework check**

2. **Administer test.**

3. Student needs ruler for les. 133.

Tuesday

Preparation

1. Chalkboard:

A
```
   534,844
   889,687
   673,716
   189,938
 + 332,859
 ─────────
```

B   1 in. = 50 mi.

C

$$35\tfrac{1}{5} \qquad\qquad 71\tfrac{5}{9}$$

$$87\tfrac{3}{10} \qquad -47\tfrac{1}{3}$$

$$+\,49\tfrac{2}{5}$$

2. *Arithmetic 4:* pp. 241–242
3. *Lesson 133 Speed Drill*
4. Visuals:
   - *Process Flashcards*
   - *Decimals (Arith Chart* 14)
   - *Concept Cards* 140–174, 24–47, 112–116, and 118–129
   - story problem clue words flashcards (optional from les. 4)
   - road map or map from history book (optional)
   - ruler

Teaching Procedure

1. **Oral review drills** (8 min.)

   Processes (3 min.)
   - *Flashcards:* Review with child.
   - Mult./Div. Tables
   - **A**   Use standard procedure.

   Decimals (2 min.)
   - *Arith Chart* **14:** Review place value.
   - *Concept Cards* **140–174:** Send him to ckbd. Show fraction side; he writes decimal equivalent. Repeat several times.

   Measures (2 min.)
   - *Concept Cards* **24–47, 112–116,** and **118–129:** After child answers several, play a game.

   Story problems (1 min.)
   - Story problem clue words flashcards

2. **Written speed drill** (6 min.) Time for 5 min.
   - Grade. Record as a speed drill/quiz grade. Count off 5 points for each incorrect answer.

3. **Introduce scale drawings.** (6 min.)
   - **Map:** Tell child what land area that map is a picture of. Ask him if map is actual size of that land area. Tell him that it is a scale drawing. **A scale drawing of a map is used to show large distances in a small amount of space.** Show scale on your map and write on ckbd. Tell child that scale tells what measured distance on map is actually equal to.
   - **B**   Tell him that this is a scale. Every in. is equal to 50 miles. Call out these distances and have him tell you how many miles they represent, using scale.
     2 in. **100 mi.**   3 in. **150 mi.**   4 in. **200 mi.**

- Read and discuss **box on p. 241.** Work **Ex. 1** together.

4. Review adding and subtracting mixed numbers. (6 min.)

- Child works on paper while you work and explain on ckbd.
- Child does **Ex. 2.**

5. Discuss story problems. (3 min.)
- Work **Ex. 3** together.

6. Review/Boardwork (9 min.) **Ex. 4–8** Student needs ruler for les. 134.

Lesson
134

Preparation

TUES

1. Chalkboard:

783,783
894,689
349,285
406,883
+ 558,399

 1 cm = 200 km

 53 ‾6,321‾

2. *Arithmetic 4:* pp. 243–244

3. *Lesson 134 Speed Drill*

4. Visuals:
- *Process Flashcards*
- *Mixed Division Facts (Arith 4, p. 322)*
- *Decimals (Arith Chart 14)*
- *Concept Cards* 140–174
- ruler

Teaching Procedure

1. Oral review drills (9 min.)

Processes (6 min.)
- *Flashcards:* Review. Encourage child to be fast with answers. If he does well, play a game.
- *Mixed Division Facts*
- Mult. Tables: Play *Just the Facts.*
- Use standard procedure.

Lesson 134
(cont.)

- Oral comb.

$9 - 4 \div 5 \times 3 - 1 = 2$ $12 \div 6 \times 3 \div 3 - 1 + 3 = 4$

$106 + 2 \div 9 \times 12 = 144$ $36 \div 6 \times 9 - 1 + 3 = 56$

$25 + 2 \div 3 \times 9 = 81$ $34 - 2 \div 4 \times 4 = 32$

$142 + 2 \div 12 \times 9 = 108$ $121 \div 11 + 13 - 4 = 20$

Decimals (3 min.)

- *Arith Chart* **14:** Review place value.
- *Concept Cards* **140–174:** Show fractions side; child writes decimals on paper.

2. Written speed drill (4 min.) Time for 3 min.

3. Review reading maps. (9 min.)

- 　B　 Remind him that this is a scale. For every 1 cm on map, real distance is 200 km. Call out these cm, he gives km, using scale.

  2 cm **400 km**　　3 cm **600 km**　　4 cm **800 km**
- Work **Ex. 1–2, p. 243** together. Encourage child to be accurate with use of ruler. In Ex. 2, he might want to make a scale drawing of their community, school community, or an imaginary community.

4. Review division. (6 min.)

- 　C　 Child works on paper as you work on ckbd. Emphasize being neat and careful. Neatness in a problem can save much confusion.
- Child does **Ex. 3.**

5. Review/Boardwork (9 min.) **Ex. 4–7**

6. Homework Ex. 8 Child needs ruler for les. 135.

Lesson
135

Preparation

1. Chalkboard:

　A　
　　574,884
　　489,259
　　749,072
　　784,847
　+ 305,447

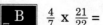

　B　 $\frac{4}{7} \times \frac{21}{22} =$ 　　$\frac{2}{5} \times \frac{5}{6} =$ 　　$\frac{3}{10} \times \frac{5}{6} =$

2. *Arithmetic 4:* pp. 245–246

3. *Lesson 135 Speed Drill*

4. Visuals:
  - *Process Flashcards*
  - *Concept Cards* 130–139, 80–104, and 140–174
  - *Decimals (Arith Chart* 14)
  - ruler
  - *1–100 Chart (Arith Chart 23)*

Teaching Procedure

1. **Oral review drills** (9 min.)

   Homework check

   Processes (4 min.)
   - *Flashcards:* Have child answer a few cards and then play a game if he does well.
   - **A** Use standard procedure.
   - Mult./Div. Tables

   Fractions (2 min.)
   - *Concept Cards* **130–139:** Show fronts; child changes to whole or mixed numbers.
   - *Concept Cards* **133–139:** Show backs; child changes to improper fractions.
   - *Concept Cards* **80–104:** He reduces to lowest terms.

   Decimals (3 min.)
   - *Arith Chart* **14:** Review place value.
   - *Concept Cards* **140–174:** Show decimal side; child reads aloud. After he reads a few cards, show decimal side and have him write equivalent fractions on ckbd.

2. **Written speed drill** (4 min.) Time for 3 min.

3. **Review bar graphs.** (6 min.)
   - Work **Ex. 1, p. 245** together. Child should use ruler to draw graph. You may want to suggest that he use a scale of 10s. If he uses a scale of 1s or 5s, graph will be too big. Child should try to keep even spacing between bars.

4. **Review factoring.** (3 min.)
   - *1–100 Chart:* Point to these numbers: 15, 22, 18, 12, 6, 8, and 9. He should list factors in numerical order.
   - Child does **Ex. 2.**

5. **Review multiplication.** (6 min.)
   - **B** Child works on paper while you work on ckbd. He should tell steps and answers.
   - Child does **Ex. 3.**

6. **Review/Boardwork** (9 min.) **Ex. 4–6**

7. **Homework Ex. 7–8** Child needs ruler for les. 136.

Preparation

1. Chalkboard:

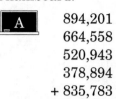

    894,201
    664,558
    520,943
    378,894
  + 835,783

 $10.00 $7.29 $5.00 $1.67

2. *Arithmetic 4:* pp. 247–248

3. *Lesson 136 Speed Drill*

4. Visuals:
   - *Process Flashcards*
   - story problem clue words flash-
     cards (optional from les. 4)
   - *Concept Cards* 80–104, 133–139,
     and 140–174
   - *Decimals (Arith Chart* 14)
   - coins
   - play bills
   - ruler

Teaching Procedure

1. **Oral review drills** (9 min.)

   Homework check

   Processes (5 min.)
   - *Flashcards:* Review. Play a favorite game.
   - Mult./Div. Tables
   - **A** Use standard procedure.
   - Oral comb.

       $5 \times 7 - 3 \div 4 + 3 = 11$ $9 \times 9 - 1 \div 10 + 9 = 17$

       $7 - 1 \div 3 + 4 \times 8 = 48$ $12 \div 6 \times 10 + 3 - 1 = 22$

       $1 + 2 \times 6 \div 9 = 2$ $2 \times 20 \div 4 + 3 - 1 = 12$

   Story problems (1 min.)
   - Story problem clue words flashcards

   Fractions/Decimals (3 min.)
   - *Concept Cards* **80–104:** Child reduces to lowest terms.
   - *Concept Cards* **133–139:** Show backs; he changes to improper
     fractions.
   - *Arith Chart* **14:** Review place value.
   - *Concept Cards* **140–174:** Child reads several cards.

2. **Written speed drill** (3 min.) Time for 2 min.

3. **Introduce counting back change.** (12 min.)
   - **B** **/Coins and play bills:** Show a 10-dollar bill and tell
     child that you have a 10-dollar bill and want to pay for items
     totaling $7.29. The clerk must give correct change. To count

back change, clerk begins with amount of purchase, which is $7.29. Then change is counted back beginning with least denominations 1st. In this case, 1 penny is counted back to make $7.30. Then 2 dimes are counted to make $7.50. (2 dimes are better than 4 nickels, since we want to give fewest pieces of money as possible.) Then 2 quarters are counted to make $8.00. Last 2 dollars are counted to make $10.00. Last amount counted should be amount given clerk.

Point to 2nd amounts. Have him give another student a 5-dollar bill. The child acting as the clerk should count back correct change. (3 pennies, 1 nickel, 1 quarter, and 3 dollars.) Clerk should say *$1.67, $1.70, $1.75, $2.00, $5.00* as coins and bills are given to customer.

If time permits, let him practice being customer and clerk.

- Read and discuss **box on p. 247.** Child does **Ex. 1.**

4. Review scale drawing. (6 min.)

- Work **Ex. 2** together.

5. Review/Boardwork (6 min.) **Ex. 3–4**

6. Homework Ex. 5 Child needs ruler in les. 137.

Preparation

1. Chalkboard:

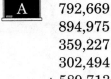

A	792,669
	894,975
	359,227
	302,494
	+ 589,713

Thurs

B   (5, 10)   (10, 15)   (10, 10)   (8, 5)

2. *Arithmetic 4:* pp. 249–250

3. *Lesson 137 Quiz*

4. Visuals:
   - *Process Flashcards*
   - *"Lion" Graph (Arith Chart 22)* and sticky circles
   - coins
   - play bills
   - ruler

Teaching Procedure

1. Oral review drills (9 min.)

Homework check

Processes (7 min.)

- *Flashcards:* Have child answer several cards. He should be quick with a response. Play a favorite game.

- Mult./Div. Tables
- **A** Use standard procedure.

Graphs (2 min.)

- *"Lion" Graph/* **B** Child plots these points. Remind him that 1st number tells how far to go across on horizontal scale and that 2nd number tells how far to go up on vertical scale.

2. **Quiz 14** (9 min.)

3. **Review making change.** (9 min.)

- **Coins/play bills:** Let child be clerk. The customer has a $20-dollar bill. Tell clerk that purchases totaled $13.81. Clerk should count back change. (4 pennies, 1 nickel, 1 dime, 1 one-dollar bill, and 1 five-dollar bill.) Clerk should say *$13.81, $13.85, $13.90, $14.00, $15.00, $20.00.* Choose different amounts.
- Read and discuss **box on p. 249.** Child does **Ex. 1.**

4. **Review scale drawings and decimals.** (3 min.)

- Work **Ex. 2** together.
- Call these decimals for **Ex. 3.** Have child write decimals.
  - **a.** .3 (Say *3 tenths.*)
  - **b.** .03 (Say *3 hundredths.*)
  - **c.** .003 (Say *3 thousandths.*)
  - **d.** .021 (Say *21 thousandths.*)
  - **e.** .21 (Say *21 hundredths.*)

5. **Review/Boardwork** (6 min.) **Ex. 4–8**

Lesson 138

Preparation

1. Chalkboard:

A
```
  468,993
  839,278
  893,830
  362,118
+ 849,586
```

B $\frac{1}{10}$ $\frac{3}{100}$ $14\frac{7}{10}$ .7   9.5   3.32

2. *Arithmetic 4:* pp. 251–252

3. *Lesson 138 Speed Drill*

4. Visuals:

- *Process Flashcards*
- *Concept Cards* 118–129 and 140–174
- *Decimals (Arith Chart* 14)

- coins
- play bills
- ruler

Teaching Procedure

1. Oral review drills (7 min.)

    Processes (4 min.)

- *Flashcards:* Review quickly.
- **A** Use standard procedure.
- Mult./Div. Tables

    Metric measures (1 min.)

- *Concept Cards* **118–129:** Child should be able to give fraction or decimal for metric prefixes of deci, centi, and milli.

    Decimals (2 min.)

- *Concept Cards* **140–174:** Show fraction side; he writes decimals on ckbd and reads decimals.
- *Chart* **14:** Review place value.

2. Written speed drill (6 min.) Time for 5 min.

- Grade. Record as a speed drill/quiz grade. Count off 10 points for each incorrect answer.

3. Introduce checking your change. (9 min.)

- **Coins/play bills:** Give customer a 5-dollar bill for a $2.50 purchase. Take 5-dollar bill and give customer $1.50 in change. He should check his change. If it is not correct, he should be able to tell what problem is.

    Give customer 10-dollar bill for a $6.35 purchase. Take 10-dollar bill and give customer $4.65 in change. He should check his change and correct mistake. Tell child he should always pay attention to amount of change received. If he receives too little, he should kindly bring it to the attention of clerk. He should return extra money if he receives too much change.

- Read and discuss **box on p. 251.** Child works **Ex. 1.**

4. Review decimals. (6 min.)

- **B** Child writes fractions as decimals and decimals as fractions.
- Child does **Ex. 2.**

5. Review/Boardwork (9 min.) **Ex. 3–7** Child needs ruler for les. 139.

Preparation

Lesson 139

1. Chalkboard:

A
```
   893,572
   903,894
   446,894
   176,210
 + 259,894
```

Fri

B hectoliter milliliter kiloliter decaliter deciliter centiliter

2. *Arithmetic 4:* pp. 253–254

3. *Lesson 139 Speed Drill*

4. Visuals:
   - *Process Flashcards*
   - *Concept Cards* 80–104, 140–174, 24–47, 112–116, and 118–129
   - *Divisibility Rules (Arith Chart* 12)
   - liter/quart containers (optional)
   - ruler
   - *Metric Units of Capacity (Arith Chart* 21)

Teaching Procedure

1. Oral review drills (9 min.)

Processes (3 min.)
   - *Flashcards:* Play a favorite game after child has answered several cards.
   - **A** Use standard procedure.
   - Mult./Div. Tables
   - *Arith Chart* **12:** Review divisibility rules.

Fractions/Decimals (3 min.)
   - *Concept Cards* **80–104:** Child reduces to lowest terms.
   - *Concept Cards* **140–174:** Child reads decimals. Show decimal side; he writes fractions on ckbd.

Measures (3 min.)
   - *Concept Cards* **24–47, 112–116,** and **118–129:** Play a game after child has answered several cards.

2. Written speed drill (4 min.) Time for 3 min.

3. Introduce metric units of capacity. (12 min.)
   - Discuss that liquids must be measured in a container. A pint and quart are 2 units of English measure. **The basic unit of capacity in the metric system is the liter.**
   - *Arith Chart* **21:** Discuss with him.
   - **liter/quart containers:** Demonstrate that liter holds slightly more than a quart. A liter of cola is a little more than a quart of cola.
   - **B** Have child point to unit that is equal to 10 liters. (decaliter) Continue with 100 liters (hectoliter), 1,000 liters (kiloliter), .1 liter (deciliter), .01 liter (centiliter), and .001 liter (milliliter). If he knows metric prefixes well, he should have no trouble with this exercise.

   Discuss that a deciliter is less than ½ cup. Both a centiliter and milliliter are very small amounts. A kiloliter is more than 264 gallons.
   - Read and discuss **box on p. 253.** Work **Ex. 1–3** together.

4. Review/Boardwork (12 min.) **Ex. 4–7**

5. Homework Ex. 8–9 Child needs ruler to complete homework.

Preparation

1. Chalkboard:

    503,784
      895,784
      330,894
      948,784
    + 774,894

2. *Arithmetic 4:* pp. 255–256

3. *Lesson 140 Speed Drill*

4. Visuals:
   - *Process Flashcards*
   - *Averaging Numbers (Arith Chart 6)*
   - *Decimals (Arith Chart 14)*
   - *Concept Cards* 140–174 and 105–110
   - Thermometer *(Arith Chart 27)* Use directions on back to complete thermometer.

Teaching Procedure

1. **Oral review drills** (9 min.)

   Homework check

   Processes (6 min.)
   - *Flashcards:* Play *Four Corners* or other favorite game.
   - Mult./Div. Tables
   - *Arith Chart* **6:** Review steps for averaging numbers.
   - 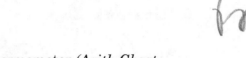 Use standard procedure.

   Decimals (3 min.)
   - *Arith Chart* **14:** Review place value.
   - *Concept Cards* **140–174:** Show fraction side; child writes decimals on paper or ckbd.
   - Call out these decimals. Have him write them on paper.
     .7   .13   .6   .014   .9   .2   .21   .78

2. **Written speed drill** (2 min.) Time for 1 min. 30 sec.

3. **Introduce temperature.** (9 min.)
   - Tell child that the scientific instrument that is used to measure temperature is the thermometer. Some thermometers have mercury that has been colored red in the glass tube. As it becomes hotter, the mercury expands and rises in the tube. As it becomes cooler, the mercury contracts and falls in the tube.
   - ***Thermometer:*** Show 2 scales: Fahrenheit and Celsius. Demonstrate mercury rising and falling. Explain that unit used to measure temperature is degrees. Show how a degree symbol is written.

   Set to several different temperatures; he gives temperatures.

Lesson 140
(cont.)

- *Concept Cards* **105–110:** Teach reference point for both scales.
- Call out these air temperatures and have child respond with hot or cold.

37 °F. **cold**	0 °C **cold**	27 °F. **cold**	92 °F. **hot**
35 °C **hot**	18 °F. **cold**	29 °F. **cold**	29 °C **hot**
3 °C **cold**	98 °F. **hot**		

- Read and discuss **box on p. 255.** Child works **Ex. 1–2.**

4. Review adding and subtracting mixed numbers. (6 min.)
- Child does **Ex. 3.**

5. Review/Boardwork (9 min.) **Ex. 4–7**

6. Homework Ex. 8–9

Tues

Lesson 141

Preparation

1. Chalkboard:

   A
   ```
      784,783
      284,784
      942,236
      796,555
   + 993,214
   ```

   B $\frac{3}{10}$ $13\frac{4}{100}$ $27\frac{82}{100}$ $7\frac{5}{1,000}$

2. *Arithmetic 4:* pp. 257–258

3. *Lesson 141 Speed Drill*

4. Visuals:
   - *Process Flashcards*
   - *Concept Cards* **105–110, 118–129,** and **140–174**
   - *Thermometer (Arith Chart 27)*
   - ruler

Teaching Procedure

1. Oral review drills (9 min.)

Homework check

Processes (4 min.)
- Mult./Div. Tables
- *Flashcards:* Review with child.
- **A** Use standard procedure.

Temperature (3 min.)
- *Concept Cards* **105–110:** Review temperature reference points.
- *Thermometer:* Call out these temperatures; he sets thermometer.

   14 °F.   37 °F.   6 °C   98 °F.   31 °C

Measures (2 min.)
- *Concept Cards* **118–129:** Review metric measures. Have him give basic metric units of length, capacity, and weight.

2. Written speed drill (3 min.) Time for 2 min.

3. Review decimals. (9 min.)
- *Concept Cards* **140–174:** Sometimes show fraction side and have child write decimals on paper or ckbd. Sometimes show decimal side and have him write fractions.
- **B** Child writes decimal equivalents on paper or ckbd. Have him read decimals aloud.
- Call out these numbers; child writes on paper.
  234.2   56.04 $15.32   78,021
- Child does **Ex. 1–2, p. 257.**

4. Review division. (6 min.)
- Child works **Ex. 3**.

5. Review/Boardwork (9 min.) **Ex. 4–7**

6. Homework Ex. 8–9 Child needs ruler for les. 142.

Tues

Preparation

Test 14, pp. 113–114 from *Student Tests and Speed Drills*

Teaching Procedure

1. Homework check

2. Administer test.
Child needs ruler.

wed

Preparation

1. Chalkboard:

A   573,782
        276,994
        559,783
        378,758
     + 839,833

B $n + 4 = 8 \times 2$ $n - 2 = 4 \times 7$

2. *Arithmetic 4:* pp. 259–260

3. *Lesson 143 Speed Drill*

4. Visuals:
   - *Process Flashcards*
   - *Decimals (Arith Chart* 14)
   - *Concept Cards* 140–174, 24–47, 112–116, 118–129, 105–110, and 56–62

   - coins
   - Story problem clue words flashcards (optional from les. 4)

Teaching Procedure

1. Oral review drills (9 min.)

Processes (3 min.)
- *Flashcards:* Review with child.
- Mult./Div. Tables
- **A** Use standard procedure.
- Oral comb.

6 x 9 + 10 − 1 ÷ 9 = *7*	7 x 1 + 10 + 1 ÷ 3 = *6*
7 x 9 + 1 ÷ 8 + 4 ÷ 3 = *4*	10 x 6 − 1 + 10 + 1 ÷ 10 = *7*
2 + 10 ÷ 3 x 4 − 1 = *15*	11 x 6 + 4 + 7 ÷ 11 = *7*

Decimals (2 min.)
- *Arith Chart* **14:** Review place value.
- *Concept Cards* **140–174:** Send child to ckbd. Show fraction side; he writes decimal equivalent. Repeat several times.

Measures (3 min.)
- *Concept Cards* **24–47, 112–116, 118–129,** and **105–110:** After child answers several, play a game.

Roman numerals (1 min.)
- *Concept Cards* **56–62**

2. Written speed drill (3 min.) Time for 2 min.

3. Introduce equations. (9 min.)
- **Coins:** Show 5 pennies in 1 hand and 1 nickel in other hand. Tell child that 2 amounts are equal. Write 5p = 1n on ckbd. Point to 2 sides of 5p = 1n. Tell him we can call this an equation because both sides are equal. Ask him if you could add 1 penny to just 1 side and keep the equation equal. You could not. You must add 1 penny to both sides to keep equality.
  Write 8 c. = 4 pt. on ckbd. Ask child if this is an equation. It is because both sides are equal. **An equation is a mathematical sentence that uses the equal symbol to show that two amounts are equal. Sometimes an equation contains an unknown number that is usually represented by a letter of the alphabet.**
- **B** Point to 1st equation. Tell him that this is an equation. The only problem is that we do not know what *n* stands for. It must stand for the one number that can make both sides equal to each other. Suppose we just guessed that *n* equaled 1. 1 could not work because 1 + 4 does not equal 8 x 2. Many

children could look at equation and know answer by inspecting problem. Tell him that is not purpose of lesson. Child needs to understand algebraic concept of solving equations. Explain problems step by step.

$n + 4 = 8 \times 2$

$n + 4 = 16$

$n + 4 - 4 = 16 - 4$

$n = 12$

$12 + 4 = 8 \times 2$

$16 = 16 \checkmark$

Step 1: Solve side without the unknown number and write the answer below. Rewrite side with unknown number.

Step 2: To solve for n, n must be left all alone. Therefore, subtract 4 from both sides of the equation. **Whatever is done to one side of an equation must be done to the other side of the equation.**

Step 3: Check the answer by rewriting the original problem, substituting the answer for n, and solving. Both sides of the equation should have the same number.

$n - 2 = 4 \times 7$

$n - 2 = 28$

$n - 2 + 2 = 28 + 2$

$n = 30$

$30 - 2 = 4 \times 7$

$28 = 28 \checkmark$

Step 1: Mult. 4 by 7 to get 28. (Solve side without unknown.)

Step 2: To get n all alone, we must get rid of –2. Since 2 is being subtracted, we use the opposite process, which is addition. We add 2 to both sides.

Step 3: Check by substituting 30 for n and working problem.

Stress to him that **unknown is isolated by using the opposite process.** For + 2, we must subt. For –2, we must add.
- Read and discuss **box on p. 259.** Do **Ex. 1–2** together.

4. Discuss story problems. (6 min.)
- Story problem clue words flashcards
- Work **Ex. 3** together.

5. Review/Boardwork (9 min.) **Ex. 4–9** Notice that Ex. 7–9 are Extra Practice and are therefore optional. Child needs a ruler in les. 144.

Thur

Preparation

Lesson
144

1. Chalkboard:

A
505,989
783,100
894,786
229,999
+ 892,759

B $x - 9 = 72 \div 12$

| C | dl | hm | mm | dkg | cl | m | dm | kg | dkl | g |

2. *Arithmetic 4:* pp. 261–262
3. *Lesson 144 Speed Drill*
4. Visuals:
   - *Process Flashcards*
   - *Concept Cards 118–129 and 105–110*
   - *Decimals (Arith Chart 14)*
   - *Metric Units of Length (Arith Chart 17)*
   - *Metric Units of Weight (Arith Chart 19)*
   - *Metric Units of Capacity (Arith Chart 21)*
   - coins
   - ruler

Teaching Procedure

1. **Oral review drills** (7 min.)

   Processes (4 min.)
   - *Flashcards:* Review. Encourage child to be fast with answers. If he does well, play a game.
   - **A** Use standard procedure.
   - Mult./Div. Tables

   Measures (2 min.)
   - *Concept Cards* **118–129:** Review metric measures.
   - *Concept Cards* **105–110:** Review temperature reference points.

   Decimals (1 min.)
   - *Arith Chart* **14:** Review place value.

2. **Written speed drill** (6 min.) Time for 5 min.
   - Grade. Record as a speed drill/quiz grade. Count off 5 points for each incorrect answer.

3. **Review equations.** (6 min.)
   - **Coins:** Show 2 dimes and 1 nickel and ask child what coin is equal to this amount. (quarter) Write 2d + 1n = 1q on ckbd. Remind him that this is called an equation. Have him explain why it is called equation. Ask if you could add 1 dime to only 1 side and keep the equation equal. (no) Ask child what you would have to do to both sides to keep the equation equal. (Add dime to both sides.) Remind him that what is done to 1 side must be done to other side.
   - **B** Work problem step by step for child. After you div. 72 by 12 to get 6, ask if you add 9 to both sides or subt 9 from both sides. Child should remember to add 9, since it is a − 9 in problem. He uses the process that is opposite of subtraction, which is addition.
   - Work **Ex. 1, p. 261** together.

4. Review metrics. (12 min.)

- *Arith Charts* **17, 19,** and **21:** Review metric units. Especially note abbreviations. Metric abbreviations do not use a period as do English abbreviations. Have him note that decimeter, deciliter, and decigram are abbreviated as dm, dl, and dg. Decameter, decaliter, and decagram are abbreviated as dkm, dkl, and dkg.

- Call out different metric units that have their abbreviations on ckbd; he points to correct abbreviation.

- Send child to ckbd to give abbreviations for metric units that you say.

- Child does **Ex. 2–6.**

5. Review/Boardwork (6 min.) **Ex. 7–8**

6. Homework Ex. 9

Fri

Preparation

1. Chalkboard:

$$744,564$$
$$274,993$$
$$922,678$$
$$796,532$$
$$+\,923,858$$

 $s + 5 = 9 + 11$

 $12 \times 3\frac{1}{2} =$

2. *Arithmetic 4:* pp. 263–264

3. *Lesson 145 Speed Drill*

4. Visuals:
   - *Process Flashcards*
   - Mixed Fact Chart (see lesson 49)
   - *Concept Cards* 130–139 and 80–104

Teaching Procedure

1. Oral review drills (9 min.)

Homework check

Processes (6 min.)

- *Flashcards:* Have child answer a few cards. Play a game if he does well.

- Use standard procedure.

- *Mixed Facts Chart (see lesson 49)*
- Mult./Div. Tables

Lesson 145
(cont.)

Fractions (3 min.)

- *Concept Cards* **130–139:** Show fronts; child changes to whole or mixed numbers.
- *Concept Cards* **133–139:** Show backs; child changes to improper fractions.
- *Concept Cards* **80–104:** He reduces to lowest terms.
- Call out these problems.

$\frac{1}{2}$ of 10 = *5*	$\frac{1}{8}$ of 64 = *8*	$\frac{1}{9}$ of 81 = *9*
$\frac{1}{3}$ of 12 = *4*	$\frac{1}{7}$ of 21 = *3*	$\frac{1}{9}$ of 18 = *2*
$\frac{1}{7}$ of 42 = *6*	$\frac{1}{11}$ of 121 = *11*	$\frac{1}{11}$ of 132 = *12*

2. **Written speed drill** (3 min.) Time for 2 min.
3. **Review equations.** (6 min.)
   - B Work as child tells you what to do. Continue to stress that what is done to 1 side must be done to other side.
   - Child works **Ex. 1, p. 263.**
4. **Review multiplying fractions.** (9 min.)
   - C He explains as you work on ckbd.
   - Child does **Ex. 2**. He should work quickly and accurately.
5. **Review/Boardwork** (9 min.) **Ex. 3–6**
6. **Homework Ex. 7–8** If time permits, work a couple of story problems together. Child needs ruler for les. 146.

Monday

Lesson 146

Preparation

1. Chalkboard:

   A $n - 7 = 64 \div 8$

   B 18 c. + 3 pt. = __ pt.

2. *Arithmetic 4:* pp. 265–266
3. *Lesson 146 Speed Drill*
4. Visuals:
   - *Process Flashcards*
   - *Concept Cards* 56–62, 24–47, 112–116, 118–129, and 105–110
   - ruler

Teaching Procedure

1. **Oral review drills** (9 min.)

   Homework check

   Processes (6 min.)

   - *Flashcards:* Review. Play a favorite game.
   - Mult./Div. Tables

- *Concept Cards* **56–62:** Child mult. each answer by 2. He gives answers in Arabic numerals.

Measures (3 min.)

- *Concept Cards* **24–47, 112–116, 118–129,** and **105–110:** Let him answer.
- Review conversion rules.

2. **Written speed drill** (3 min.) Time for 2 min.

3. **Review equations.** (6 min.)

- **A** Have him copy and work equation on ckbd. Have him explain each step.
- Child does **Ex. 1, p. 265.**

4. **Review measurement equations.** (6 min.)

- **B** Child works on paper while you work on ckbd. Stress importance of knowing measures to be able to correctly and easily solve measurement equations.
- Child works **Ex. 2.**

5. **Review/Boardwork** (12 min.) **Ex. 3–8**

6. **Homework Ex. 9–11** Child needs ruler to complete hwk.

Tues

Lesson 147

Preparation

1. Chalkboard:

   (10, 5)   (15, 10)   (5, 5)   (9, 9)

2. *Arithmetic 4:* pp. 267–268

3. *Lesson 147 Quiz*

4. Visuals:

   - *Process Flashcards*
   - *"Lion" Graph (Arith Chart 22)* and sticky circles
   - *Concept Cards* 118–129, 105–110, and 117
   - *Thermometer (Arith Chart 27)*
   - *English Measures of Capacity (Arith Chart 11)*

Teaching Procedure

1. **Oral review drills** (9 min.)

   Homework check

   Processes (3 min.)

   - *Flashcards:* Play a favorite game.
   - Mult./Div. Tables

   Graphs (2 min.)

   - *"Lion" Graph/* Child plots these points. Remind him that 1st number tells how far to go across on horizontal scale and that 2nd number tells how far to go up on vertical scale.

Lesson 147
(cont.)

Metrics (1 min.)
- *Concept Cards* **118–129:** Let child answer. If child is weak be sure he gets plenty of practice.

Temperature (3 min.)
- *Concept Cards* **105–110:** Review temperature reference points.
- *Thermometer:* Child sets to these temperatures.
  5 °C   88 °F.   25 °F.   40 °C   47 °F.

2. Quiz 15 (9 min.)

3. Introduce teaspoons and tablespoons. (6 min.)
- *Arith Chart* **11:** Introduce teaspoons and tablespoons. Point out correct abbreviations.
- *Concept Card* **117:** Practice measure.
- Read and discuss **box on p. 267.** Child does **Ex. 1–2.**

4. Discuss story problem. (3 min.)
- Work **Ex. 3** together. He may want to use a red pencil to make thermometer more attractive.

5. Review/Boardwork (9 min.) **Ex. 4–8**

Lesson 148

Preparation

1. Chalkboard:

    MCCCXXIV   LVIII   MMMVI   XLIV   CCLXXV

2. *Arithmetic 4:* pp. 269–270

3. *Lesson 148 Speed Drill*

4. Visuals:
   - *Process Flashcards*
   - *Concept Cards* 56–62, 105–110, 140–174, and 175–183
   - *Thermometer (Arith Chart 27)*
   - *Decimals (Arith Chart* 14)
   - *Lion Graph (Arith Chart* 22)/sticky circles

Teaching Procedure

1. Oral review drills (7 min.)

Processes (3 min.)
- *Flashcards:* review
- Mult./Div. Tables
- Oral comb.

7 x 5 + 2 + 1 + 3 = *41*	8 x 2 + 3 − 1 ÷ 6 = *3*
4 x 5 + 2 + 3 + 4 = *29*	7 x 3 + 4 ÷ 5 + 15 = *20*
6 x 9 + 6 ÷ 10 = *6*	9 x 2 + 7 ÷ 5 = *5*
7 x 2 + 1 ÷ 3 = *5*	10 x 6 + 7 − 3 ÷ 8 = *8*

Roman numerals (1 min.)
- *Concept Cards* **56–62**
- Child gives Arabic numerals.

Temperature (1 min.)
- *Concept Cards* **105–110:** Review temperature reference points.
- *Thermometer:* Tell child to set thermometers to freezing point of water on Fahrenheit scale. Use other reference points that are on thermometers.

Decimals (2 min.)
- *Concept Cards* **140–174:** Show fraction side; he writes decimals on ckbd and reads decimal.
- *Arith Chart* **14:** Review place value.

2. **Written speed drill** (6 min.) Time for 5 min.
- Grade. Record as a speed drill/quiz grade. Count off 5 points for each incorrect answer.

3. **Introduce geometry.** (9 min.)
- *"Lion" Graph*/**sticky circles:** Place a circle on graph and remind him that it is called a point. **A point is just one dot on the grid. A point can be a dot placed anywhere.** Place another point on grid. Tell him that we could draw a line to connect 2 points. The line is really a line segment. **A line segment has a beginning point and an ending point. A line never ends. It does not have a beginning or ending point.** Draw a line and line segment on ckbd. Tell child we put arrows on end of line to show that it continues forever in both directions.

  Draw a ray. **A ray has a beginning point but no ending point.**
- *Concept Cards* **175–183:** Use cards to introduce geometric concepts.
- Send child to ckbd to draw the geometric models.
- Read and discuss **box on p. 269.** Child works **Ex. 1–2.**

4. **Review multiplying fractions.** (6 min.)
- Child does **Ex. 3.**

5. **Review/Boardwork** (9 min.) **Ex. 4–8**

Thurs

Preparation

1. Chalkboard:
   XV   III   MC   XL   DC   CD   XXIX   CL

2. *Arithmetic 4:* pp. 271–272

3. *Lesson 149 Speed Drill*

4. Visuals:
- *Process Flashcards*
- *Mixed Multiplication Facts (Arith 4, p. 319)*

Lesson 149
(cont.)

- *Divisibility Rules (Arith Chart* 12)
- *Concept Cards* 80–104, 140–174, 24–47, 112–129, 175–183, 184–185, and 48–54
- cola can or box (optional)

Teaching Procedure

1. **Oral review drills** (12 min.)

   Processes (6 min.)
   - *Flashcards:* Review. Play *Beat the Clock.* If time permits, play again, trying to beat time just set.
   - *Mixed Multiplication Facts*
   - Mult./Div. Tables
   - *Arith Chart* **12:** Review divisibility rules.

   Fractions/Decimals (2 min.)
   - *Concept Cards* **80–104:** Child reduces to lowest terms.
   - *Concept Cards* **140–174:** He reads decimals. Show decimal side; he writes fractions on ckbd.

   Roman numerals (1 min.)
   - He gives Arabic numerals.

   Measures (3 min.)
   - *Concept Cards* **24–47** and **112–129:** Play a game after child has answered several cards.

2. **Written speed drill** (4 min.) Time for 3 min.
3. **Introduce geometric shapes.** (12 min.)
   - ***Concept Cards* 175–183:** Review geometric concepts.
   - ***Concept Cards* 184–185:** Show card 184 and discuss how shape has no openings and no intersections. Look at card 185. Ask child if it is a simple closed shape. It is because it has no openings and no intersections. It is also called a polygon. **A polygon is a simple closed figure made up of many line segments.** Ask him if 2 line segments could form a polygon. He should say no, since only 2 line segments cannot form a simple closed figure.
   - ***Concept Cards* 48–54:** Hand cards to child and have him look at each shape. Ask if each shape is a simple closed figure. (They all are.) Ask which shape is not a polygon. (circle)

   Tell him that they are all plane shapes because they are all flat. Show a can or box and explain that it is not a plane shape because it is not flat. A can or box can hold something and is called a solid shape.

   Discuss each shape and its special characteristic.
   - Read and discuss **box on p. 271.** Child works **Ex. 1–3.** You may need to work a few together.
4. **Review/Boardwork** (9 min.) **Ex. 4–5**
5. **Homework Ex. 6**

Friday

Preparation

1. *Arithmetic 4:* pp. 273–274
2. *Lesson 150 Speed Drill*
3. Visuals:
   - *Process Flashcards*
   - *Concept Cards* 56–62, 105–110, 175–185, and 48–55
   - *1–100 Chart (Arith Chart 23)*
   - *Thermometer (Arith Chart 27)*

Teaching Procedure

1. **Oral review drills** (9 min.)

   Homework check

   Processes (5 min.)
   - *Flashcards:* Play *Four Corners* or other favorite game.
   - Mult./Div. Tables

   Roman numerals (1 min.)
   - *Concept Cards* **56–62**
   - *1–100 Chart:* Point to several numbers; child gives Roman numerals.

   Temperature (3 min.)
   - *Concept Cards* **105–110:** Review temperature reference points.
   - *Thermometer:* Call out several temperatures for him to set.

2. **Written speed drill** (2 min.) Time for 1 min.

3. **Review geometric shapes.** (6 min.)
   - *Concept Cards* **175–185** and **48–55:** Review with child.
   - Have him look for objects and give geometric shape.
   - Child does **Ex. 1–2, p. 273.**

4. **Review thermometers.** (3 min.)
   - Child does **Ex. 3.** Let him set *Thermometer* to temperatures in Ex. 3.

5. **Discuss story problems.** (6 min.)
   - Work **Ex. 4** together.

6. **Review/Boardwork** (9 min.) **Ex. 5–8**

7. **Homework** **Ex. 9–10**

mon

Preparation

1. Chalkboard:

   $n + 8 = 6 \times 12$
2. *Arithmetic 4:* pp. 275–276
3. *Lesson 151 Speed Drill*

Lesson 151
(cont.)

4. Visuals:
   - *Process Flashcards*
   - *Averaging Numbers (Arith Chart 6)*
   - *Concept Cards* 175–185, 48–55, and 118–129
   - ruler

Teaching Procedure

1. **Oral review drills** (9 min.)

   Homework check

   Processes (6 min.)
   - Mult./Div. Tables
   - *Flashcards:* Review with child.
   - *Arith Chart* **6:** Review steps in averaging numbers.
   - Oral comb.

$7 \times 3 + 3 \div 4 \times 2 = 12$	$2 \times 8 \div 8 \times 3 \div 2 = 3$
$5 \times 3 + 5 \div 5 \times 9 = 36$	$45 \div 9 \times 9 = 45$
$5 \times 10 + 10 \div 5 = 12$	$54 \times 2 \times 1 \div 2 = 54$
$10 + 2 \div 2 \times 10 = 60$	$18 \div 3 \times 3 \div 2 \times 2 = 18$

   Geometry (1 min.)
   - *Concept Cards* **175–185** and **48–55:** Review.

   Measures (2 min.)
   - *Concept Cards* **118–129:** Review metric measures. Have child give basic metric units of length, capacity, and weight.

2. **Written speed drill** (4 min.) Time for 3 min.

3. **Review equations.** (6 min.)
   - ▮ Work problem on ckbd while he tells you what to do.
   - Child does **Ex. 1, p. 275.**

4. **Discuss story problems.** (6 min.)
   - Work **Ex. 2** together. Encourage child to read carefully and think through each story problem.

5. **Review problem solving.** (4 min.)
   - Give child 4 min. to do **Ex. 3.** Check. Praise child if he got them all correct.

6. **Review/Boardwork** (9 min.) **Ex. 4–7** Encourage him to use ruler and colored pencils to make Ex. 5 attractive.

7. **Homework Ex. 8–10**

Preparation

Test 15, pp. 121–122 from *Student Tests and Speed Drills*.

Teaching Procedure

1. **Homework check**   2. **Administer test.**

Preparation

1. Chalkboard:

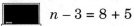 $n - 3 = 8 + 5$

2. *Arithmetic 4:* pp. 277–278

3. *Lesson 153 Speed Drill*

4. Visuals:
   - *Process Flashcards*
   - *Mixed Division Facts (Arith 4, p. 322)*
   - *Concept Cards* 80–104, 130–139, 140–174, 24–47, 112–129, 105–110, 175–185, and 48–55

Teaching Procedure

1. **Oral review drills** (9 min.)

   Processes (3 min.)
   - *Flashcards:* Review.
   - Mult./Div. Tables
   - *Mixed Division Facts*

   Fractions/Decimals (3 min.)
   - *Concept Cards* **80–104:** Child reduces to lowest terms.
   - *Concept Cards* **130–139:** Child changes to whole or mixed numbers.
   - *Concept Cards* **140–174:** Show decimal side; child writes fractions on ckbd.

   Measures (3 min.)
   - *Concept Cards* **24–47, 112–129,** and **105–110:** After he answers several cards, play a game.

2. **Written speed drill** (3 min.) Time for 2 min.

3. **Review geometry.** (9 min.)
   - *Concept Cards* **175–185** and **48–55:** Let child answer and then play a game.
   - Send child to ckbd to draw shapes.
   - He does **Ex. 1–3, p. 277.**

4. Review equations. (6 min.)

- Child works on paper as you work on ckbd.

- Child doe **Ex. 4.**

5. Review/Boardwork (9 min.) **Ex. 5–10**

Lesson 154

Preparation

1. Chalkboard:

    $l = 8$ ft. $l = 19$ in.

   $w = 6$ ft. $w = 7$ in.

    $x + 5 = 6 \times 3$

2 *Arithmetic 4:* pp. 279–280

3. *Lesson 154 Speed Drill*

4. Visuals:
   - *Process Flashcards*
   - *Mixed Addition Facts (Arith 4, p. 311)*
   - *Concept Cards* 175–185, 48–55, 118–129, 105–110, 1–15, 186, and 188
   - *Place Value (Arith Chart* 2)
   - cookie (optional)
   - *Decimals (Arith Chart 14)*
   - *Perimeter (Arith Chart 16)*

Teaching Procedure

1. Oral review drills (9 min.)

   Processes (4 min.)
   - *Flashcards:* Review. If child does well, play a game.
   - *Mixed Addition Facts*
   - Mult./Div. Tables

   Geometry (1 min.)
   - *Concept Cards* **175–185** and **48–55**

   Measures (2 min.)
   - *Concept Cards* **118–129:** Review metric measures.
   - *Concept Cards* **105–110:** Review temperature reference points.

   Place value (2 min.)
   - *Arith Charts* **2** and **14:** Review place value.
   - *Concept Cards* **1–15:** Hand 5 cards to child. He puts in order from least to greatest.

2. Written speed drill (4 min.) Time for 3 min.

3. Introduce perimeter. (12 min.)
   - Write *perimeter* on ckbd and underline *meter*. Child tells you what a meter measures. (length) Pronounce *perimeter* and

tell him that it measures length as well. **Perimeter measures the length around a polygon.** Point to floor of room and tell him that it is in shape of a rectangle, which is a polygon. To find perimeter, we must measure length of 4 sides and add lengths together.

- *Arith Chart* **16:** Discuss perimeter and how to find perimeter of rectangle. Because opposite sides of a rectangle are congruent (same size), we can mult. length and width by 2 to find perimeter. This special characteristic of a rectangle allows us to use formula $P = (2 \times l) + (2 \times w)$. Write formula on ckbd.
- **Cookie:** Explain to child that a formula is like a recipe. When we buy a certain brand cookie, we expect it to taste a certain way. The reason we can count on it is that the manufacturer has a recipe that he always follows. The recipe tells exactly how much of each ingredient to use and how to put ingredients together. A formula is like a recipe. If we follow it exactly, we will get correct results. Of course, if we want a pizza, we do not follow a cookie recipe. Child must learn to use correct formula for what they are looking for.
- *Concept Cards* **186** and **188:** Review definition of perimeter and formula for perimeter of a rectangle.

- ▐ A ▌ Work 1st problem step by step for him.

$P = (2 \times l) + (2 \times w)$
$P = (2 \times 8) + (2 \times 6)$
$P = 16 + 12$
$P = 28$ ft.

Step 1: Since we are finding perimeter of a rectangle, we use formula for perimeter of rectangle. (Child should always write formula. It is his *blueprint* to follow.)

Step 2: Work within parentheses 1st. Mult. 2 times length and 2 times width.

Step 3: Add 2 products together.

Step 4: Include feet in answer. (Since perimeter is a linear measure, the linear unit is an essential part of answer.)

Use same steps to work 2nd problem.
- Read and discuss **box on p. 279.** Work **Ex. 1–2** together.

4. Review equations. (6 min.)

- ▐ B ▌ Child works on paper as you work on ckbd.
- Child does **Ex. 3.**

5. Review/Boardwork (6 min.) **Ex. 4–6**

6. Homework Ex. 7

Preparation

1. Chalkboard:

   ▐ A ▌ $l = 12$ ft.
   $w = 8$ ft.

   ▐ B ▌ $s = 7$ yd. $s = 18$ in.

2. *Arithmetic 4:* pp. 281–282

3. *Lesson 155 Speed Drill*

4. Visuals:
   - *Process Flashcards*
   - *Concept Cards* 24–47, 112–129, 175–185, 48–55, and 186–188
   - *Perimeter (Arith Chart* 16)

Teaching Procedure

1. **Oral review drills** (7 min.)

   Homework check

   Processes (4 min.)
   - *Flashcards:* Have child answer a few cards. Play a game if he does well.
   - Mult./Div. Tables
   - Oral comb.

$10 + 10 \div 2 \times 50 = 500$	$5 \times 5 \div 5 \times 3 + 4 = 19$
$5 \times 4 \div 2 \times 10 \div 10 = 10$	$2 + 8 \times 7 - 6 = 64$
$9 \times 7 + 6 - 8 = 61$	$10 - 6 + 4 \times 8 = 64$

   Measures (2 min.)
   - *Concept Cards* **24–47** and **112–129**
   - Review metric abbreviations.

   Geometry (1 min.)
   - *Concept Cards* **175–185** and **48–55**

2. **Written speed drill** (6 min.) Time for 5 min.
   - Grade. Record as a speed drill/quiz grade. Count off 5 points for each incorrect answer.

3. **Introduce perimeter of a square.** (12 min.)
   - *Concept Cards* **186** and **188:** Review definition of perimeter and formula for perimeter of a rectangle.

   - **A** Find perimeter of rectangle.

   - *Arith Chart* **16:** Introduce formula for perimeter of square. Because a square has 4 congruent (equal) sides, we can mult. length of 1 side by 4. Tell child that formulas are easy to remember if he thinks about special characteristics of shapes.
   - *Concept Card* **187:** Review formula for perimeter of a square.

   - **B** Work problems step by step with child. Be sure he understands how to write formula 1st. He must finish up by including unit of length in answer.
   - Read and discuss **box on p. 281.** Child does **Ex. 1–3.**

4. **Review metric prefixes.** (3 min.)
   - Have him write fraction equivalent for metric prefixes that are decimals in **Ex. 4.** Child then completes ex.

5. **Review/Boardwork** (9 min.) **Ex. 5–7**

6. **Homework Ex. 8** Child needs ruler for les. 156.

Preparation

1. Chalkboard:

   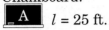 $l = 25$ ft.
   $w = 18$ ft.

   [B] $s = 13$ yd.

   Mon

2. *Arithmetic 4:* pp. 283–284

3. *Lesson 156 Speed Drill*

4. Visuals:
   - *Process Flashcards*
   - *Concept Cards* 175–185, 48–55, 24–47, 112–129, 105–110, and 186–188
   - *Perimeter (Arith Chart* 16)
   - *Thermometer (Arith Chart* 27)
   - ruler

Teaching Procedure

1. **Oral review drills** (9 min.)

   Homework check

   Processes (5 min.)
   - *Flashcards:* Review. Play a favorite game.
   - Mult./Div. Tables

   Geometry (1 min.)
   - *Concept Cards* **175–185** and **48–55**

   Measures (3 min.)
   - *Concept Cards* **24–47, 112–129,** and **105–110:** Let child answer. If time permits, play *Beat the Clock.*

2. **Written speed drill** (4 min.) Time for 3 min.

3. **Review perimeter.** (9 min.)
   - *Arith Chart* **16:** Review definition and formulas.
   - *Concept Cards* **186–188:** Drill briefly. Send child to ckbd to write formulas.
   - [A] Child explains how to find perimeter of a rectangle.
   - [B] Review how to find perimeter of square.
   - Child does **Ex. 1–2, p. 283.**

4. **Review temperature.** (3 min.)
   - *Thermometer:* Call out several temperatures on both scales; he sets thermometers.
   - *Concept Cards* **105–110:** Review temperature reference points.
   - Child works **Ex. 3.** Have him set thermometers to temperatures in Ex. 3.

5. **Review/Boardwork** (12 min.) **Ex. 4–9**

6. **Homework** Ex. 10–11

Lesson
157

Tues (handwritten)

Preparation

1. Chalkboard:

   rectangle: $l = 9$ ft. $w = 6$ ft.   square: $s = 25$ yd.

2. *Arithmetic 4:* pp. 285–286
3. *Lesson 157 Quiz*
4. Visuals:
   - *Process Flashcards*
   - coins
   - play bills
   - *Concept Cards* 105–110 and 186
   - *Thermometer (Arith Chart 27)*
   - *Perimeter (Arith Chart 16)*

Teaching Procedure

1. **Oral review drills** (9 min.)

   Homework check

   Processes (3 min.)
   - *Flashcards:* Play a favorite game.
   - Mult./Div. Tables

   Money (3 min.)
   - Coins/play bills: Parent plays customer and child the clerk. Customer hands clerk a bill and tells him how much he is spending. Clerk should count back change correctly. Customer should check to be sure change was counted back correctly.

   Temperature (3 min.)
   - *Concept Cards* **105–110:** Review temperature reference points.
   - *Thermometer:* Child sets to these temperatures.
     12°C   89°F.   33°F.   19°C   102°F.

2. **Quiz 16** (9 min.)

3. **Review perimeter.** (6 min.)
   - *Arith Chart* **16:** Review definition and formulas.
   - *Concept Card* **186:** Tell him that you have a triangle with all sides a different length. Ask him to tell you what to do to find perimeter. He should use definition of perimeter to give answer. (Measure length of each side and add 3 lengths together.)
   - ▮ Child gives correct formula to use for each shape. He tells you how to find perimeter of each.
   - Child does **Ex. 1–3, p. 285.**

4. **Discuss story problems.** (3 min.)
   - Work **Ex. 4** together.

5. **Review/Boardwork** (9 min.) **Ex. 5–11** Remind child that as he does **Ex. 7** that he can add 0s to end of a decimal without changing its value. We only change name of decimal when we add 0s to end. **Decimals should have same name to be compared.** That means if 1 of 2 decimals being compared is tenths and other is hundredths, a 0 is added to tenths to make it hundredths. It is easy to compare hundredths to hundredths.

Preparation

wed

1. Chalkboard:

 $7\frac{1}{8}$

$-2\frac{1}{3}$

2. *Arithmetic 4:* pp. 287–288

3. *Lesson 158 Speed Drill*

4. Visuals:

- *Process Flashcards*
- story problems clue words flash-cards (optional from les. 4)

- *Concept Cards* 80–104, 189, 175–185, and 48–55
- *Area (Arith Chart* 18)

Teaching Procedure

1. Oral review drills (9 min.)

Processes (5 min.)
- *Flashcards:* Play a game.
- Mult./Div. Tables
- Oral comb.

$6 \times 9 + 2 \div 8 \times 9 - 5 + 2 = 60$ $11 \times 11 - 21 \div 50 \times 9 = 18$

$108 \div 12 \times 6 - 5 \div 7 \times 3 = 21$ $44 - 8 \div 6 \times 3 - 9 \times 5 + 1 = 46$

$99 \div 11 + 2 - 6 \times 7 + 1 \div 9 = 4$ $53 - 4 \div 7 \times 8 + 4 \div 10 \times 4 + 5 = 29$

$87 + 5 - 2 \div 9 \times 3 \div 5 \div 2 - 3 = 0$ $41 - 9 \div 8 \times 7 + 2 \div 6 \times 8 = 40$

Story problems (1 min.)
- Story problem clue words flashcards

Fractions (3 min.)
- *Concept Cards* **80–104:** Send child to ckbd. Show card; he writes reduced fraction on ckbd. Show backs of 2 cards; he gives l.c.d.
- ▮ Child works on paper or on ckbd. Praise child who works hard to get correct answer and is continuing to do well with fractions. A good background in fractions in 4th grade helps children have confidence to continue to do well in later grades. Be sure to give special help to child who is still struggling with fractions.

2. Written speed drill (3 min.) Time for 2 min. 30 sec.

3. Introduce area. (9 min.)
- Have him give shape of room floor. (rectangle) Tell him that you want to put new carpet on floor. Would knowing perimeter help? He should realize that floor would look strange if it only had carpet along baseboards. Tell him we need to know the inside portion to be able to know how much carpet we need. **Area is the inside of a shape. To find area we must divide the inside of a shape into square units.** Child has probably heard commericals where carpet is sold

Lesson 158
(cont.)

by the square yard. A square yard is 1 yard long and 1 yard wide. If you have 4 yardsticks, place them so he can see square yard.

- *Arith Chart* **18:** Discuss top of chart. Child should count squares to find area of top rectangle. Stress that area must be in square units.
- *Concept Card* **189:** Review definition of area.
- Read and discuss **box on p. 287.** Child works **Ex. 1–2.** As he does Ex. 2, have him count squares across and squares down. Write 6 across and 3 down on ckbd. Then have him count squares in all. Write 18 on ckbd. Child should see that 6 times 3 gives 18. This discovery helps him as he learns the formula for area of rectangle later.

4. Review geometric figures. (6 min.)
- *Concept Cards* **175–185** and **48–55**
- Send child to ckbd to draw shapes and give formulas for perimeter of rectangle and square.
- Child does **Ex. 3.**

5. Review/Boardwork (9 min.) **Ex. 4–7**

Lesson
159

Preparation

1. Chalkboard:

 l = 4 ft. l = 9 in.

   w = 3 ft. w = 6 in.

2. *Arithmetic 4:* pp. 289–290

3. *Lesson 159 Speed Drill*

4. Visuals:
   - *Process Flashcards*
   - *Divisibility Rules (Arith Chart* 12)
   - *Area (Arith Chart* 18)

   - *Concept Cards* 175–185, 48–55, 187–188, 56–62, 24–47, 112–129, and 191

Teaching Procedure

1. Oral review drills (8 min.)

   Processes (3 min.)
   - *Flashcards:* Play a game.
   - *Arith Chart* **12:** Review divisibility rules.
   - Oral comb.

   $\frac{1}{4}$ of 12 x 5 − 9 = *6* $\frac{1}{5}$ of 45 ÷ 3 x 6 ÷ 2 x 5 = *45*

   $\frac{1}{10}$ of 90 x 4 ÷ 6 x 2 ÷ 4 = *3* $\frac{1}{8}$ of 24 x 7 − 6 ÷ 5 x 9 = *27*

   $\frac{1}{11}$ of 121 x 12 − 12 ÷ 10 = *12* $\frac{1}{7}$ of 56 ÷ 4 x 9 − 9 ÷ 3 x 4 = *12*

   $\frac{1}{7}$ of 49 + 8 ÷ 5 x 8 ÷ 6 = *4* $\frac{1}{11}$ of 44 ÷ 4 x 8 + 5 − 9 x 4 = *16*

Geometry (2 min.)
- *Concept Cards* **175–185** and **48–55:** Show name of shape (back of card); child draws on ckbd.
- *Concept Cards* **187–188:** Review formulas for perimeter of rectangle and square.

Roman numerals (1 min.)
- *Concept Cards* **56–62**

Measures (2 min.)
- *Concept Cards* **24–47** and **112–129:** Play a game after child has answered several cards.

2. **Written speed drill** (6 min.) Time for 5 min.
- Grade. Record as a speed drill/quiz grade. Count off 15 points for each incorrect answer.

3. **Introduce formula for area of a rectangle.** (12 min.)
- *Arith Chart* **18:** Review definition of area and contrast to perimeter. Tell child that we could find area of all rectangles by dividing them into square units and counting number of squares. That method is very time consuming and trouble. Show formula that makes finding area of rectangle quite easy. Write formula on ckbd. Remind him that length is always the longer side.
- *Concept Card* **191:** Review formula.
- Work 1st problem step by step.

  $A = l \times w$

  $A = 4 \times 3$

  $A = 12$ sq. ft.

  Step 1: Write formula for finding area of a rectangle.
  Step 2: Substitute correct dimensions in formula and find product.
  Step 3: Include sq. ft. in answers. It is essential to include square units in answer of an area problem.

  Use same steps to find area of 2nd rectangle.
- Read and discuss **box on p. 289.** Child works **Ex. 1–2.**

4. **Review division.** (3 min.)
- Have child do **Ex. 3** in text.

5. **Review/Boardwork** (9 min.) **Ex. 4–6**

6. **Homework Ex. 7–8**

Lesson

160

Preparation

1. Chalkboard:

   A rectangle: l = 13 yd. w = 7 yd.

   B square: s = 7 ft.

   C 300 cm – 2 m = __ cm

2. *Arithmetic 4:* pp. 291–292

3. *Lesson 160 Speed Drill*

4. Visuals:
   - *Process Flashcards*
   - *Concept Cards* 175–185, 48–55, 187–188, 191, 105–110, and 190
   - *Thermometer (Arith Chart 27)*
   - *Area (Arith Chart* 18)

Teaching Procedure

1. Oral review drills (9 min.)

Homework check

Processes (3 min.)
- *Flashcards:* Play *Four Corners* or other favorite game.
- Mult./Div. Tables

Geometry (3 min.)
- *Concept Cards* **175–185** and **48–55:** Play *Beat the Clock.*
- *Concept Cards* **187–188** and **191:** Review formulas.
- **A** Child tells you how to find perimeter and area of rectangle.

Temperature (3 min.)
- *Concept Cards* **105–110:** Review temperature reference points.
- *Thermometer:* Call out several temperatures for him to set.

2. Written speed drill (3 min.) Time for 2 min.

3. Introduce formula for area of a square. (12 min.)
- *Arith Chart* **18:** Review concept of area and formula for area of a rectangle. Introduce formula for area of a square. Tell him that we could use same formula that we used for area of a rectangle, but since length and width are same, we can use this simpler formula. Again stress that if child understands concepts of area and perimeter and special characteristics of shapes, he will not get formulas confused.
- *Concept Card* **190:** Review formula.
- **B** Work problem step by step for child. Be sure to begin with formula and end with square feet in answer.
- Read and discuss **box on p. 291.** Child does **Ex. 1–3.**

4. Review measurement problems. (3 min.)
- **C** Work problem for him.
- Child does **Ex. 4.**

5. Review multiplication. (3 min.)
- Child does **Ex. 5**. Encourage him to work accurately, quickly, and neatly.

6. Review/Boardwork (6 min.) **Ex. 6–7**

7. Homework **Ex. 8–9**

Preparation

1. Chalkboard:

1 ft.	1 ft.	1 ft.
1 ft.	1 ft.	1 ft.
1 ft.	1 ft.	1 ft.

B $l = 8$ m $w = 6$ m

2. *Arithmetic 4:* pp. 293–294
3. *Lesson 161 Speed Drill*
4. Visuals:
   - *Calculator (Arith Chart 20)*
   - *Process Flashcards*
   - *Concept Cards 175–185, 48–55, 186–191, and 192–193*
   - *Area (Arith Chart 18)*

Teaching Procedure

1. **Oral review drills** (9 min.)

   Homework check

   Processes (6 min.)
   - *Calculator:* Point to numbers; child mult. by 8, 9, 11, or 12.
   - Mult./Div. Tables
   - *Flashcards:* Review with child.
   - Oral comb.

     $14 \div 7 \times 5 \div 2 \times 6 \div 10 \times 4 = 12$ $100 - 90 \times 5 \div 2 + 3 = 28$

     $16 + 4 \div 10 \times 6 \div 3 + 1 \div 5 = 1$ $11 \times 12 - 32 \times 10 + 1 = 1{,}001$

     $57 + 3 \div 6 \div 5 \div 2 \times 3 = 3$ $9 \times 9 - 1 \div 10 \times 8 + 6 = 70$

     $24 + 3 \div 9 \times 8 - 5 + 4 = 23$ $97 - 7 \div 30 \times 2 \times 0 = 0$

   Geometry (3 min.)
   - *Concept Cards* **175–185** and **48–55:** Review.
   - *Concept Cards* **186–191:** Review concepts of area and perimeter and formulas.

2. **Written speed drill** (4 min.) Time for 3 min.

3. **Introduce square measures.** (9 min.)
   - Have him tell you what you get when you mult. in. by in. (sq. in.) Repeat for ft. times ft. and yd. times yd.
   - Send child to ckbd to write number of inches in foot. Tell him that to find number of sq. in. in sq. ft., we must take 12 and mult. it by itself. When we square a number, we always use number as a factor twice. Mult. 12 times 12 to get 144.
   - ***Arith Chart* 18/*Concept Card* 192:** Show child that there are 144 sq. in. in 1 sq. ft.

Lesson 161
(cont.)

- See if he can determine number of sq. ft. in 1 sq. yd. by using same steps given above. He should know that there are 3 ft. in 1 yd. He should understand that to find the square, we use 3 as a factor twice to get 9.
- *Arith Chart* **18**/*Concept Card* **193:** Show that there are 9 sq. ft. in 1 sq. yd. Review 2 measures with him.
- **A** Look at diagram that proves there are 9 sq. ft. in 1 sq. yd. Each side of square represents 3 feet or 1 yard. The square has a total of 9 sq. ft.
- **B** Find area and perimeter of rectangle. Child should give formulas and explain how to work.
- Read and discuss **box on p. 293.** Child does **Ex. 1–2.**

4. Review division and multiplication. (6 min.)
- Child does **Ex. 3–4.**

5. Review/Boardwork (9 min.) **Ex. 5–7**

6. Homework Ex. 8–9

Lesson 162

Preparation

Test 16, pp. 129–130 from *Student Tests and Speed Drills*

Teaching Procedure

1. Homework check   **2. Administer test.**

Lesson 163

Preparation

1. Chalkboard:

   A 784,843
   930,830
   732,884
   903,265
   + 744,884

   B rectangle: $l = 1\frac{1}{2}$ ft.   square: $s = 43$ in.
   $w = \frac{3}{4}$ ft.

2. *Arithmetic 4:* pp. 295–296

3. *Lesson 163 Speed Drill*

4. Visuals:
   - *Process Flashcards*
   - *Concept Cards* 175–185, 48–55, 186–193, and 1–15
   - *Place Value (Arith Chart* 2)
   - *Decimals (Arith Chart* 14)

1. Oral review drills (9 min.)

Processes (4 min.)
- *Flashcards:* Review with child.
- Mult./Div. Tables
- **A** Use standard procedure.

Geometry (3 min.)
- *Concept Cards* **175–185** and **48–55:** Review shapes.
- *Concept Cards* **186–193:** Review concepts of area and perimeter, formulas, and square units.

Place value (2 min.)
- *Charts* **2** and **14:** Review place value.
- *Concept Cards* **1–15:** Hand him several cards; he puts them in order from least to greatest.

2. Written speed drill (2 min.) Time for 1 min. 30 sec.

3. Review area and perimeter. (15 min.)
- **B** Point to dimensions for rectangle. Tell child that even though dimensions are fractions, we use same formula and same steps. Have him find perimeter 1st. He should write formula of $P = (2 \times l) + (2 \times w)$. He should substitute into formula. Remind him that length is always longer side. He mult. a whole number by mixed number as usual. He changes 2 to $^2/_1$ and 1 $^1/_2$ to $^3/_2$. Continue through each step with him. He should find area of rectangle as well.

  Demonstrate on ckbd how to find perimeter and area of the square.
- Child does **Ex. 1–4, p. 295.** Work Ex. 4 together.

4. Review/Boardwork (9 min.) **Ex. 5–9**

Preparation

Lesson 164

1. Chalkboard:

   A 756,483
   903,783
   277,883
   894,766
   + 664,937

   B rectangle: $\frac{3}{4}$ ft. by $2\frac{2}{3}$ ft.   **C** $x + 4 = 9 \times 5$

2 *Arithmetic 4:* pp. 297–298

3. *Lesson 164 Speed Drill*

Thurs

4. Visuals:
   - *Process Flashcards*
   - *Divisibility Rules (Arith Chart* 12)
   - *Concept Cards 24–47, 112–129, 56–62, 186–193, 175–185,*
     and 48–55
   - *1–100 Chart (Arith Chart 23)*
   - *Roman Numerals (Arith Chart 10)*

Teaching Procedure

1. **Oral review drills** (10 min.)

   Processes (5 min.)
   - *Flashcards:* Review.
   - ▮ A ▮ Use standard procedure.
   - Mult./Div. Tables
   - *Arith Chart* **12:** Review divisibility rules.
   - Oral comb. Play *Speedy Sam.*

$1/11$ of $121 + 7 \div 3 \times 9 = 54$	$1/11$ of $132 \div 4 \times 9 - 18 = 9$
$1/9$ of $72 \div 4 \times 8 \div 4 + 8 - 9 = 3$	$1/4$ of $36 \div 3 \times 5 - 7 + 3 = 11$
$1/8$ of $64 \div 8 + 15 \div 4 \times 8 = 32$	$1/5$ of $25 \times 6 \div 10 \times 7 - 11 \times 10 = 100$
$1/7$ of $84 \div 6 \times 9 \div 3 \times 7 = 42$	$1/9$ of $27 \times 8 \div 6 \times 9 \div 3 \div 6 \times 5 = 10$

   Measures (2 min.)
   - *Concept Cards* **24–47** and **112–129**

   Fractions (1 min.)
   - Call out these fractions; child stands if proper. He remains
     seated if improper.
     $4/5$ $7/9$ $3/2$ $4/3$ $6/8$ $9/5$

   Roman numerals (2 min.)
   - *Arith Chart* **10**
   - *Concept Cards* **56–62**
   - *1–100 Chart:* Point to numbers; child gives as Roman numerals.

2. **Written speed drill** (3 min.) Time for 2 min. 30 sec.

3. **Review area and perimeter.** (12 min.)
   - *Concept Cards* **186–193:** Review concepts of area and perime-
     ter, formulas, and square units.
   - ▮ B ▮ Demonstrate how to find area and perimeter on ckbd.
     Encourage child to tackle problems with fractions with same
     confidence as problems without fractions. He follows through
     with his knowledge of fractions and geometry.
   - *Concept Cards* **175–185** and **48–55:** Briefly review geometric
     shapes.
   - Child does **Ex. 1–4, p. 297.**

4. **Review equations.** (3 min.)
   - ▮ C ▮ He explains as you work on ckbd. Child does **Ex. 5.**

5. **Review/Boardwork** (9 min.) **Ex. 6–8**

6. **Homework Ex. 9–10** Child needs ruler for les. 165.

Preparation

1. Chalkboard:

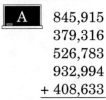 845,915
379,316
526,783
932,994
+ 408,633

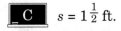 $l = 33$ ft.
$w = 17$ ft.

 $s = 1\frac{1}{2}$ ft.

Fri

2. *Arithmetic 4:* pp. 299–300

3. *Lesson 165 Speed Drill*

4. Visuals:
   - *Process Flashcards*
   - *Divisibility Rules (Arith Chart* 12)
   - Concept Cards 24–47, 112–129, 175–185, 48–55, 186–193, and 105–110
   - *Thermometer (Arith Chart 27)*
   - ruler

Teaching Procedure

1. **Oral review drills** (9 min.)

   Homework check

   Processes (4 min.)
   - *Flashcards:* Have child answer.
   - Mult./Div. Tables
   - *Arith Chart* **12:** Review divisibility rules.
   - A Use standard procedure.
   - Oral comb.

     $6 \times 7 - 2 \div 10 \times 8 + 3 = 35$ $18 + 4 \div 11 \times 6 \div 2 \times 3 = 18$

     $11 \times 5 - 1 \div 9 \times 3 + 2 - 3 = 17$ $82 + 18 + 20 \div 10 \times 8 = 96$

     $23 - 7 \div 4 \times 8 + 32 + 6 = 70$ $47 - 5 + 7 \div 7 \times 3 + 4 = 25$

   Measures (3 min.)
   - *Concept Cards* **24–47** and **112–129**
   - Review metric abbreviations.

   Geometry (2 min.)
   - *Concept Cards* **175–185** and **48–55**
   - *Concept Cards* **186–193:** Review concepts of area and perimeter, formulas, and square units.

2. **Written speed drill** (4 min.) Time for 3 min.

3. **Review area and perimeter.** (6 min.)
   - B Find perimeter and area of rectangle. Child explains as you work on ckbd.
   - C Child explains how to find area and perimeter of square.
   - Child does **Ex. 1, p. 299.**

4. **Review temperature.** (3 min.)
   - *Thermometer:* Call out several temperatures for him to set on thermometer.
   - *Concept Cards* **105–110:** Review temperature reference points.
   - Child does **Ex. 2.**

5. **Review bar graphs.** (3 min.)
   - Work **Ex. 3** together. Encourage him to use ruler and colored pencils to make graph more attractive.

6. **Review/Boardwork** (12 min.) **Ex. 4–7**

7. **Homework Ex. 8–9**

Lesson 166

Preparation

1. Chalkboard:

   A   148,558
            258,935
            894,795
            184,295
          + 940,668

   B $s = 4\frac{1}{2}$ ft.

   C $6\frac{4}{9}$

2. *Arithmetic 4:* pp. 301–302

3. *Lesson 166 Speed Drill*

4. Visuals:
   - *Calculator (Arith Chart 20)*
   - Mixed Facts Chart (see lesson 49)
   - *Concept Cards* 186–193, 80–104, and 130–139

Teaching Procedure

1. **Oral review drills** (9 min.)

   Homework check

   Processes (5 min.)
   - *Calculator:* Push buttons; child adds 9 or 7 to numbers pushed.
   - Mixed Facts Chart
   - **A** Use standard procedure.

   Area and Perimeter (1 min.)
   - *Concept Cards* **186–193**

   Fractions (3 min.)
   - *Concept Cards* **80–104:** Child reduces to lowest terms.
   - Call out these fractions; he stands if proper. He remains seated if improper.

     $\frac{8}{9}$ $\quad$ $\frac{9}{8}$ $\quad$ $\frac{11}{9}$ $\quad$ $\frac{4}{5}$ $\quad$ $\frac{2}{3}$ $\quad$ $\frac{6}{5}$ $\quad$ $\frac{4}{3}$

   - *Concept Cards* **130–139:** Child changes improper fractions to whole or mixed numbers.
   - Call out these improper fractions; he gives correct mixed number.

     $\frac{8}{7}$ $\quad$ $\frac{6}{5}$ $\quad$ $\frac{11}{9}$ $\quad$ $\frac{8}{5}$ $\quad$ $\frac{9}{7}$

2. **Written speed drill** (3 min.) Time for 2 min.

3. **Review area and perimeter.** (6 min.)
  - Send child to ckbd to write formula that you say.
  - **B** Child explains how to find perimeter and area while you work on ckbd.
  - Child does **Ex. 1, p. 301.**

4. **Review division.** (6 min.)
  - Give him 5 min. to work and check **Ex. 2.** Then check. Praise child who made a perfect score.

5. **Review changing improper fractions.** (3 min.)
  - **C** Send child to ckbd to change to improper fraction. Use *Concept Cards* **133–139** with him. Show backs; he changes to improper fractions.
  - Child works **Ex. 3.**

6. **Review/Boardwork** (9 min.) **Ex. 4–7**

7. **Homework Ex. 8–9**

Preparation

Lesson
167

1. Chalkboard:

A
784,783
284,784
942,236
796,555
+ 993,214

B $\frac{4}{7} = \frac{}{28}$

C $\frac{16}{18} =$

D $\frac{19}{12} =$

E $5\frac{4}{9} =$

F $2\frac{2}{5}$

$7\frac{1}{3}$

G $\frac{4}{7} \times 1\frac{3}{4} =$

$+ \frac{4}{15}$

2. *Arithmetic 4:* pp. 303–304

3. *Lesson 167 Speed Drill*

4. Visuals:
  - *Process Flashcards*
  - *Concept Cards* 56–62, 24–47, 112–129, and 192–193

Teaching Procedure

1. **Oral review drills** (9 min.)

   Homework check

Lesson 167
(cont.)

Processes (5 min.)
- *Flashcards:* Play a favorite game.
- Mult./Div. Tables
- **A** Use standard procedure.

Roman numerals (1 min.)
- *Concept Cards* **56–62**

Measures (3 min.)
- *Concept Cards* **24–47, 112–129,** and **192–193:** Review with class and then play a favorite game.

2. Written speed drill (5 min.) Time for 4 min.

3. Review fractions. (15 min.)

- **B** Child gives missing number. Remind him to find what he must mult. original denominator by to get new denominator. He must mult. original numerator by same factor.
- Child does **Ex. 1, p. 303.**
- **C** He reduces to lowest terms.
- Child does **Ex. 2.**
- **D** He changes to a mixed number.
- Child does **Ex. 3.**
- **E** He changes to improper fraction.
- Child does **Ex. 4**
- **F** He explains as you work problem on ckbd.
- Child does **Ex. 5.**
- **G** He explains as you work on ckbd.
- Child does **Ex. 6.**

4. Review/Boardwork (9 min.) **Ex. 7–12**

Lesson 168

Preparation

1. Chalkboard:

A
457,346
893,893
904,884
284,894
+ 995,994

B $4 \frac{3}{1,000}$

C 17.07

D
13.00
− 1.91

2. *Arithmetic 4:* pp. 305–306

3. *Lesson 168 Speed Drill*

4. Visuals:
  - *Process Flashcards*
  - *Divisibility Rules (Arith Chart 12)*
  - *Decimals (Arith Chart 14)*
  - *Concept Cards 186–191, 175–185, 48–55, 24–47, 112–129, 192–193,* and 140–174

Teaching Procedure

1. **Oral review drills** (9 min.)

   Processes (4 min.)
   - *Flashcards:* Play a game.
   - Mult./Div. Tables
   - **A** Use standard procedure.
   - *Arith Chart* **12:** Review divisibility rules.

   Geometry (3 min.)
   - *Concept Cards* **186–191**
   - Write *l* x *w* on ckbd. Child tells what it is formula for. Repeat for *s* x *s*, 4 x *s*, and (2 x *l*) + (2 x *w*).
   - *Concept Cards* **175–185** and **48–55:** Review geometric shapes.

   Measures (2 min.)
   - *Concept Cards* **24–47, 112–129,** and **192–193**

2. **Written speed drill** (3 min.) Time for 2 min.

3. **Review decimals.** (12 min.)
   - *Arith Chart* **14:** Review decimal place value.
   - Child does **Ex. 1–2, p. 305.**
   - *Concept Cards* **140–174:** Show fractions; he writes decimals on ckbd.
   - **B** He writes as a mixed decimal.
   - Child does **Ex. 3.**
   - **C** He writes as a fraction.
   - Child does **Ex. 4–5.**
   - **D** Work on ckbd as he explains.
   - Child does **Ex. 6.**

4. **Review/Boardwork** (12 min.) **Ex. 7–10** Child needs ruler for les. 169.

5. **Homework Ex. 11–12** Homework may be omitted since this is not a usual day for homework.

Lesson
169

Thurs

Preparation

1. Chalkboard:

A	843,950
	430,158
	584,947
	904,229
	+ 784,036

B	$l = 98$ ft.
	$w = 87$ ft.

C	$s = 1\frac{1}{2}$ yd.

2. *Arithmetic 4:* pp. 307–308
3. *Lesson 169 Speed Drill*
4. Visuals:
   * *Process Flashcards*
   * *Concept Cards* 175–185, 48–55, 186–191, 24–47, and 112–129
   * ruler

Teaching Procedure

1. **Oral review drills** (9 min.)

   Homework check

   Processes (4 min.)
   * *Flashcards:* Play *Beat the Clock.*
   * Mult./Div. Tables
   * | A | Use standard procedure.
   * Oral comb.

$6 \times 7 - 2 \div 4 \times 5 + 3 = 53$	$9 \div 3 \times 6 + 2 \div 5 \times 8 = 32$
$11 - 3 \times 5 + 3 - 1 \div 6 = 7$	$14 \div 7 \times 4 \times 8 + 3 = 67$
$67 + 5 \div 8 \times 4 - 5 = 31$	$28 \div 4 \times 7 + 1 \div 5 + 2 = 12$

   Geometry (2 min.)
   * *Concept Cards* **175–185** and **48–55:** Review shapes.
   * *Concept Cards* **186–191:** Review concepts and formulas.

   Measures (3 min.)
   * *Concept Cards* **24–47** and **112–129:** Play a game after child has answered several cards.

2. **Written speed drill** (3 min.) Time for 2 min.

3. **Review area and perimeter.** (9 min.)

   * | B | Find area and perimeter of rectangle.
   * | C | Find area and perimeter of square.
   * Child does **Ex. 1–2, p. 307.**

4. **Review problem solving.** (4 min.)
   * Give him 4 min. to work **Ex. 3.** Check. Praise child who gets them all correct.

5. **Discuss story problems.** (3 min.)
   • Work **Ex. 4** together.
6. **Review/Boardwork** (9 min.) **Ex. 5–8** Child should use ruler to connect points in Ex. 8.
7. **Homework** Study for Final Exam. Student needs ruler for les. 170, Final Exam.

Lesson

170

Preparation

Final Exam, pp. 133–136 from *Student Tests and Speed Drills*

Teaching Procedure

Administer exam. Allow ample time to complete exam. Child should use ruler to draw the square and trapezoid.